FISHING TACKLE ANTIQUES
AND COLLECTABLES
PLUGS

VOLUME I

IDENTIFICATION AND EVALUATION OF
PRE-1970 TACKLE

BY KARL T. WHITE
P.O. Box 190
Luther, OK 73054
(405) 277-3636
ktwhite@swbell.net

All pictures were taken from the
KARL T. WHITE FISHING TACKLE COLLECTION

OKLAHOMA AQUARIUM

P.O. Box 910 · 300 Aquarium Drive · Jenks, OK 74037

(918) 296-FISH (3474) · FAX: 296-FINS (3467) · www.aquarium.org

On the Arkansas River at the Creek Turnpike in Tulsa metro...

A major feature of the Oklahoma Aquarium is the world-class, one-of-a-kind Karl and Beverly White National Fishing Tackle Museum...the largest collection of tackle encompassing the complete history of sports fishing. The Karl T. White Collection, housed in over 4,000 square feet of exhibit space, features historical plugs, baits, rods, reels, boats and motors...over 20,000 pieces valued at more than $4 million!

The Oklahoma Aquarium welcomes visitors of all ages! With over 200 exhibits, nearly a million gallons of water, and thousands of aquatic animals...the Oklahoma Aquarium offers a fascinatiing look at the amazing variety of aquatic life from around the world!

The Oklahoma Aquarium is a compelling family attraction with unique opportunities to learn about aquatic conservation, sports fishing and outdoor recreation through fishing clinics and other education programs in partnership with the Oklahoma Department of Wildlife Conservation. In addition, the 34-acre Aquarium campus and its 72,000 square-foot building includes laboratories dedictated to aquatic research and education progams available to students and researchesr of all levels of study.

Along with the Karl T. White Collection, the Aquarium exhibits include giant sharks, octopi, catfish, moray eels piranhas, sunfish, barracudas, seahorses, anemones, bass, Alaskan king crabs, mudskippers, sea jellies, sea turtles, lobsters, coral reefs, and touch tanks...you can SEA IT ALL at the Oklahoma Aquarium.

ACKNOWLEDGEMENTS

A very special thanks to Ann Money, Curator of Museum Collections at the Oklahoma Aquarium for her tireless efforts in helping prepare the Collection for transfer to the Aquarium and being responsible for cataloging and displaying the Collection for public viewing.

A special thanks to the National Fishing Lure Collectors Club (NFLCC) -without its 6000 members and 26 years of existence, it would not have been possible to obtain these items for the Museum Collection and this book.
www.nflcc.com

A special thanks to B.A.S.S , (P.O. Box 17116, Montgomery, AL, 36141-0116), for the exposure of myself and this book to the fishing industry.

Also a special thanks to Bob Lang of Lang's Sporting Collectable, Inc., (14 Fisherman's Lane, Raymond ME, 04071), for helping all collectors to evaluate the tackle by way of his auctions, as the only true test of value is at auction.

PUBLISHED BY HOLLI ENTERPRISES
P.O. BOX 190
LUTHER, OK 73054
(405) 277-3636 FAX (405) 277-3733
COPYRIGHT 2002
ALL RIGHTS RESERVED
FIRST EDITION

FIRST PRINTING   ISBN 0-9634515-6-1 (Volume I)   JULY 2002

ABOUT THE AUTHOR

Since 1948, at age 9, Karl White has been interested in fishing. This began when he was living next to a sandpit lake. One day while he was fishing, another young boy came along who threw a red and white River Runt bait in the water. Trying to be helpful, Karl told the boy to leave his cork in the water or he would never catch a fish. You can guess what happened next. "Bang! A Bass!" From that point on, Karl has been a collector. A few years passed, then Karl's father took him to an old hotel in Claremore, Oklahoma, where probably the best collection of antique firearms is kept. Karl was fascinated by this. He thought "If there is a museum on hunting material, why isn't there one for fishing, since it is more popular?" Hence, his collecting fishing tackle began.

In 1961 Karl married Beverly Wright and they had three daughters, Crystal, Leesa and Holli.

In 1962 Karl received his degree in Biology and Chemistry from Central State University in Edmond, Oklahoma.

By 1976, Karl's business, Crystal Laboratory, Inc., which manufactures raw allergenic products, was growing fast and supplied him the income to purchase some of the best antique fishing tackle collections that have existed.

In 1976, the National Fishing Lure Collectors Club (NFLCC) was founded by three gentlemen in the School of the Ozarks. Karl had previously contacted these people and was instrumental in the formation of the club and is one of it's founding members. This club has now grown to over 6000 members at the present time. During this time Karl has seen a 'gasp' when someone paid $50.00 for a lure, to a 'gasp' when someone paid $40,000.00 for one. The NFLCC has given him the means to seek out the best collections available and to trade his duplicates to add to his collection.

Karl currently is the consultant to BASSMASTER Magazine and has a column in their magazine titled 'What's It Worth? in which he answers readers' questions concerning antique fishing tackle and related items.

In 2002 he donated his entire collection to the Oklahoma Aquarium, located in Jenks, Oklahoma, a suburb of Tulsa. It has a building in it which houses his collection and is named the 'Karl & Beverly White National Fishing Tackle Museum'.

Picture taking and editing
typing, and assembling done by
Leesa Yvette Christy
and
Jackie Ann Simpson

Leesa Christy is Karl's daughter and works in his business where she is the Production Supervisor and Quality Assurance Manager there. She is married to Kent Christy and has three children Julie, Shelby and Kodee Christy.

Jackie Simpson has worked in Karl's business since 1980 and is Secretary/Bookeeper there. She is married to Joe Simpson and they have three children, Jeanette and Michael Montgomery, Joe Jr. and 5 grandchildren.

PICTURE EDITING ALSO DONE BY:
Robert Jackson Cole and Guy Lyle Lindsey

INTRODUCTION OF CONTENTS

The purpose of this book is to identify and evaluate plugs and plug boxes dated up to 1970. Plugs are identified as a bodied lure made from wood, metal, plastic or any counterpart.

Prices can fluctuate up to 50%, according to the demand of antique tackle. One thing to remember is that the better items keep getting more valuable and the common items stay about the same. Lure Sets (items of one company's production) and Color Sets (all colors produced of one item), should be at least 25% more valuable. The values in this book are rated as to excellent condition, although the items pictured might not be.

Rarity, demand, condition and age determine value. Keep in mind that the higher the number of items found and in circulation, the lower the value is.

A true collector obtains tackle for love of the hobby and not for the investment. The only common denominator that everyone understands is putting a dollar value on it. Good finds of antique fishing tackle are hard to come by and more people are collecting the 1940's, and later.

In this book the lures are indexed alphabetically by manufacturer and by common name. To find a particular item name or manufacturer

There are two indexes: *Lure by Manufacturer* and *Lure by Common Name.*

Included is a page to help identify lures and their age by their hardware entitled *Hardware Types.* The pictures in this book were done to give the best view of the item to help with identification. The sizes of the actual lures and or boxes are not relative to the picture size. In many cases the size of the lure is stated in inches and/or ounces or descriptive names (ie Musky, Tiny etc.). All picture were done by digital camera and are computer enhanced. Enlarged pictures may be obtained for a nominal fee.

Best of luck and good hunting,
Karl T White

GENERAL GRADING SYSTEM OF LURES

IN BOX	Pristine, in box, with papers.
FLAWLESS	Pristine, but without a box and or papers.
EXCELLENT	Bright paint with few scratches or minor scrapes.
VERY GOOD	Shows use, little varnish loss, duller finish.
GOOD	Minor problems; hook scars, rust, little loss to primer.
AVERAGE	Loss of paint, maybe 10%, to primer, cracks, starting to look at age in relation to condition.
FAIR	Major defects, looking at possible replacement, showing wood 10% or more.
POOR	Looking at reconditioning or touching up, replacing hardware.
REPAINTED	A reconditioned, beaten plug, no dents.
BEATER	Ready to strip for repaint or to use parts.
PLUG BODY	Rig and paint yourself, use for fishing.

Comment: 1/4 of Value should be taken off, or added to, between each grade.

The lures in this book are valued very good to excellent even though many are not.

THIS BOOK IS DEDICATED TO MY WIFE OF 41 YEARS, BEVERLY
AND MY THREE CHILDREN:
CRYSTAL, WHO IS MARRIED TO JERRY RAINS, AND HER CHILDREN CLINT AND JESSICA CASWELL
LEESA, WHO IS MARRIED TO KENT CHRISTY, AND THEIR CHILDREN JULIE, SHELBY, AND KODEE CHRISTY
HOLLI, WHO IS MARRIED TO MARK VAUGHN, AND THEIR CHILDREN JAXON, JADIE AND JACIE VAUGHN

LURE HARDWARE TYPES

BASIC HOOK HANGERS

OF 6 MAJOR COMPANIES

CREEK CHUB (CCBC0)

1. Washer Rig   1911-1915
2. Shallow Cup   1916-1919
3. Cup Rig   1920-____

PFLUEGER

1. Wire Rig   1900-1925
2. Eye Screw   1910-1941
3. Paper Clip Rig   1912-1913
4. Bent Wire   1914-1927
5. Surface Rig   1929-____

SHAKESPEARE

1. Wire Rig   1899-1920
2. Staple Rig   1908-1912
3. Eye Screw   1907-1941
4. Paper Clip Rig   1907-1912
5. Flat Wire Through   1913-1941
6. Cup Rig   1945-____

HEDDON

1. Cup Rig   1903-1914
2. L-Rig   1915-1930
3. Toilet Seat   1926-1930
4. Flap Rig   1931-1948
5. Surface Rig   1949-____

MOONLIGHT (PAW PAW)

1. Shallow Cup   1906-1919
2. Eye Screw   1920-1941
3. Cup Rig   1920-____
4. Built-in Cup   1945-____
5. Surface Rig   1945-____

SOUTH BEND (WORDEN)

1. Eye Screw   1903-1909
2. Aluminum Cup   1910-1912
3. Cup Rig   1913-1950
4. Surface Rig   1951-____

L-RIG

TOILET SEAT

FLAP RIG

SURFACE RIG

EYE SCREW

WASHER RIG

BENT WIRE

STAPLE RIG

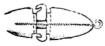

WIRE RIG

FLAT WIRE THROUGH

PAPER CLIP RIG

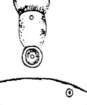

CUP RIG

SHALLOW CUP

BUILT-IN CUP

LURE WANT LIST

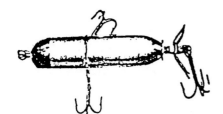

A. BLEE & HELMKAMP
SUBMARINE
IN   1914 $1000

B. BOWERSOX
BOWERSOX MINNOW
IN   1907 $1500

C. BROWN
WIGGLETAIL MINNOW
IN   1907 $1500

D. CREEK CHUB BAIT CO.
DECOY
IN   1919 $1500

E. DONALY, JIM
DIVER
NJ   1938 $750

F. EWERT
ARTIFICIAL BAIT
CA   1919 $2000

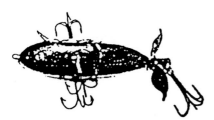

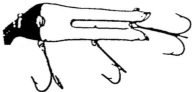

G. GARRISON
GARRISON MINNOW
WA   1910 $2000

H. GARST
CLOSE PIN
IL   1925   300

I. HOMSER
MECHANICAL FROG
MI   1928 $2000

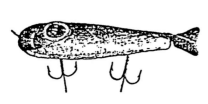

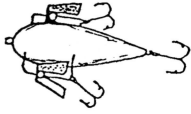

J. KNIGHT & WALL
COSTA LURE
FL   1930 $750

K. MEADOWS
MEADOWS WOODEN MINNOW
FL   1937 $300

L. PARKER
AEROPLANE BAIT
MI   1912 $1500

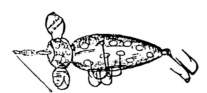

M. PEPPER, JOE E.
REVOLVING MINNOW
NY   1915 $750

N. SMITH
SMITH MINNOW
IN   1905 $3000

O. VANDECAR
BONIFIED MINNOW
MI   1907 $3000

007-0215 A.L.& W.
PIKIE, DOUBLE JOINTED, A.L. & W.
CAN   1947   5 1/2 IN
ALLCOCK-LAIGHT & WESTWOOD $40

007-0216 A.L.& W.
PIKIE, DOUBLE JOINTED, A.L. & W.
CAN   1947   5 1/2 IN
PLASTIC (CREEK CHUB) $40

007-0217 A.L.& W.
PIKIE, JOINTED,   A.L.&W.
CAN   1947   5 1/2 IN
PLASTIC (CREEK CHUB) $40

007-0218 A.L.& W.
PIKIE, JOINTED, A.L.&W.
CAN   1947   5 IN
PLASTIC (CREEK CHUB) $40

007-0214 A.L.& W.
RIVER RUSTLER, A.L. & W.
CAN   1947   2 1/2 IN
PLASTIC (CREEK CHUB) $40

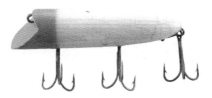

007-0064 ABBEY & IMBRIE
BASSER
NY   1925
(HEDDON) $300

007-0065 ABBEY & IMBRIE
CRAB WIGGLER
NY   1925
(HEDDON) $300

007-0066 ABBEY & IMBRIE
SPIN DIVER, ABBEY & IMBRIE
NY   1925
(HEDDON) $1000

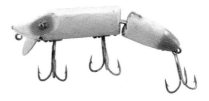

007-0063 ABBEY & IMBRIE
VAMP, JOINTED
NY   1925
(HEDDON) $200

007-2909 ABBEY & IMBRIE
RIDEAU
MI   1928   4 IN
CUP-RIG, (MOONLIGHT BAIT CO) $300

007-0043 ABBEY & IMBRIE
WHIRLING CHUB, JOINTED
NY   1925
(PAW PAW) $100

007-1502 ABBEY & IMBRIE
MINNEHAHA
NY   1925
PFLUEGER $150

007-1504 ABBEY & IMBRIE
OCTOPUS MINNOW
NY   1903
$2000

007-0077 ABBEY & IMBRIE
TORPEDO, ABBEY & IMBRIE
NY   1899
GEORGE JENNINGS $750

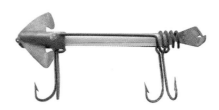

007-0062 ABBEY & IMBRIE
GLOWBODY MINNOW
NY   1920
$300

008-0027 ABBEY & IMBRIE
ASTRA
NY   1952   2 1/2 IN   1/4 OZ
WOOD (HORROCKS-IBBOTSON) $50

008-0053 ABBEY & IMBRIE
BABE-ORENO TYPE, GO-GETTER
NY   1952
(HORROCKS-IBBOTSON) $40

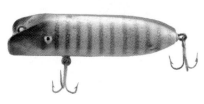

008-0051 ABBEY & IMBRIE
BASS-ORENO TYPE, GO-GETTER
NY   1952
(HORROCKS-IBBOTSON) $40

008-0028 ABBEY & IMBRIE
BIG BROTHER TEASER
NY   1952   8 IN
(HORROCKS-IBBOTSON) $50

008-0025 ABBEY & IMBRIE
CLEARWATER
NY   1925   4 IN   1/2 OZ
(HORROCKS-IBBOTSON) $50

008-0009 ABBEY & IMBRIE
GO-GETTER
NY   1952
(HORROCKS-IBBOTSON) $30

008-0016 ABBEY & IMBRIE
GO-GETTER
NY   1952   3 1/4 IN
(HORROCKS-IBBOTSON) $40

008-0037 ABBEY & IMBRIE
GO-GETTER
NY   1952
(HORROCKS-IBBOTSON) $40

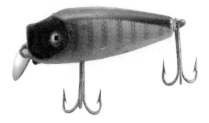

008-0038 ABBEY & IMBRIE
GO-GETTER
NY   1952
(HORROCKS-IBBOTSON) $40

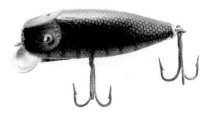

008-0039 ABBEY & IMBRIE
GO-GETTER
NY   1952
(HORROCKS-IBBOTSON) $40

008-0040 ABBEY & IMBRIE
GO-GETTER
NY   1952
(HORROCKS-IBBOTSON) $40

008-0044 ABBEY & IMBRIE
GO-GETTER
NY   1952
HORROCKS-IBBOTSON) $50

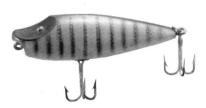

008-0058 ABBEY & IMBRIE
GO-GETTER
NY   1952
(HORROCKS-IBBOTSON) $40

008-0059 ABBEY & IMBRIE
GO-GETTER
NY   1952
(HORROCKS-IBBOTSON) $30

008-0036 ABBEY & IMBRIE
GO-GETTER, RIVER RUNT TYPE
NY   1952
(HORROCKS-IBBOTSON) $40

009-0032 ABBEY & IMBRIE
GO-GETTER, S.O.S. TYPE
NY   1952   2 1/2 IN
(HORROCKS-IBBOTSON) $40

009-0057 ABBEY & IMBRIE
NJURED MINNOW TYPE
NY   1952
(HORROCKS-IBBOTSON) $40

009-0061 ABBEY & IMBRIE
MOUSE, GO-GETTER
NY   1952
HORROCKS-IBBOTSON $50

009-0050 ABBEY & IMBRIE
TWO-ORENO TYPE, GO-GETTER
NY   1952
(HORROCKS-IBBOTSON) $75

009-0190 ACCETTA, TONY
JIGOLET
OH   2 1/2 IN
PLASTIC $20

009-0189 ACCETTA, TONY
JIGOLET SNAGLESS
OH   2 1/2 IN
PLASTIC $20

009-0200 ACTION LURE CO.
ACTION LURE
CA   1952   2 IN
PLASTIC $20

009-0246 ACTIVATED LURE CO.
HI-YO LURE
OH   1947   4 IN
RUBBER & METAL/W DRY ICE $60

009-0195 ACTUAL LURE CO.
ACTUAL CRAWDAD
NY   1950   2 IN
REAL CRAWDAD $20

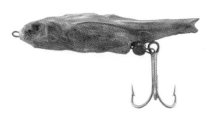

009-0198 ACTUAL LURE CO.
ACTUAL MINNOW
NY   1950   3 IN
REAL MINNOW $30

009-0199 ACTUAL LURE CO.
ACTUAL MINNOW
NY   1950   2 IN
REAL MINNOW $20

009-0196 ACTUAL LURE CO.
ACTUAL SHAD
NY   1950   5 IN
REAL SHAD $20

009-0197 ACTUAL LURE CO.
ACTUAL SHAD
NY   1950   3 IN
REAL SHAD $30

009-3353 ADAMS, L.D , ' POP'
BASS GETTER
OK   1960
$30

009-5721 ADAMS, L.D , ' POP'
BASS GETTER
OK   1960
$40

# FISHING PLUGS

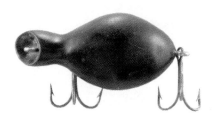

010-0209 ADAMS, L.D , ' POP'
LEECH, ADAMS
OK   1920 's   2 IN
WOOD $300

010-0210 ADAMS, L.D , ' POP'
PLUNKER, ADAMS
OK   1940 's   3 IN
WOOD $50

010-0201 AIREX BAIT CO.
HOPPIE
NY   1958   2 3/4 IN
PLASTIC $20

010-0203 AIREX BAIT CO.
HOPPIE
NY   1952   2 3/4 IN
PLASTIC $20

010-0204 AIREX BAIT CO.
MINNOW, AIREX
NY   1950   2 3/4 IN
PLASTIC $20

010-2681 ALASKAN BAIT CO
ALASKAN SALMON PLUG
OH   1885
     $75

010-0194 ALCOE LURE CO
MAGIC MINNOW, ALCOE
FL   1958   5 IN
RUBBER $50

010-0229 ALGER, FRANK CO.
ALGER'S MINNOW
MI   1910   4 IN
WOOD $1200

010-5914 ALLEN TACKLE CO.
DUBL-MINO
IL   1959
     $30

010-5705 AL-LURE-O BAIT CO.
AL-LURE-O BAIT
MN   1946
     $20

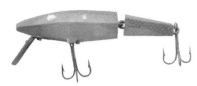

010-1112 AL'S GOLDFISH LURE CO.
DIAMOND JIM LURE
MA   1960   1/2 OZ
LARGE $30

010-1117 AL'S GOLDFISH LURE CO.
DIAMOND JIM LURE
MA   1960   1/4 OZ
SMALL $30

010-0227 ALSTAR BAIT CO.
GEE WIZ FROG
IL   1931   5 IN
RUBBER & WOOD $150

010-0228 ALSTAR BAIT CO.
GEE WIZ FROG,
IL   1931   6 IN
RUBBER & WOOD, MUSKY $300

010-0298 AMER. & NATIONAL TACKLE
RANGER TYPE
OK   1940's   2 1/2 IN
WOOD, USES BLOOD TABLETS $100

FISHING PLUGS

011--0289 AMER. & NATIONAL TACKLE
RIVER FLASH
OK   1954
BLEEDER BAIT/ DOES NOT BLEED $90

011-0299 AMER. & NATIONAL TACKLE
RIVER FLASH
OK   1940's   3 IN   LARGE
WOOD, USES BLOOD TABLETS $150

011-0300 AMER. & NATIONAL TACKLE
RIVER FLASH
OK   1940's   2 1/2 IN   SMALL
WOOD, USES BLOOD TABLETS $150

011-0232 AMERICAN ROD & GUN
LUCKY BUNNY
CT   1954   3 IN
RABBIT FOOT AND PLASTIC $75

011-0233 AMERICAN ROD & GUN
LUCKY BUNNY JR.
CT   1965
RABBIT FOOT AND PLASTIC $60

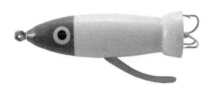

011-0241 ANDERSON & SON
WEEDLESS WONDER
RI   1969   2 3/4 IN
SPRING LOADED $75

011-0240 ANDERSON & SON
WEEDLESS WONDER PROTOTYPE
RI   1968   2 3/4 IN
SPRING-LOADED $75

011-0234 ANDERSON BAIT CO.
ANDERSON MINNOW
IL   1949   3 1/2 IN   7/8 OZ
  $90

011-0238 APEX BAIT CO.
BULL NOSE BAIT
IL   1913   4 1/2 IN
WOOD $300

011-0239 APEX BAIT CO.
BULL NOSE BAIT JR.
IL   1914   3/1/2 IN
WOOD $300

011-0251 AQUASPORT, INC.
DOODLE BUG, DIVING
OK   1965   2 1/2 IN
PLASTIC (SELTZER ACTIVATED) $30

011-0126 ARBOGAST, FRED
JITTERBUG PROTOTYPE
OH   1938
2 TREBLES $400

011-0129 ARBOGAST, FRED
JITTERBUG
OH   1937   2 3/4 IN   5/8 OZ
WOOD, MEDIUM $200

011-0128 ARBOGAST, FRED
JITTERBUG
OH   1944   2 3/4 IN   5/8 OZ
WOOD WITH PLASTIC LIP $150

011-0127 ARBOGAST, FRED
JITTERBUG
OH   1950   2 3/4 IN   5/8 OZ
PLASTIC, OLD COLOR $20

012-0125 ARBOGAST, FRED
JITTERBUG, MUSKY
OH   1939   3 3/4 IN   1 1/4 OZ
2 TREBLES $200

012-0124 ARBOGAST, FRED
JITTERBUG
OH   1950   3 3/4 IN   1 1/4 OZ
MUSKY, 3 TREBLES $50

012-0134 ARBOGAST, FRED
JITTERBUG, JOINTED
OH   1964   2 1/2 IN   1/2 OZ
PLASTIC W/ METAL LIP $20

012-0133 ARBOGAST, FRED
JITTERBUG, JOINTED, SMALL
OH   1964   3 IN   1/2 OZ
PLASTIC W/ METAL LIP $20

012-0130 ARBOGAST, FRED
JITTERBUG, SMALL
OH   1944   2 1/4 IN   1/2 OZ
WOOD W/ PLASTIC LIP $300

012-0132 ARBOGAST, FRED
JITTERBUG, SMALL
OH   1944   2 1/4 IN   1/2 OZ
PLASTIC W/ PLASTIC LIP, 2 HK $150

012-0131 ARBOGAST, FRED
JITTERBUG, SMALL
OH   1939   2 1/4 IN   1/2 OZ
WOOD W/ ALUMINUM LIP, 1 HK $400

012-0145 ARBOGAST, FRED
ARBOGASTER
OH   1956   1 3/4 IN   1/2 OZ
SMALL, PLASTIC $10

012-0146 ARBOGAST, FRED
ARBOGASTER
OH   1955   2 IN   5/8 OZ
LARGE, PLASTIC $10

012-5117 ARBOGAST, FRED
DeKALB BAIT
OH   1960
 $30

012-0148 ARBOGAST, FRED
DORADO
OH   1960
 $40

012-0136 ARBOGAST, FRED
HULA DANCER
OH   1947   1 1/2 IN   1/2 OZ
PLASTIC $20

012-0137 ARBOGAST, FRED
HULA DIVER
OH   1949   2 IN   5/8 OZ
PLASTIC $20

012-0147 ARBOGAST, FRED
HULA HOOPLE
OH   1960   4 1/2 IN   5/8 OZ
PLASTIC $10

012-0154 ARBOGAST, FRED
HULA PIKIE, JOINTED
OH   1962   2 3/4 IN   1/2 OZ
PLASTIC $10

FISHING PLUGS

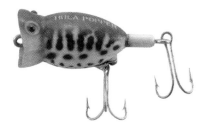

013-0140 ARBOGAST, FRED
HULA POPPER
OH   1948   2 IN   1/2 OZ
PLASTIC, SMALL $10

013-0141 ARBOGAST, FRED
HULA POPPER
OH   1947   2 1/2 IN   5/8 OZ
PLASTIC, BELLY MARKED $60

013-0139 ARBOGAST, FRED
HULA POPPER WOODEN PROTOTYPE
OH   1946   2 1/2 IN   5/8 OZ
WOOD, LAST LURE BY FRED $400

013-0153 ARBOGAST, FRED
HUSTLER, ARBOGAST
OH   1962   3 3/4 IN   5/8 OZ
PLASTIC $10

013-0162 ARBOGAST, FRED
LIL' BASS
OH   1959   2 1/2 IN   1/4 OZ
RUBBER $20

013-7052 ARBOGAST, FRED
LUMINOUS WORM
OH   1968
 $10

013-0151 ARBOGAST, FRED
SCOOTER, ARBOGAST
OH   1962   3 3/4 IN   5/8 OZ
PLASTIC, LARGE $10

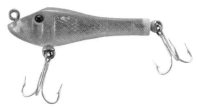

013-0152 ARBOGAST, FRED
SCOOTER, ARBOGAST
OH   1962   2 1/4 IN   1/2 OZ
PLASTIC, SMALL $10

013-0157 ARBOGAST, FRED
SCUDDER
OH   1965   5 IN   1 1/4 OZ
PLASTIC $20

013-0155 ARBOGAST, FRED
SKINNY MINNY
OH   1959   5 IN   5/8 OZ
LARGE, PLASTIC $10

013-0156 ARBOGAST, FRED
SKINNY MINNY
OH   1960   3 1/2 IN   1/2 OZ
SMALL, PLASTIC $10

013-0138 ARBOGAST, FRED
SPIN DANCER
OH   1949   1 3/4 IN   1/2 OZ
PLASTIC $20

013-0149 ARBOGAST, FRED
SPUTTERBUG
OH   1955   3 3/4 IN   5/8 OZ
LARGE, PLASTIC $10

013-0150 ARBOGAST, FRED
SPUTTERBUG
OH   1955   2 1/4 IN   1/2 OZ
PLASTIC, BABY $10

013-0158 ARBOGAST, FRED
WEEDLER
OH   1964   8 IN
RUBBER $20

014-1386 ARBY'S TACKLE
FIRE FISH
　1955
　$30

014-0535 ARCO MFG.
HORNET SR
MO　1952
　$20

014-6031 ARJON
ARJON BASSY
SWE　1960
SWEDEN　$10

014-0242 ARNOLD, S. & CO.
HOPALONG
MO　1947　3 IN
　$20

014-5422 ARWOOD, J.
DECOY, SUCKER, ARWOOD
MN　1933
　$300

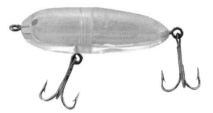

014-0612 ASHING GROUNDS, INC.
THREE-IN-ONE
TN　1959
COLORED PAPER INSIDE　$30

014-0244 ASSOCIATED SPECIALTY CO
COOL RIPPLE FROG
IL　1949　2 IN
RUBBER　$100

014-0245 ASSOCIATED SPECIALTY CO
GENTLEMAN JIM
IL　1949　4 IN
PLASTIC　$30

014-5201 ATOM MFG. CO.
ATOM
MA　1960's
PLASTIC　$50

014-0266 ATOM MFG. CO.
STRIPER ATOM
MA　1947　7 1/4 IN
WOOD　$75

014-0250 ATOMIC FISHING TACKLE
TRIP-LURE
NJ　1946　2 IN
PLASTIC　$75

014-3842 AU CLAIRE, T.F.
OSCAR THE FROG
MI　1947
　$200

014-24682 AVON
SURE CATCH AFTER SHAVE

　$10

014-0323 B & M PRODUCTS
INVADER
CT　1946　4 IN
RUBBER BODY　$100

014-0508 BABBITT, E.S.
BABBITT WEEDLESS BAIT
OH　1926　2 IN
　$400

FISHING PLUGS

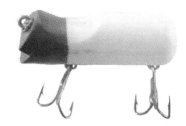

015-0550 BABY- RATTLE BAIT MFG.
BABY- RATTLE BAIT
  1960
  $30

015-0343 BAILER BAITS
FISH-ALL
MI   1950-60's
  $30

015-0546 BAILEY & ELLIOT
MANITOU MINNOW
IN   1905   3 3/4 IN
WITH WRENCH $1500

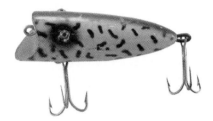

015-0267 BAKER, BILL CO.
LITTLE LUCKY 'LEVENS
OK   1947
WOOD, SMALL $40

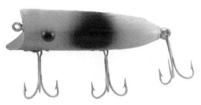

015-0268 BAKER, BILL CO.
LITTLE LUCKY 'LEVENS
OK   1947
WOOD, LARGE $40

015-0274 BAKER, BILL CO.
LITTLE LUCKY 'LEVENS
OK   1947
WOOD, SURFACE $50

015-0270 BAKER, BILL CO.
NIGHT CRAWLER, WEEDLESS
OK   1965
WOOD $10

015-0275 BAKER, BILL CO.
POPPER, BAKER
OK   1947   2 IN
WOOD, SMALL $50

015-0276 BAKER, BILL CO.
POPPER, BAKER
OK   1952   3 IN
WOOD, LARGE $50

015-0273 BAKER, BILL CO.
SURFACE MINNOW, BAKER
OK   1952   3 1/2 IN
WOOD $50

015-0269 BAKER, BILL CO.
TOPPER, BAKER
OK   1952   2 IN
WOOD $50

015-0277 BAKER, BILL CO.
WOBBLER, BABE-ORENO TYPE, BAKER
OK   1952   2 IN
WOOD, SMALL $50

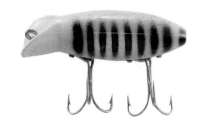

015-0278 BAKER, BILL CO.
WOBBLER, BABE-ORENO TYPE, BAKER
OK   1952   3 1/2 IN
WOOD, LARGE $50

015-0271 BAKER, BILL CO.
WOBBLER, BAKER
OK   1947   1 1/2 IN
WOOD, SMALL $50

015-0272 BAKER, BILL CO.
WOBBLER, BAKER
OK   1947   2 IN
WOOD, LARGE $50

016-2617 BAL-DART INC,
BAL-DART BAIT
MI   1957
  $50

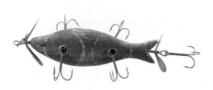

016-0325 BALDWIN BAITS (PFLUEGER)
BALDWIN MINNOW
MI   1910's   5 1/2 IN
ONLY ONE KNOWN $3000

016-0507 BALLARD, IKE
BINGO
IN   1960   2 1/2 IN
  $20

016-0506 BALLARD, IKE
IKE BALLARD BAIT
IN   1955
  $30

016-5441 BAR LAKE
DECOY, KINGFISH

  $300

016-0505 BARBEE BAIT CO,
SLO-POKE
IN   1955   1 3/4 IN
  $10

016-0503 BARBER, E.E.
REEL SHAD
KY   1960   2 1/4 IN
  $20

016-0547 BARNES E. & B.D.
BARNES BAIT
  1906   3 1/2 IN
HAND PAINTED $3000

016-0346 BARR-ROYERS CO.
FROG, BARR-ROYERS
IA   1925
LARGE $200

016-0347 BARR-ROYERS CO.
FROG, BARR-ROYERS
IA   1925
SMALL $200

016-0318 BARR-ROYERS CO.
MINNOW, BARR-ROYERS
IA   1931   2 1/4 IN
WOOD $200

016-0331 BARR-ROYERS CO.
MINNOW, BARR-ROYERS
IA   1931   4 1/4 IN
MUSKY SIZE $400

016-0319 BARR-ROYERS CO.
WATER PUPPY
IA   1931   3 3/4 IN
WOOD, LARGE $200

016-0320 BARR-ROYERS CO.
WATER PUPPY
IA   1931   2 1/4 IN
WOOD, SMALL $200

016-0350 BARR-ROYERS CO.
WOOD CRAB, BARR-ROYERS
IA   1931   3 IN
LARGE $200

FISHING PLUGS

017-0351 BARR-ROYERS CO.
WOOD CRAB, BARR-ROYERS
IA 1931 3 IN
SMALL $200

017-24770 BASS BUSTER BAIT CO.
BASS BUSTER TOPPER
MO 1952
$30

017-0341 BASS-BUSTER LURES
BASS BAIT DIVER
MO 1952
DEEP DIVER $30

017-0340 BASS-BUSTER LURES
DEEP RUNT TYPE
MO 1952 2 1/2 IN
AB SAINT LIP $20

017-0534 BASSKIL CO.
BASSKIL
TX 1950 2 1/2 IN
SMALL $30

017-0533 BASSKIL CO.
SEAHAWK
TX 1950 3 IN
$30

017-3259 BATES, FANNY
LADYBUG WEEDLESS
MN 1946 2 1/2 IN 1/2 OZ
SMALL $90

017-3260 BATES, FANNY
LADYBUG WEEDLESS
MN 1946 3 1/4 IN 5/8 OZ
LARGE $90

017-3265 BATES
FANNY BATES
MN 1946 3 1/4 IN 5/8 OZ
LARGE $90

017-3266 BATES, FANNY
LADYBUG
MN 1946 2 3/4 IN 1/2 OZ
SMALL $90

017-0532 BATSELL BAITS
BATSELL KILLER
TX 1950 3 IN
$10

017-0513 BEAR CREEK BAIT CO.
DECOY, BEAR CREEK
MI 1940 6 1/2 IN
WOOD $200

017-0514 BEAR CREEK BAIT CO.
DECOY, BEAR CREEK
MI 1940 6 1/2 IN
WOOD $200

017-5359 BEAR CREEK BAIT CO.
DECOY, BEAR CREEK
MI 1940's
BEAR CREEK $100

017-5381 BEAR CREEK BAIT CO.
FISH DECOY, BEAR CREEK
MI 1940's
$100

018-5382 BEAR CREEK BAIT CO.
FISH DECOY, BEAR CREEK
MI   1952
 $100

018-5383 BEAR CREEK BAIT CO.
FISH DECOY, BEAR CREEK
MI   1940's
 $100

018-5384 BEAR CREEK BAIT CO.
FISH DECOY, BEAR CREEK
MI   1940's
 $100

018-5387 BEAR CREEK BAIT CO.
FISH DECOY, BEAR CREEK
MI   1940's
 $100

018-5425 BEAR CREEK BAIT CO.
FISH DECOY, BEAR CREEK
MI   1952
 $100

018-5428 BEAR CREEK BAIT CO.
FISH DECOY, BEAR CREEK
MI   1952
 $100

018-0510 BEAR CREEK BAIT CO.
SUCKER MINNOW, BEAR CREEK
MI   1952   2 1/2 IN
SMALL $30

018-0511 BEAR CREEK BAIT CO.
SUCKER MINNOW, BEAR CREEK
MI   1952   3 3/4 IN
LARGE $30

018-0509 BEAR CREEK BAIT CO.
SUCKER MINNOW, DEEP DIVE
MI   1926
 $30

018-0545 BEAR CREEK BAIT CO.
TWEEDLER
MI   1952   2 1/2 IN
2 SIZES $30

018-3363 BEAVER BAIT CO.
OLE FIGHTER
PA   1955
 $30

018-0504 BENDER FISHING TACKLE
DILLIE
FL   1955   2 3/4 IN
 $20

018-0260 BENO BAIT CO
BENO BAIT
TX
 $30

018-0261 BENO BAIT CO
BENO EEL
TX
SURFACE $30

018-0262 BENO BAIT CO
BENO EEL
TX
DIVING $30

FISHING PLUGS

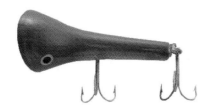

019-0499 BERRY-LEBECK MFG. CO.
TALKY-TOPPER
MO   1947   3 IN
OZARKA LURE $40

019-3164 BERRY-LEBECK MFG. CO.
WEE-GEE
MO   1960   2 1/4 IN
SMALL $20

019-5545 BESSINGER, FRANK
BESS LURE
MI   1951
   $30

019-5442 BETHEL, C.
DECOY, SUCKER , BETHEL
MN   1950
   $300

019-5399 BETHEL, C.
DECOY, TROUT
MN   1950
   $150

019-4090 BEYERLEIN, G.B.
BEYERLEIN LURE
MO   1920   5 1/2 IN
MUSKY $200

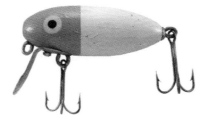

019-4091 BEYERLEIN, G.B.
BEYERLEIN LURE
MI   1928
   $150

019-0536 BIDDLE BAIT CO.
BIDDLE WOBBLER
MO
   $20

019-0537 BIDDLE BAIT CO.
BIDDLE WOBBLER
MO
SMALL $20

019-0531 BIDDLE BAIT CO.
MAGGOT WOBBLER
MO   1958
   $30

019-0538 BIDDLE BAIT CO.
BIDDLE BAIT
MO
SURFACE $20

019-0542 BIDDLE BAIT CO.
BIDDLE POPPER
MO
   $20

019-0543 BIDDLE BAIT CO.
BIDDLE POPPER
MO
   $20

019-0392 BIDWELL, C.W.
BOTTLE BAIT
MI   1915
   $1500

019-0393 BIDWELL, C.W.
BOTTLE BAIT
MI   1915   3 1/2 IN
3 VERSIONS $700

FISHING PLUGS

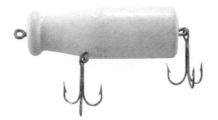

020-0394 BIDWELL, C.W.
BOTTLE BAIT
MI   1920
  $120

020-0491 BIEK BAIT CO.
BALSA MINNOW, BIEK
MI   1960
  $50

020-0494 BIEK BAIT CO.
GOLF TEE
MI   1947   2 3/4 IN
  $100

020-0490 BIEK BAIT CO.
MINNOW, BIEK
MI   1960
  $50

020-7143 BIEK BAIT CO.
PADDLER
MI   1947   3 IN
  $150

020-0311 BIFF BAIT CO
MR. BIFF
WI   1925   2 3/4 IN
WOOD, HOLE IN PLUG $200

020-0312 BIFF BAIT CO.
MASTER BIFF BAIT
WI   1925   2 IN
WOOD, JR. SIZE $250

020-0310 BIFF BAIT CO.
BIFF BAIT
WI   1926   2 IN
CORK & METAL, BASS SIZE $150

020-0313 BIFF BAIT CO.
GO DEVIL
WI   1926   1 1/2 IN
CORK & METAL $150

020-0314 BIFF BAIT CO.
MICKEY THE MOUSE
WI   1926   1 1/2 IN
CORK & METAL $150

020-0501 BIGNALL & SCHAAF
DIAMOND WIGGLER
MI   1914   3 3/4 IN
HOLE IN BAIT $400

020-0518 BINGENHEIMER, A.F.
BING'S MINNOW
WI   1905
SMALL, 1-HK $500

020-0519 BINGENHEIMER, A.F.
BING'S MINNOW, FLOATING
WI   1905
  $500

020-0520 BINGENHEIMER, A.F.
NEMAHBIN MINNOW
WI   1910   4 IN
UNDERWATER $500

020-0427 BITE-EM-BATE SALES CO.
BITE-EM BATE, UNKNOWN
IN   1922   3 IN
WEIGHTED HOOKS $300

FISHING PLUGS

021-0749 BITE-EM-BATE SALES CO.
BITE-EM BATE, UNKNOWN
IN   1922
$300

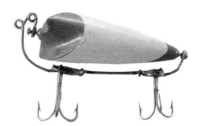

021-0420 BITE-EM-BATE SALES CO.
BITE-EM-BATE
IN   1919   3 IN
$200

021-0424 BITE-EM-BATE SALES CO.
BUG, BITE-EM-BATE
IN   1920   1 1/2 IN
$400

021-0432 BITE-EM-BATE SALES CO.
LIPPED WIGGLER
IN   1940
SMALL $200

021-0433 BITE-EM-BATE SALES CO.
LIPPED WIGGLER
IN   1920   3 1/2 IN
ADJUSTABLE $200

021-0425 BITE-EM-BATE SALES CO.
MINNOW, BITE-EM-BATE
IN   1921   2 1/2 IN
FLOATING $600

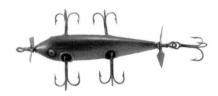

021-0426 BITE-EM-BATE SALES CO.
MINNOW, BITE-EM-BATE
IN   1921   3 3/4 IN
UNDERWATER $750

021-0422 BITE-EM-BATE SALES CO.
WATER MOLE
IN   1921   3 IN
$300

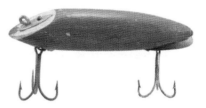

021-0423 BITE-EM-BATE SALES CO.
WIGGLER, BITE-EM-BATE
IN   1920   3 3/4 IN
$200

021-1433 BITTLECOME BAITS
CAL'S CRIPPLE MINNOW
CA   1966
$10

021-0389 BLAZ-O-LURE MFG. CO.
BLAZ-O-LURE
CA   1954
$40

021-0296 BLEEDING BAIT CO
BLEEDER BAIT, MUSKY
TX   1940's   4 IN
WOOD, USES BLOOD TABLETS $300

021-0291 BLEEDING BAIT CO
BROKEN BACK
TX   1940's   4 IN
WOOD, USES BLOOD TABLETS $200

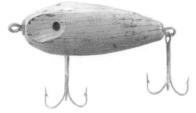

021-0301 BLEEDING BAIT CO
BUBBLER
TX   1940's   2 1/2 IN
WOOD, USES BLOOD TABLETS $150

021-0292 BLEEDING BAIT CO
CHUNKER, BLEEDING BAIT
TX   1940's   2 1/4 IN
WOOD, USES BLOOD TABLETS $150

022-0295 BLEEDING BAIT CO
DARTER, JOINTED, BLEEDING BAIT
TX   1947
WOOD, USES BLOOD TABLETS $200

022-0293 BLEEDING BAIT CO
DIDO
TX   1940   2 5/8 IN   5/8 OZ
WOOD, USES BLOOD TABLETS $150

022-0290 BLEEDING BAIT CO
MOUSE, BLEEDING BAIT CO
TX   1940   2 5/8 IN   1/2 OZ
WOOD, USES BLOOD TABLETS $300

022-0294 BLEEDING BAIT CO
RANGER DIVER
TX   1939   2 5/8 IN   1/2 OZ
WOOD, USES BLOOD TABLETS $150

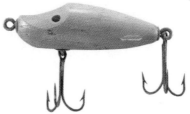

022-0302 BLEEDING BAIT CO
RANGER FLOATER
TX   1940's   3 IN
WOOD $150

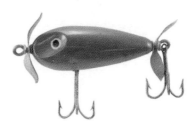

022-0297 BLEEDING BAIT CO
SPINNER, THE
TX   1941   2 5/8 IN
WOOD, USES BLOOD TABLETS $150

022-5125 BLIMPS BAIT CO.
SQUEAKY MOUSE

   $40

022-5567 BLOODY GOOD LURE CO.
BLOODY GOOD LURE
CO   1959
   $20

022-0348 BOBOPEN BAIT CO.
BOBOPEN BAIT
CO   1960
   $20

022-5380 BOB'S FLY TYING CO.
FISH DECOY, BOB'S

$200

022-5395 BOB'S FLY TYING CO.
FISH DECOY, BOB'S

$200

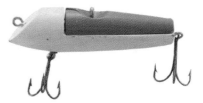

022-0493 BOLTON, GEORGE W.
A-B-C MINNOW
MI   1925   4 IN
MULTI-BODIED $600

022-24731 BOLTON, GEORGE W.
A-B-C MNNOW BODIES
MI   1925
GOES WITH A-B-C MINNOW $100

022-0352 BOMBER BAIT CO.
BOMBER, HANDMADE
TX   1939   3 IN
   $300

022-0353 BOMBER BAIT CO.
BOMBER LURE
TX   1940   2 1/2 IN
1st MANUFACTURED $75

FISHING PLUGS

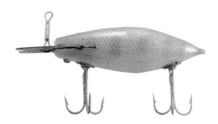

023-0354 BOMBER BAIT CO.
BOMBER LURE
TX   1942   2 1/2 IN
2stT MANUFACTURED $50

023-0355 BOMBER BAIT CO.
BOMBER LURE
TX   1944
3rd MANUFACTURED $40

023-0356 BOMBER BAIT CO.
BOMBER LURE
TX   1945
PLASTIC, 4th MANUFACTURED $40

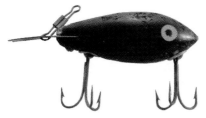

023-0357 BOMBER BAIT CO.
BOMBER LURE
TX   1950
5th MANUFACTURED $30

023-0358 BOMBER BAIT CO.
BOMBER LURE
TX   1953
6th MANUFACTURED $30

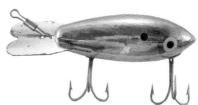

023-0359 BOMBER BAIT CO.
BOMBER LURE
TX   1965
CHROMED $30

023-0360 BOMBER BAIT CO.
BOMBER LURE
TX   1964
METAL FLAKES $30

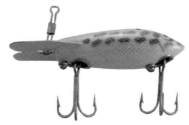

023-0361 BOMBER BAIT CO.
BOMBER LURE, HEAVY DUTY
TX   1965
   $50

023-0365 BOMBER BAIT CO.
BOMBER SPECIAL
TX   1948   2 1/2 IN
SPECIAL MADE $400

023-0384 BOMBER BAIT CO.
TOPPER, BOMBER
TX   1948   2 1/2 IN
   $30

023-0378 BOMBER BAIT CO.
BOMBERETTE
TX   1948   2 1/2 IN
LARGE $30

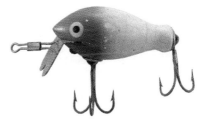

023-0379 BOMBER BAIT CO.
BOMBERETTE
TX   1948
MEDIUM $30

023-0380 BOMBER BAIT CO.
BOMBERETTE
TX   1948   2 IN
SMALL $30

023-0362 BOMBER BAIT CO.
JERK, BIG
TX   1952
LARGE $40

023-0363 BOMBER BAIT CO.
JERK, BOMBER BAIT CO
TX   1952   3 3/4 IN
MEDIUM $40

FISHING PLUGS

024-0364 BOMBER BAIT CO.
JERK, BOMBER BAIT CO
TX   1952   3 IN
SMALL $40

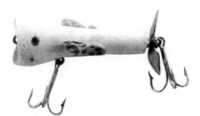

024-5471 BOMBER BAIT CO.
BOMBER BAIT
TX   1940's
 $200

024-0369 BOMBER BAIT CO.
KNOTHEAD
TX   1948
LARGE $150

024-0370 BOMBER BAIT CO.
KNOTHEAD
TX   1948   3 IN
SMALL $150

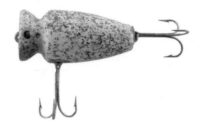

024-0371 BOMBER BAIT CO.
KNOTHEAD
TX   1948   3 IN
SMALL $150

024-0381 BOMBER BAIT CO.
SPIN STICK
TX   1952   3 1/2 IN
LARGE $30

024-0383 BOMBER BAIT CO.
SPIN STICK
TX   1950
SMALL $30

024-0382 BOMBER BAIT CO.
STICK
TX   1952   3 1/2 IN
SMALL $30

024-0375 BOMBER BAIT CO.
WATER DOG
TX   1948
LARGE $20

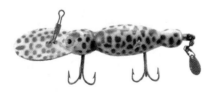

024-0376 BOMBER BAIT CO.
WATER DOG
TX   1948   3 1/2 IN
MEDIUM $20

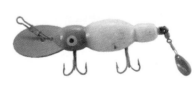

024-0377 BOMBER BAIT CO.
WATER DOG
TX   1948
SMALL $20

024-0368 BOMBER BAIT CO.
SPEED SHAD, BOMBER
TX   1963
 $20

024-0327 BONNER CO.
BONNER CASTING MINNOW
FL   1931   3 IN
SALTWATER $400

024-0326 BONNETT, C.E.
BONNETT MINNOW
LA   1932   4 IN
WOOD, GLASS EYES $600

024-0428 BOONE BAIT CO.
BLUE RIBBON MINNOW
FL   1955   3 IN
 $15

FISHING PLUGS

025-0523 BOONE BAIT CO.
NEEDLEFISH
FL   1957
  $20

025-0524 BOONE BAIT CO.
NEEDLEFISH
FL   1957   5 1/2 IN
LARGE $20

025-0525 BOONE BAIT CO.
NEEDLEFISH
FL   1957
  $20

025-0526 BOONE BAIT CO.
NEEDLEFISH
FL   1957   3 3/4 IN
SMALL $20

025-0527 BOONE BAIT CO.
NEEDLEFISH
FL   1957   4 1/2 IN
SMALL $20

025-5530 BOONE BAIT CO.
SURE-IMP
FL   1957
  $20

025-0329 BOSHEAR TACKLE CO.
RAZZLE DAZZLE
AR   1951   2 1/4 IN
  $20

025-0496 BOULTON, T.J.
BASS HOG
MI   1911   4 1/4 IN
  $300

025-0497 BOULTON, T.J.
BASS HOG
MI   1910   4 1/4 IN
  $300

025-0488 BOULTON, T.J.
DECOY, BOULTON
MI   1925   5 IN
  $2000

025-0548 BRAIDWOOD STAMP CO.
GAYLURE
NJ   1938
LARGE $75

025-0544 BRAIDWOOD STAMP CO.
GAYLURE
NJ   1934
  $100

025-0390 BRAINERD BAIT CO.
GOLD CAP DODGER
MN   1932   4 IN
FRONT PLATE, LARGE $200

025-0391 BRAINERD BAIT CO.
GOLD CAP DODGER
MN   1932
SMALL $200

015-0334 BRAINERD BAIT CO.
HORSEFLY
MN   1938   2 1/2 IN
TOPWATER $100

FISHING PLUGS

026-0530 BRIGHTE-EYE LURE PROD.
BRIGHTE-EYE-LURE
MI   1933   3 1/2 IN
LARGE $200

026-0529 BRIGHTE-EYE LURE PROD.
BRIGHTE-EYE-LURE
MI   1933   3 IN
SMALL $200

026-0411 BROOKS BAITS (R-JAY IND)
BROOKS WEEDLESS
OH   1941   1 3/4 IN   5/8 OZ
LARGE $20

026-0412 BROOKS BAITS (R-JAY IND)
BROOKS WEEDLESS
OH   1941   1 1/2 IN   1/2 OZ
SMALL $20

026-0414 BROOKS BAITS (R-JAY IND)
BROOKS TOPWATER
OH
SMALL $20

029-0413 BROOKS BAITS (R-JAY IND)
BROOKS TOPWATER NO.5
OH   1940   2 1/4 IN   1/2 OZ
LARGE $20

026-0407 BROOKS BAITS (R-JAY IND)
BUZZER
OH   1950
   $20

026-0409 BROOKS BAITS (R-JAY IND)
DIGGER
OH   1948   3 1/4 IN   1/2 OZ
   $20

026-0408 BROOKS BAITS (R-JAY IND)
DOUBLE OO
OH   1939   3 IN   1/2 OZ
   $20

026-0406 BROOKS BAITS (R-JAY IND)
O BROOKS BAIT
OH   1938   2 IN   1/2 OZ
   $20

026-0417 BROOKS BAITS (R-JAY IND)
REEFER
OH
LARGE $10

026-0418 BROOKS BAITS (R-JAY IND)
REEFER
OH
SMALL $10

026-0415 BROOKS BAITS (R-JAY IND)
REEFER, JOINTED
OH   1947   4 IN   1/2 OZ
LARGE $20

026-0416 BROOKS BAITS (R-JAY IND)
REEFER, JOINTED
OH   1940   3 IN
SMALL $20

026-0419 BROOK'S SHINER BAIT CO.
BROOK'S SHINER
WI   1926   3 3/4 IN
2 SIZES $600

FISHING PLUGS

027-6994 BROOKS-EIDSON TACKLE CO.
WHIZ BANG!
TX   1964
  $30

027-0431 BROWN BAIT CO.
DECOY, FISHERETTO
MN   1940   4 1/2 IN
TACK EYES $200

027-0430 BROWN BAIT CO.
FISHERETTO
MN   1915   4 IN
GLASS EYES $300

027-4088 BROWN BAIT CO.
FISHERETTO
MN   1915
  $300

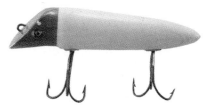

027-0429 BROWN BAIT CO.
FISHERETTO WIGGLER
MN   1918   4 IN
GLASS EYES $300

027-5715 BROWN'S TACKLE CO.
BASS HELPER
MI   1940
  $100

027-5417 BRU-ELL
DECOY, PERCH
MN   1950
GREENLEE $100

027-0500 BUCKEYE BAIT CO.
BUG & BASS
KS   1960   3 1/4 IN
LARGE, NOVELTY BAIT $40

027-5114 BUCKEYE BAIT CO.
BUG & BASS
KS   1960
SMALL $30

027-0386 BURGESS, BENJAMIN F.
BURGESS BAIT
MI   1898   2 1/2 IN
  $4000

027-0330 BURKE, B.F. BAITS
BUG, BURKE
IL   1914   2 1/4 IN
RUBBER $350

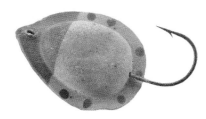

027-0344 BURKE, B.F. BAITS
BURKE BASS BAIT
IL   1913   2 IN
RUBBER $350

027-0345 BURKE, B.F. BAITS
BURKE BASS BAIT
IL   1913   2 IN
RUBBER $350

027-0528 BURMEK, TONY
BURMEK'S SECRET BAIT
WI   1960   7 1/2 IN
MUSKY BAIT $30

027-3921 BURRELLURE BAIT CO.
BURRELLURE MINNOW
NJ   1947   5 1/2 IN
LARGE $30

028-3920 BURRELLURE BAIT CO.
BURRELLURE MINNOW
NJ   1947   4IN
SMALL $30

028-0549 BURROUGHS, F.S. & CO.
AQUA BAIT
NJ   1947
  $30

028-6988 BURROUGHS, F.S. & CO.
BURROUGHS BAIT
NJ   1947
  $30

028-5469 BURROUGHS, F.S. & CO.
CROAKER, BURROUGHS
NJ   1950
  $30

028-0305 BYLER, AL
BASGETER SURFACE MOLE
WA   1930   3 1/2 IN
WOOD $300

028-0306 BYLER, AL
BASGETER, UNDERWATER
WA   1930   5 1/2 IN
WOOD $300

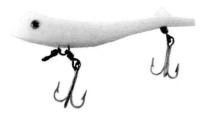

028-5208 C & E SPORTFISHING
SEA PEARL
MA
  $30

028-0724 CAIN, RALPH
GRASSHOPPER POPPER, CAIN
OK   1937 2 3/4 IN
$400

028-0725 CAIN, RALPH
GRASSHOPPER, CAIN
OK   1940   3 1/4 IN
THIN FLAT BODY $300

028-0790 CALKIN
CALKIN MINNOW TUBE

  $500

028-0717 CAMPBELL, F.C.
WILCOX BAIT
OH   1909   2 1/4 IN
  $1000

028-0718 CAMPBELL, F.C.
WILCOX POPPER
OH   1909   2 7/8 IN
  $1500

028-7138 CAMPBELL, F.C.
WILCOX WIGGLER
OH   1907   3 3/4 IN
  $3000

028-3847 CANADIAN MAKER, UNKNOWN
TNT BAIT
CAN
  $20

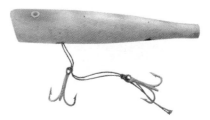

028-5197 CAP'N BILL
POPPER, CAP'N BILL
  1947
  $30

FISHING PLUGS

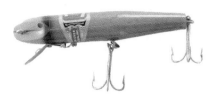

029-5126 CAPTIVATED LURES, INC.
EL PRODUCTO LURE
FL   1970's
KING EDWARD PROMOTIONAL $40

029-3376 CAPTIVATED LURES, INC.
LULU LURE
FL   1960   6 IN
BATTERY OPERATED $90

029-0721 CARNES, JACK LURES
FANCY-DANCER
AR   1953   3 1/4 IN
HOLE IN PLUG $40

029-0641 CARR MFG. CO.
BAIT PILOT
CA   1954
    $20

029-0723 CARSWELL, M.
CARSWELL FROG
    1898
LARGE, SCOTLAND $300

029-0722 CARSWELL, M.
CARSWELL FROG
    1898
SMALL, SCOTLAND $300

029-0744 CARTER BAIT CO.
BESTEVER BAIT
IN   1923   3 5/8 IN   3/4 OZ
'OLD BLACK JOE' $75

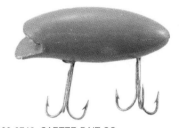

029-0746 CARTER BAIT CO.
BESTEVER BAIT
IN   1923   3 1/8 IN
MED $75

029-0739 CARTER BAIT CO.
BESTEVER BAIT
IN
    $75

029-0737 CARTER BAIT CO.
BESTEVER BAIT
IN   1931   3 1/8 IN
GLASS EYES $150

029-0741 CARTER BAIT CO.
BESTEVER BAIT
IN   1924   1 3/4 IN   1/8 OZ
BABY SIZE $100

029-0748 CARTER BAIT CO.
BESTEVER BAIT
IN   1927   2 5/8 IN
WEEDLESS $150

029-0747 CARTER BAIT CO.
MOUSE, CARTER
OH   1926
OLD $150

029-0738 CARTER BAIT CO.
MOUSE, CARTER
IN   1933   2 5/8 IN   1/2 OZ
    $200

029-0742 CARTER BAIT CO.
DAY-R-NIGHT
IN   1930   3 IN
    $150

FISHING PLUGS

030-0743 CARTER BAIT CO.
DUBBLE-HEADER BAIT
IN   1930   3 1/4 IN
OLD, ADJUSTABLE HEAD $150

030-0745 CARTER BAIT CO.
SHORE MINNOW, CARTER
IN   3 1/4 IN   3/4 OZ
   $150

030-0732 CARTER-DUNK'S
DUBBLE-HEADER BAIT
OH   1933   2 1/2 IN
LARGE $200

030-0733 CARTER-DUNK'S
DUBBLE-HEADER BAIT
OH   1933   2 IN
BABY SIZE $200

030-0735 CARTER-DUNK'S
MINNOW
OH   1931   3 1/4 IN   3/4 OZ
SURFACE $150

030-0734 CARTER-DUNK'S
PIKE BAIT
OH   1924   1 1/4 IN   3/4 OZ
   $250

030-0736 CARTER-DUNK'S
POPPER
OH
   $150

030-0752 CARTER-DUNK'S
STUBBY'S HYDROPLUG
OH   1923   2 3/4 IN   5/8 OZ
AMERICAN DISPLAY CO. $75

030-0763 CARTER-DUNK'S
SWIM-A-LURE BLUE GILL
OH   1939   3 IN
   $300

030-0766 CARTER-DUNK'S
SWIM-A-LURE CHIPMUNK
OH   1939
   $500

030-0761 CARTER-DUNK'S
SWIM-A-LURE DUCKLING
OH   1939
   $300

030-0760 CARTER-DUNK'S
SWIM-A-LURE FROG
OH   1939   2 1/2 IN
   $300

030-0762 CARTER-DUNK'S
SWIM-A-LURE JOINTED PIKE
OH   1939   4 1/2 IN   3/4 OZ
   $300

030-0759 CARTER-DUNK'S
SWIM-A-LURE PIKE
OH   1939   4 1/2 IN
   $300

030-0765 CARTER-DUNK'S
SWIM-A-LURE STRIPED MINNOW
OH   1944
   $300

031-0764 CARTER-DUNK'S
SWIM-A-LURE YELLOW JACKET
OH   1944
  $300

031-0730 CASE BAIT CO.
ROTARY MARVEL
MI   1910   3 IN
  $1500

031-0731 CASE BAIT CO.
ROTARY MARVEL
MI   1911   3 IN
(PFLUEGER) $1500

031-2807 CASTING, INC.
FLIPPER FISH, CASTING INC.
MI   1948
WEEDLESS $40

031-0607 CEDAR SQUID BAIT CO.
CEDAR SQUID
NY   1900-1910
SALTWATER $60

031-0608 CEDAR SQUID BAIT CO.
CEDAR SQUID
NY   1900-1910
SALTWATER $60

031-0609 CEDAR SQUID BAIT CO.
CEDAR SQUID
NY   1900-1910
SALTWATER $60

031-0610 CEDAR SQUID BAIT CO.
CEDAR SQUID
NY   1900-1910
SALTWATER $60

031-0643 CEDAR STUMP BAIT CO.
CEDAR STUMP
  1958
  $20

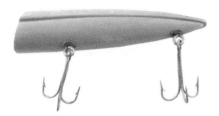

031-0715 CELLU-ART BAIT CO.
CELLU-ART BAIT
MA   1920
  $400

031-0639 CHALLENGE TACKLE
ADJUSTABLE WING BAIT
PA   1952
  $30

030-0653 CHARMER MINNOW CO., THE
CHARMER MINNOW
MO   1910   3 1/4 IN
  $500

031-0654 CHARMER MINNOW CO., THE
CHARMER MINNOW
MO   1910
JR. SIZE $500

031-0655 CHARMER MINNOW CO., THE
CHARMER MINNOW
MO   1912   3 IN
BABY $500

031-0656 CHARMER MINNOW CO., THE
CHARMER MINNOW
MO   1912   3 1/2 IN
TOPWATER $1000

032-0658 CHARMER MINNOW CO., THE
CHARMER MINNOW
MO   1915   3 IN
METAL HEAD $300

032-0785 CHASE ROD & TACKLE
FISH GETTER
FL   1952   3 3/4 IN
  $60

032-5762 CHEVALIER, FRANK
FRENCHY SPECIAL
FL   1938
  $200

032-5767 CHEVALIER, FRANK
FRENCHY SPECIAL
FL   1938
  $200

032-5769 CHEVALIER, FRANK
FRENCHY SPECIAL
FL   1938
  $200

032-5770 CHEVALIER, FRANK
FRENCHY SPECIAL
FL   1938
  $200

032-5771 CHEVALIER, FRANK
FRENCHY SPECIAL
FL   1938
  $100

032-0615 CHICAGO TACKLE CO.
KING CHUB
IL   1952   3 1/2 IN   5/8 OZ
LARGE $50

032-0616 CHICAGO TACKLE CO.
KING CHUB
IL   1952   2 1/2 IN   3/8 OZ
MEDIUM $50

032-0617 CHICAGO TACKLE CO.
KING CHUB
IL   1952   2 IN   1/4 OZ
SMALL $50

032-0779 CHICAGO TACKLE CO.
THOREN MINNOW CHASER
IL   1937
  $400

032-2678 CHIX FISH LURE CO.
SALMON PLUG, CHIX
WA   1935   5 IN
SMALL $40

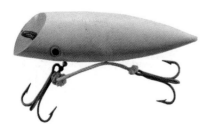

032-2679 CHIX FISH LURE CO.
SALMON PLUG, CHIX
WA   1939   6 IN
LARGE $40

032-2680 CHIX FISH LURE CO.
SALMON PLUG, CHIX
WA
MEDIUM $75

032-5806 CHOICE, RUA
CHOICE BAIT
OK   1959
  $40

FISHING PLUGS

033-0562 CHRISTENSEN, O.
CHRISTENSEN FROG
MN   1936   3 IN
WORKING LEGS $2000

033-5154 CHUM LURE CO.
CHUM CHUM BAIT
FL
GOES WITH 5183 $30

033-5183 CHUM LURE CO.
CHUM CHUM BAIT FOOD
FL
GOES WITH 5154 $15

033-0590 CHURCH ST. TACKLE
CHURCH ST. MINNOW
IL   1949
    $20

033-0587 CHURCH ST. TACKLE
CHURCH ST. WIGGLER
IL   1949
    $30

033-0589 CHURCH ST. TACKLE
CHURCH ST. WIGGLER
IL   1949
    $30

033-0588 CHURCH ST. TACKLE
CHURCH ST. TOPWATER
IL   1949
    $30

033-2573 CINCINNATI SUPERIOR BAITS
LUCKY DEVIL
OH   1933   1 3/4 IN
MILNERS $40

033-0787 CIRCLE H LURES
BUTCH
OH   1949   2 3/4 IN
HOLDENLINE CO $60

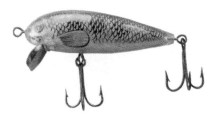

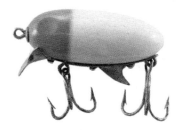

033-0786 CIRCLE H LURES
SOURPUSS
OH   1949   3 IN
HOLDENLINE CO $60

033-0726 CLARK BROTHERS
MAKE 'EM BITE
IN   1926   3 IN
    $500

033-0693 CLARK, C.A. , CO.
WATER SCOUT
MO
NO EYE, OLDEST $75

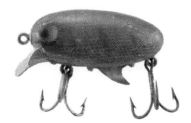

033-0692 CLARK, C.A. , CO.
WATER SCOUT
MO   1936   2 1/4 IN
LARGE, OLD $75

033-0691 CLARK, C.A. , CO.
WATER SCOUT
MO   1936   2 IN
SMALL, OLD $75

033-0699 CLARK, C.A. , CO.
SCOUT SINKER
MO   1946   2 1/4 IN
LARGE, DOT ON TAIL $40

FISHING PLUGS

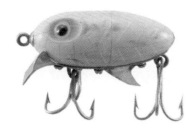

034-0700 CLARK, C.A. , CO.
SCOUT SINKER
MO
SMALL, DOT ON TAIL $40

034-0698 CLARK, C.A. , CO.
SCOUT FLOATER
MO
LARGE $40

034-0701 CLARK, C.A. , CO.
SCOUT FLOATER
MO 1946 2 IN
SMALL $40

034-0702 CLARK, C.A. , CO.
SCOUT WITH AB SAINT LIP
MO 1947 2 IN
DEEP DIVING WATER SCOUT $100

034-0703 CLARK, C.A. , CO.
LITTLE EDDIE
MO 1946 1 3/4 IN
  $75

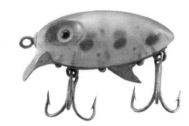

034-0704 CLARK, C.A. , CO.
STREAMLINER, CLARK
MO 1948 2 1/4 IN
PLASTIC $50

034-0696 CLARK, C.A. , CO.
DUCK BILL,   LARGE
MO 1946 2 1/4 IN
  $100

034-0697 CLARK, C.A. , CO.
DUCKLING
MO 1946 2 IN
SMALL $100

034-0695 CLARK, C.A. , CO.
DUCK BILL,   JOINTED
MO 1946 3 IN
  $100

034-0694 CLARK, C.A. , CO.
POPPER SCOUT
MO 1936 2 1/2 IN
  $30

034-0689 CLARK, C.A. , CO.
DARTER, C LARK
MO 1948 3 IN
  $100

034-0690 CLARK, C.A. , CO.
GOOFY GUS
MO 1948 3 1/4 IN
  $150

034-5677 CLARK, ISADORE
WOODPECKER TYPE
  1932
  $100

034-0727 CLARK, J.L. MFG. CO.
CLARK EXPERT
IL 1907 4 IN 1 OZ
MUSKY SIZE, REVERSE GILLS $2000

034-0728 CLARK, J.L. MFG. CO.
CLARK EXPERT
IL 1907 4 IN
REVERSE GILLS $1000

FISHING PLUGS

035-0729 CLARK, J.L. MFG. CO.
CLARK EXPERT
IL 1907 3 IN 1/2 OZ
BABY SIZE, REVERSE GILLS $800

035-0784 CLEWELL, R.L.
SNAKERBAIT
OH 1926 4 1/4 IN
CERAMIC $1000

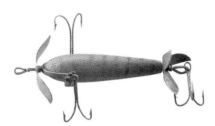

035-0652 CLINTON WILT
CHAMPION
MO 1912 3 1/4 IN
$1500

035-0651 CLINTON WILT
LITTLE WONDER, CLINTON WILT
MO 1913 2 1/4 IN
$1500

035-7137 COLD LIGHT MFG. CO.
MARVELITE RADIUM MINNOW

DOTS ON BELLY (PLUEGER) $300

035-0769 COLDWATER BAITS
COLDWATER BAIT
MI 1912 4 1/2 IN
$200

035-0770 COLDWATER BAITS
COLDWATER BAIT
MI 1912
$200

035-0771 COLDWATER BAITS
COLDWATER BAIT
MI 1912
$200

035-0772 COLDWATER BAITS
FINCH
MI 1912 4 1/2 IN
$600

035-0774 COLDWATER BAITS
GHOST
MI 1915 4 IN
NEWER $200

035-0768 COLDWATER BAITS
HELLDIVER
MI 1917 4 3/8 IN
$250

035-0775 COLDWATER BAITS
KING WIGGLER, COLDWATER
MI 1920 4 IN
$300

035-0776 COLDWATER BAITS
KING WIGGLER, COLDWATER
MI 1931
SMALL $350

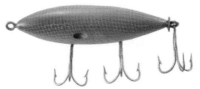

035-0773 COLDWATER BAITS
WIGGLER, COLDWATER
MI 1931 4 IN
$250

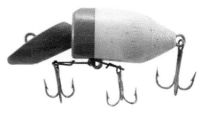

035-0613 COLGER MFG.
GROOVEHEAD
MI 1953
$100

FISHING PLUGS

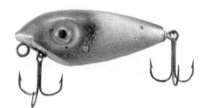

036-1208 COLT DISTRIBUTING CO.
PONY LURE
FL   1950
  $60

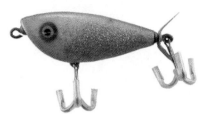

036-3310 COLT DISTRIBUTING CO.
PONY LURE
FL   1953   3 IN
LARGE, SERV-A-LURE CO. $40

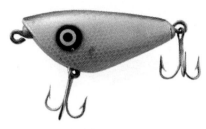

036-3311 COLT DISTRIBUTING CO.
PONY LURE
FL   1953   2 1/4 IN
SMALL, SERV-A-LURE $40

036-0593 COMBS, E.E.
COMBS MINNOW
MO   1946
SMALL $90

036-0594 COMBS, E.E.
COMBS MINNOW
MO   1946   2 3/4 IN
LARGE $90

036-0595 COMBS, E.E.
COMBS WOBBLER
MO   1946   1 3/4 IN
SMALL $90

036-0781 COMSTOCK, HARRY
FLYING HELLGRAMITE
NY   1883   3 IN
RED GLASS EYES $10000

036-0777 COMSTOCK, F.E.
COMSTOCK CHUNK
MI   1939
  $300

036-0778 COMSTOCK, F.E.
COMSTOCK CHUNK
MI   1939   4 IN
  $350

036-0600 COOK, F.W.
COOK'S "500" BEER LURE
IN
  $100

036-0599 COOK, F.W.
COOK'S BEER LURE
IN
  $100

036-0565 COOL RIPPLE LURES, INC.
COOL RIPPLE FROG,   FEMALE
IL   1947   2 3/4 IN
HUMAN PARTS $60

036-0566 COOL RIPPLE LURES, INC.
COOL RIPPLE FROG,   MALE
IL   1947   2 3/4 IN
HUMAN PARTS $60

036-0627 COOPER LURES
BIG DADDY
IL   1952
  $30

036-0626 COOPER LURES
BIG LUNKER POPPER
IL   1952
  $30

FISHING PLUGS

037-0597 COOPER LURES
COOPER LOOR
IL   1951   2 IN   5/8 OZ
GENE COOPER $40

037-0637 COOPER LURES
DUDE
IL   1952
BABY $20

037-0628 COOPER LURES
HUSKY DUDE
IL   1952
   $30

037-0633 COOPER LURES
HUSTLE, JOINTED
IL   1952
   $30

037-0631 COOPER LURES
HUSTLER, COOPER
IL   1952
   $30

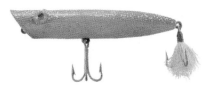

037-0634 COOPER LURES
LUNKER POPPER
IL   1952
   $30

037-0635 COOPER LURES
SHARKIE JR.
IL   1952
   $30

037-0632 COOPER LURES
SUPER HUSTLER
IL   1952
   $30

037-0629 COOPER LURES
SUPER SHARKIE
IL   1952
   $30

037-0598 COOPER LURES
UBANGI
IL   1952   2 IN
   $20

037-5120 CORDELL
ARKANSAS RAZORBACK
AR   1977
   $10

037-5116 CORDELL
CORDELL, UNKNOWN
AR   1977
   $20

037-5119 CORDELL
PEANUT LURE
AR   1977
   $20

037-0611 CORONADO TACKLE
DRAGONFLY, CORONADO

   $60

037-0596 COX, ARTHUR
COX TAMPA BAY MINNOW
FL   1922   4 IN
   $1000

FISHING PLUGS

038-0584 CRABUG BAIT CO.
CRABUG
MI   1939   3 3/4 IN
  $150

038-5133 CRACKERJACK PRIZES
CRACKER JACK CO.
  1951
LURE AND KEYCHAIN $50

038-5122 CRAZY LEGS BAIT CO.
CRAZY LEGS
MO
  $40

038-5123 CRAZY LEGS BAIT CO.
CRAZY LEGS
MO
  $40

038-0798 CREEK CHUB BAIT CO.
BASS-ORENO
IN   1930-1939   3 3/4 IN
SALTWATER, SHUR-STRIKE $50

038-0799 CREEK CHUB BAIT CO.
BASS-ORENO
IN
SHUR-STRIKE   BO TYPE $90

038-0800 CREEK CHUB BAIT CO.
BABE-ORENO
IN   1930's   3 IN
SHUR-STRIKE   BO TYPE $90

038-0828 CREEK CHUB BAIT CO.
PETITE SPINNER
IN   1930-1939   2 IN
SHUR-STRIKE $90

038-0817 CREEK CHUB BAIT CO.
BIG MOUTH
IN   1928   2 3/4 IN
SHUR-STRIKE $120

038-0846 CREEK CHUB BAIT CO.
DARTER
IN   1930-1939   3 1/2 IN
SHUR-STRIKE $120

038-1029 CREEK CHUB BAIT CO.
DINGER
IN
SHUR-STRIKE, NO METAL PLATE $90

038-0814 CREEK CHUB BAIT CO.
FLAT FISH
IN
SHUR-STRIKE   FF TYPE $90

038-0815 CREEK CHUB BAIT CO.
FLAT FISH
IN   1930-1939   3 IN
SHUR-STRIKE   FF TYPE $90

038-0826 CREEK CHUB BAIT CO.
INJURED MINNOW
IN   1930-1193   3 3/4 IN
SHUR-STRIKE $50

038-0919 CREEK CHUB BAIT CO.
INJURED MINNOW
IN
SHUR-STRIKE $90

FISHING PLUGS

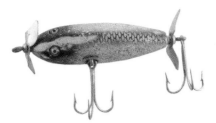

039-0923 CREEK CHUB BAIT CO.
INJURED MINNOW
IN
SHUR-STRIKE, BABY $75

039-0840 CREEK CHUB BAIT CO.
ANTEATER, MIDGET
IN   1930-1939   2 3/4 IN
SHUR-STRIKE $90

039-0839 CREEK CHUB BAIT CO.
ANTEATER
IN   1930's   3 1/4 IN
BABY, SHUR-STRIKE $90

039-0834 CREEK CHUB BAIT CO.
PIKIE, MIDGET
IN   1938   2 3/4 IN
SHUR-STRIKE   MP TYPE $90

039-0827 CREEK CHUB BAIT CO.
UNDERWATER MINNOW
IN   1930-1939   3 1/4 IN
SHUR-STRIKE $120

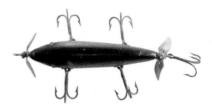

039-0907 CREEK CHUB BAIT CO.
UNDERWATER SPINNER
IN   1925   3 3/4 IN
SHUR-STRIKE? $2000

039-0832 CREEK CHUB BAIT CO.
PIKIE
IN   1938   4 1/4 IN
SHUR-STRIKE   P TYPE $90

039-0833 CREEK CHUB BAIT CO.
PIKIE
IN
SHUR-STRIKE   P TYPE $90

039-0835 CREEK CHUB BAIT CO.
PIKIE
IN   1938   3 1/4 IN
SHUR-STRIKE , BABY, BP TYPE $90

039-0836 CREEK CHUB BAIT CO.
PIKIE
IN
SHUR-STRIKE   P TYPE $90

039-0842 CREEK CHUB BAIT CO.
APIKIE, JOINTED
IN   1930-1939   4 1/4 IN
SHUR-STRIKE   PJ TYPE $90

039-0841 CREEK CHUB BAIT CO.
PIKIE, JOINTED, BABY
IN   1930-1939   3 1/2 IN
SHUR-STRIKE, BJP TYPE. $90

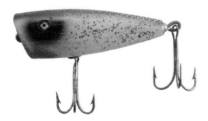

039-0824 CREEK CHUB BAIT CO.
PLUNKER
IN
OLD STYLE $150

039-0825 CREEK CHUB BAIT CO.
PLUNKER
IN
SHUR-STRIKE $50

039-0805 CREEK CHUB BAIT CO.
POINTED NOSE
IN
SHUR-STRIKE $120

FISHING PLUGS

040-0806 CREEK CHUB BAIT CO.
POINTED NOSE WIGGLER
IN   1930-1939   4 IN
SHUR-STRIKE $100

040-0984 CREEK CHUB BAIT CO.
POP ' N' DUNK
IN   1930-1939   2 3/4 IN
SHUR-STRIKE $120

040-0830 CREEK CHUB BAIT CO.
MINNIE MOUSE WOBBLER
IN   1930-1939   3 IN
SHUR-STRIKE $120

040-0829 CREEK CHUB BAIT CO.
MINNIE MOUSE, TOPWATER
IN   1930-1939   3 IN
SHUR-STRIKE $120

040-0831 CREEK CHUB BAIT CO.
MINNIE MOUSE, UNDERWATER
IN   1930-1939   3 IN
SHUR-STRIKE $60

040-0804 CREEK CHUB BAIT CO.
RIVER RUNT, CREEK CHUB
IN
SHUR-STRIKE   RR TYPE $120

040-0810 CREEK CHUB BAIT CO.
RIVER RUNT, CREEK CHUB
IN   1930-1939   2 1/2 IN
SHUR-STRIKE $90

040-0812 CREEK CHUB BAIT CO.
RIVER RUNT, CREEK CHUB
IN
SHUR-STRIKE   RR TYPE $50

040-0813 CREEK CHUB BAIT CO.
RIVER RUNT, CREEK CHUB
IN
SHUR-STRIKE   RR TYPE $90

040-0843 CREEK CHUB BAIT CO.
RIVER RUNT, JTD, CREEK CHUB
IN   1930-1939   3 1/2 IN
SHUR-STRIKE   JRR TYPE $90

040-0844 CREEK CHUB BAIT CO.
RIVER RUNT, JTD, CREEK CHUB
IN
SHUR-STRIKE   JRR TYPE $50

040-0811 CREEK CHUB BAIT CO.
WOBBLER, CREEK CHUB
IN
SHUR-STRIKE $90

040-0838 CREEK CHUB BAIT CO.
ROUND NOSE
IN   1930-1939   4 1/2 IN
SHUR-STRIKE $90

040-0809 CREEK CHUB BAIT CO.
SHUR-STRIKE BAIT
IN
    $50

040-0797 CREEK CHUB BAIT CO.
SLANT-NOSE
IN   1930-1939   3 3/4 IN
SHUR-STRIKE,   STYLE A $90

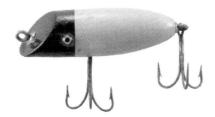

041-0801 CREEK CHUB BAIT CO.
SLANT-NOSE
IN   1930-1939   3 IN
SHUR-STRIKE,   SMALL $90

041-0845 CREEK CHUB BAIT CO.
SLANT-NOSE WOODPECKER
IN   1930-1939   4 1/4 IN
SHUR-STRIKE $120

041-0823 CREEK CHUB BAIT CO.
SLIM JIM
IN   1930-1939   4 IN
SHUR-STRIKE   SJ TYPE $90

041-0802 CREEK CHUB BAIT CO.
SURF-ORENO
IN   1930's   3 3/4 IN
SHUR-STRIKE   SO TYPE $90

041-0803 CREEK CHUB BAIT CO.
SURF-ORENO
IN   1930-1939   2 3/4 IN
BABY,SHUR-STRIKE, BSO TYPE $90

041-0816 CREEK CHUB BAIT CO.
ZARGOSSA
IN   1920-1929
SHUR-STRIKE   Z TYPE $200

041-0987 CREEK CHUB BAIT CO.
BEETLE, CREEK CHUB
IN   1932
BABY $200

041-0998 CREEK CHUB BAIT CO.
BEETLE, CREEK CHUB
IN   1931   2 1/2 IN   3/4 OZ
#3800 SERIES $200

041-0985 CREEK CHUB BAIT CO.
BOMBER
IN   1942   2 1/4 IN   3/8 OZ
#6500 SERIES, BABY $90

041-0990 CREEK CHUB BAIT CO.
BOMBER KREEKER
IN   1942   2 3/4 IN   1/2 OZ
#6600 SERIES $150

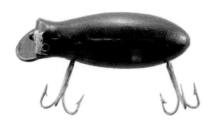

041-0986 CREEK CHUB BAIT CO.
BOMBER, BIG
IN   1939   3 1/2 IN
#6700 SERIES $500

041-0819 CREEK CHUB BAIT CO.
BUG WIGGLER
IN
EARLY $1000

041-0950 CREEK CHUB BAIT CO.
CASTROLA
IN   1927   3 5/8 IN   3/4 OZ
#3100 SERIES $200

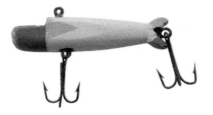

041-0969 CREEK CHUB BAIT CO.
CLOSE-PIN BAIT
IN   1936   3 1/4 IN   1 1/2 OZ
#5000 SERIES $900

041-0848 CREEK CHUB BAIT CO.
CRAWDAD
IN   1926   2 1/4 IN   1/2 OZ
#400 SERIES, LATER $50

042-0849 CREEK CHUB BAIT CO.
CRAWDAD
IN   2 1/4 IN   1/2 OZ
#400 SERIES, LATER $50

042-0860 CREEK CHUB BAIT CO.
CRAWDAD
IN
#300 $100

042-0861 CREEK CHUB BAIT CO.
CRAWDAD
IN   1918   2 3/4 IN   3/4 OZ
#300, OLD STYLE $400

042-0862 CREEK CHUB BAIT CO.
CRAWDAD
IN   1926   2 3/4 IN   3/4 OZ
#300, NEW STYLE $50

042-0847 CREEK CHUB BAIT CO.
CRAWDAD   ALBINO
IN   1918   2 1/4 IN   1/2 OZ
#400 SERIES, EARLY, BABY $400

042-0859 CREEK CHUB BAIT CO.
CRAZY CRAB
IN
#9900 SERIES $40

042-0905 CREEK CHUB BAIT CO.
CREEK & RIVER FISHING LURE
IN   1924   2 3/4 IN   5/8 OZ
#1800 SERIES $1500

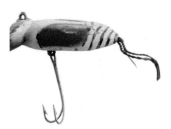

042-0912 CREEK CHUB BAIT CO.
CREEK BUG WIGGLER, BIG
IN   1924   2 1/2 IN   1/2 OZ
#1400 SERIES $400

042-2340 CREEK CHUB BAIT CO.
CREEK CHUB-ORENO
IN   1938
V GROOVE, SHUR-STRIKE $90

042-0940 CREEK CHUB BAIT CO.
DARTER
IN   1960   3 1/4 IN
GLASS-EYED $75

042-0941 CREEK CHUB BAIT CO.
DARTER
IN   1924   3 3/4 IN   1/2 OZ
#2000 SERIES, NO EYES $75

042-0942 CREEK CHUB BAIT CO.
DARTER
IN   3 1/4 IN
#2000 SERIES, OLD STYLE $100

042-0943 CREEK CHUB BAIT CO.
DARTER
IN   3 3/4 IN
#2000 SERIES $50

042-1008 CREEK CHUB BAIT CO.
DARTER
IN   1957   7 1/4 IN
#7600 SERIES, SALTWATER $300

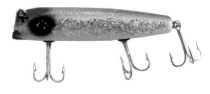

042-7018 CREEK CHUB BAIT CO.
DARTER
IN
GLASS EYES $100

FISHING PLUGS

043-0936 CREEK CHUB BAIT CO.
DARTER, SPINNERED
IN
#9000S SERIES, BABY $75

043-0935 CREEK CHUB BAIT CO.
DARTER, CONCAVE
IN   1930   3 1/4 IN
$90

043-0944 CREEK CHUB BAIT CO.
DARTER, METALIZED
IN   1924   3 3/4 IN
$500

043-0929 CREEK CHUB BAIT CO.
DARTER, MIDGET
IN   1938   3 IN   3/8 OZ
#8000 SERIES $40

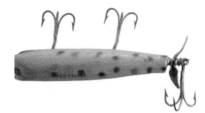

043-0934 CREEK CHUB BAIT CO.
DARTER, SPINNERED
IN
#2000S SERIES $75

043-0937 CREEK CHUB BAIT CO.
DARTER, SPINNING
IN   1953   2 3/4 IN   1/4 OZ
#9000S SERIES $75

043-0930 CREEK CHUB BAIT CO.
DARTER, JOINTED
IN   1938   3 3/4 IN   1/2 OZ
#4900 SERIES $75

043-0992 CREEK CHUB BAIT CO.
DEEPSTER, SPINNING
IN   1953   2 1/4 IN   1/4 OZ
#9600 SERIES $90

043-0977 CREEK CHUB BAIT CO.
DING BAT
IN   1960   1 1/2 IN
#5300 SERIES, PLASTIC $30

043-0981 CREEK CHUB BAIT CO.
DING BAT
IN   1937   2 IN   5/8 OZ
#5100 SERIES $50

043-0983 CREEK CHUB BAIT CO.
DING BAT
IN   1930-1939   2 1/4 IN
#5300 SERIES, HUSKY $350

043-0989 CREEK CHUB BAIT CO.
DING BAT
IN   1938
#5200 SERIES, MIDGET $90

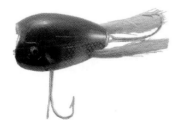

043-1005 CREEK CHUB BAIT CO.
DING BAT
IN   1938   1 3/4 IN   5/8 OZ
#5400 SERIES, SURFACE $150

043-1018 CREEK CHUB BAIT CO.
DINGER
IN   1939   4 IN   1/2 OZ
#5600 SERIES $90

043-1014 CREEK CHUB BAIT CO.
DINGER, HUSKY
IN   1939   3 1/4 IN
#5700 SERIES $500

FISHING PLUGS

044-1011 CREEK CHUB BAIT CO.
DINGER, MIDGET
IN   1940   4 IN   3/8 OZ   SPECIAL COLOR
#6100 SERIES $500

044-7148 CREEK CHUB BAIT CO.
DINGER, PLUNKING
IN   1940   4 IN   5/8 OZ
#6200 SERIES $150

044-0909 CREEK CHUB BAIT CO.
FINTAIL SHINER
IN   1924   4 IN   3/4 OZ
#2100 SERIES, OLD STYLE $300

044-0911 CREEK CHUB BAIT CO.
FINTAIL SHINER
IN   1930   4 IN   3/4 OZ
#2100 SERIES, NEW STYLE $300

044-0910 CREEK CHUB BAIT CO.
FINTAIL SHINER SPECIAL
IN   1930   4 IN   3/4 OZ
$1000

044-0947 CREEK CHUB BAIT CO.
FLIP FLAP
IN   1942   2 IN
#4400 SERIES $300

044-0945 CREEK CHUB BAIT CO.
GAR MINNOW, CREEK CHUB
IN   1927   5 1/4 IN   3/4 OZ
#2900 SERIES $900

044-0866 CREEK CHUB BAIT CO.
HUSKY MUSKIE
IN   5 IN
#600 SERIES, EARLY $400

044-0867 CREEK CHUB BAIT CO.
HUSKY MUSKIE
IN   5 IN
#600 SERIES, LATER $150

044-0868 CREEK CHUB BAIT CO.
HUSKY MUSKIE
IN   1919   5 IN
#600 SERIES $300

044-0869 CREEK CHUB BAIT CO.
HUSKY MUSKIE
IN   1922
NO EYES $200

044-0916 CREEK CHUB BAIT CO.
INJURED MINNOW
IN
#1500 SERIES, PLASTIC $35

044-0917 CREEK CHUB BAIT CO.
INJURED MINNOW
IN
#1500 SERIES, NEWER $40

044-0918 CREEK CHUB BAIT CO.
INJURED MINNOW
IN
#1500 SERIES $75

044-0920 CREEK CHUB BAIT CO.
INJURED MINNOW
IN   1924   3 3/4 IN   3/4 OZ
#1500 SERIES, OLDEST $120

FISHING PLUGS

045-0921 CREEK CHUB BAIT CO.
INJURED MINNOW
IN
#1500 SERIES $75

045-0925 CREEK CHUB BAIT CO.
INJURED MINNOW
IN
#1600 SERIES, BABY $100

045-0927 CREEK CHUB BAIT CO.
INJURED MINNOW
IN   1924   2 3/4 IN   1/2 OZ
#1600 , OLD STYLE, BABY $120

045-6191 CREEK CHUB BAIT CO.
PIKIE
IN   PRODUCTION STEPS OF
MANUFACTURING PIKIES $300

045-7130 CREEK CHUB BAIT CO.
INJURED MINNOW, HUSKY
IN
#3500 SERIES $400

045-7136 CREEK CHUB BAIT CO.
INJURED MINNOW, MUSKY
IN   1929   5 IN
#3500 SERIES $400

045-0913 CREEK CHUB BAIT CO.
INJURED MINNOW, SPINNING
IN   1953   2 IN   1/4 OZ
#9500 SERIES $30

045-0922 CREEK CHUB BAIT CO.
INJURED MINNOW, SPINNING
IN
#9500 SERIES $30

045-0924 CREEK CHUB BAIT CO.
INJURED MINNOW, SPINNING
IN
#9500 SERIES, OLDEST $75

045-0967 CREEK CHUB BAIT CO.
JIGGER
IN   1935   3 1/4 IN   3/4 OZ
BABY $600

045-0972 CREEK CHUB BAIT CO.
JIGGER
IN   1933   3 5/8 IN   3/4 OZ
#4100 SERIES $400

045-0975 CREEK CHUB BAIT CO.
LUCKY MOUSE
IN   1929   2 1/2 IN   3/4 OZ
#3600 SERIES $400

045-0795 CREEK CHUB BAIT CO.
MITY MOUSE
IN
#600P SERIES $20

045-0996 CREEK CHUB BAIT CO.
NIKIE
IN   1960   3 1/4 IN   1/2 OZ
#1000P SERIES $30

045-0997 CREEK CHUB BAIT CO.
NIKIE
IN
#9800P SERIES $30

FISHING PLUGS

046-0863 CREEK CHUB BAIT CO.
OPEN MOUTH SHINER
IN   1918   3 1/4 IN   3/4 OZ
#500 SERIES $400

046-0864 CREEK CHUB BAIT CO.
OPEN MOUTH SHINER
IN   3/4 OZ
#500 SERIES $300

046-0865 CREEK CHUB BAIT CO.
OPEN MOUTH SHINER
IN   1926   3 IN   3/4 OZ
#500 SERIES, LATER $200

046-0881 CREEK CHUB BAIT CO.
PETERS SPECIAL
IN
#2600 SERIES $120

046-0873 CREEK CHUB BAIT CO.
PIKID, JOINTED MIDGET
IN   1933   2 3/4 IN   1/4 OZ
#4200 SERIES $75

046-0897 CREEK CHUB BAIT CO.
PIKIE MINNOW
IN   1926   4 1/2 IN   3/4 OZ
#700 SERIES, NO EYES $150

046-0898 CREEK CHUB BAIT CO.
PIKIE MINNOW
IN   1920   4 1/2 IN   3/4 OZ
#700 SERIES $200

046-0899 CREEK CHUB BAIT CO.
PIKIE MINNOW
IN
#700 SERIES $100

046-0876 CREEK CHUB BAIT CO.
PIKIE, BABY
IN
#900 SERIES, TACK-EYES, $50

046-0886 CREEK CHUB BAIT CO.
PIKIE, BABY
IN   1921   3 1/4 IN   1/2 OZ
#900 SERIES, INVERTED LIP $125

046-0887 CREEK CHUB BAIT CO.
PIKIE, BABY
IN
#900 SERIES $75

046-0888 CREEK CHUB BAIT CO.
PIKIE, BABY
IN   1926   3 1/4 IN   1/2 OZ
#900 SERIES, NO EYES $200

046-0874 CREEK CHUB BAIT CO.
PIKIE, CHROMED
IN
#700 SERIES, LATE $50

046-0875 CREEK CHUB BAIT CO.
PIKIE, FIREFINISH
IN
#700 SERIES $75

046-0877 CREEK CHUB BAIT CO.
PIKIE, FIREFINISH, BABY
IN
#900 SERIES $40

FISHING PLUGS

047-1032 CREEK CHUB BAIT CO.
PIKIE, FIREFINISH, MUSKY
IN
#2300 SERIES $200

047-1024 CREEK CHUB BAIT CO.
PIKIE, HUSKY
IN   1950   7 1/4 IN   1 1/2 OZ
#3000 SERIES, JOINTED $225

047-1034 CREEK CHUB BAIT CO.
PIKIE, HUSKY
IN
#2300 SERIES, NEW $150

047-1036 CREEK CHUB BAIT CO.
PIKIE, HUSKY
IN   1925   6 3/4 IN   1 1/2 OZ
#2300 SERIES $200

047-0879 CREEK CHUB BAIT CO.
PIKIE, JOINTED
IN   1927   3 1/4 IN   1/2 OZ
#2700 SERIES, BABY $100

047-0882 CREEK CHUB BAIT CO.
PIKIE, JOINTED
IN
#2600 SERIES $40

047-0890 CREEK CHUB BAIT CO.
PIKIE, JOINTED
IN   1926   4 1/4 IN   3/4/OZ
#2600 SERIES, EARLY $175

047-0891 CREEK CHUB BAIT CO.
PIKIE, JOINTED
IN
#2600 SERIES $40

047-0880 CREEK CHUB BAIT CO.
PIKIE, JOINTED DEEP DIVE
IN
#2600D SERIES $50

047-1021 CREEK CHUB BAIT CO.
PIKIE, JOINTED GIANT
IN
#800 SERIES $200

047-1023 CREEK CHUB BAIT CO.
PIKIE, JOINTED GIANT
IN   1957   13 IN   4 OZ
#800 SERIES, GLASS EYES $225

047-1025 CREEK CHUB BAIT CO.
PIKIE, JOINTED MUSKY
IN
#3000 SERIES, JOINTED $200

047-1013 CREEK CHUB BAIT CO.
PIKIE, JOINTED SNOOK
IN
#5500 SERIES $150

047-1026 CREEK CHUB BAIT CO.
PIKIE, JOINTED SNOOK
IN   1950   5 1/2 IN   1 1/8 OZ
#5500 SERIES $200

047-1022 CREEK CHUB BAIT CO.
PIKIE, JOINTED STRIPER
IN   1950   6 1/2 IN   3 1/4 OZ
#6800 SERIES $150

FISHING PLUGS

048-0878 CREEK CHUB BAIT CO.
PIKIE, JOINTED, BABY
IN
#2700 SERIES,TACK-EYES $40

048-1012 CREEK CHUB BAIT CO.
PIKIE, JTD. STRIPER, FIREFINISH
IN   1950   6 1/2 IN   3 1/4 OZ
#6800 SERIES $150

048-1035 CREEK CHUB BAIT CO.
PIKIE, KINGFISH
IN   5 1/4 IN
   $1000

048-0894 CREEK CHUB BAIT CO.
PIKIE, MIDGET
IN   1926   2 3/4 IN   1/4 OZ
#2200 SERIES, NO EYES $200

048-0895 CREEK CHUB BAIT CO.
PIKIE, MIDGET
IN   1924   2 3/4 IN   1/4 OZ
#2200 SERIES, GLASS EYES $100

048-1028 CREEK CHUB BAIT CO.
PIKIE, MUSKY
IN
#3000, TACK EYES $100

048-1031 CREEK CHUB BAIT CO.
PIKIE, MUSKY
IN
#2300 SERIES $150

048-0889 CREEK CHUB BAIT CO.
PIKIE, PICKEREL
IN   1926   4 1/4 IN   3/4 OZ
#2600 SERIES $125

048-0896 CREEK CHUB BAIT CO.
PIKIE, SNOOK
IN   1929   4 7/8 IN
#3400 SERIES $125

048-0892 CREEK CHUB BAIT CO.
PIKIE, SPINNING
IN   1953   2 1/4 IN   1/4 OZ
   $50

048-0893 CREEK CHUB BAIT CO.
PIKIE, SPINNING
IN
   $75

048-1033 CREEK CHUB BAIT CO.
PIKIE, STRIPER
IN   1950   6 IN   3 3/4 OZ
#6900 SERIES $150

048-1037 CREEK CHUB BAIT CO.
PIKIE, STRIPER
IN   1950   5 1/4 IN   3 3/4 OZ
#6900 SERIES $150

048-1040 CREEK CHUB BAIT CO.
PIKIE, SURFSTER
IN   1953   4 1/2 IN   1 7/8 OZ
#7200 SERIES, SMALL $150

048-1041 CREEK CHUB BAIT CO.
PIKIE, SURFSTER
IN   1953   7 1/4 IN   4 OZ
#7400 SERIES, LARGE $150

049-1038 CREEK CHUB BAIT CO.
PIKIE, SURSTER
IN
#7300 SERIES, MEDIUM $150

049-1039 CREEK CHUB BAIT CO.
PIKIE, TARPON
IN 1933 6 3/4 IN
#4000 SERIES $300

049-0955 CREEK CHUB BAIT CO.
PLUNKER
IN
#3200 SERIES, TACK EYES $20

049-0966 CREEK CHUB BAIT CO.
PLUNKER
IN 1929 3 IN 3/4 OZ
#3200 SERIES $90

049-0995 CREEK CHUB BAIT CO.
PLUNKER, HUSKY
IN 1939 4 1/2 IN
#5800 SERIES $300

049-0958 CREEK CHUB BAIT CO.
PLUNKER, MIDGET
IN 1939 2 1/4 IN 3/8 OZ
#5900 SERIES $60

049-0974 CREEK CHUB BAIT CO.
PLUNKER, SNOOK
IN 1953 4 1/2 IN
#7100 SERIES $200

049-0957 CREEK CHUB BAIT CO.
PLUNKER, SPINNING
IN 1953 2 1/4 IN 1/4 OZ
#9200 SERIES $40

049-1007 CREEK CHUB BAIT CO.
POCKET ROCKET
IN 1960
#7000 SERIES $120

049-0956 CREEK CHUB BAIT CO.
POLYWIGGLE
IN 1924 1 3/4 IN 1/2 OZ
#1700 SERIES $900

049-0988 CREEK CHUB BAIT CO.
POP 'N' DUNK
IN 1941 2 3/4 IN 5/8 OZ
#6300 SERIES $150

049-0818 CREEK CHUB BAIT CO.
PRACTICE PLUG
IN
$100

049-0821 CREEK CHUB BAIT CO.
RESEARCH CRAWDAD WIGGLER
IN
$100

049-0962 CREEK CHUB BAIT CO.
RIVER RUSTLER
IN 1930 2 5/8 IN 5/8 OZ
#3700 SERIES $300

049-0908 CREEK CHUB BAIT CO.
RIVER SCAMP
IN 1933 2 1/2 IN 1/2 OZ
#4300 SERIES $200

FISHING PLUGS

050-0953 CREEK CHUB BAIT CO.
SARASOTA
IN   1927   4 1/4 IN   5/8 OZ
#3300 SERIES $500

050-0976 CREEK CHUB BAIT CO.
SARASOTA, SIDE-HOOK
IN   1927   4 1/4 IN   5/8 OZ
#3300 SERIES $1200

050-1020 CREEK CHUB BAIT CO.
SEVEN THOUSAND
IN   1950   2 3/4 IN
#7000 SERIES, LARGE $90

050-1027 CREEK CHUB BAIT CO.
SEVEN THOUSAND
IN   1950   2 1/4 IN
#7000 SERIES $90

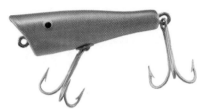

050-0951 CREEK CHUB BAIT CO.
SIMMONS SPECIAL
IN   1947   3 IN
SMALL $200

050-0964 CREEK CHUB BAIT CO.
SIMMONS SPECIAL
IN
LARGE $250

050-0973 CREEK CHUB BAIT CO.
SKIPPER
IN   1936   3 IN   5/8 OZ
#4600 SERIES $100

050-0993 CREEK CHUB BAIT CO.
SNARK-EEL
IN   1958
#1300 SERIES $75

050-0994 CREEK CHUB BAIT CO.
SNARKIE
IN   1958
#1200 SERIES $75

050-0991 CREEK CHUB BAIT CO.
SPOON-TAIL
IN   1954   2 1/2 IN
#9100 SERIES $50

050-1001 CREEK CHUB BAIT CO.
SPOON-TAIL
IN   1954   3 1/2 IN   1/2 OZ
#500 SERIES, LARGE $30

050-0946 CREEK CHUB BAIT CO.
SUCKER
IN   1932   3 1/2 IN   3/4 OZ
#3900 SERIES $900

050-1009 CREEK CHUB BAIT CO.
SURF POPPER
IN   1953   7 1/4 IN   3 3/4 OZ
#7500 SERIES $300

050-0792 CREEK CHUB BAIT CO.
SWIMMING MOUSE
IN   1940-1950   2 3/4 IN
#6300, OLD STYLE $40

050-0793 CREEK CHUB BAIT CO.
SWIMMING MOUSE
IN
#6400 $40

Page 50

051-0794 CREEK CHUB BAIT CO.
SWIMMING MOUSE
IN
#6500 $30

051-0796 CREEK CHUB BAIT CO.
SWIMMING MOUSE
IN   1960   2 3/4 IN
#6000 SERIES, NEW STYLE $20

051-1006 CREEK CHUB BAIT CO.
TINY TIM
IN   1941   1 3/4 IN   1/2 OZ
#6400 SERIES, NO EYES $120

051-1010 CREEK CHUB BAIT CO.
TINY TIM
IN   1941   1 3/4 IN
#6400 SERIES $90

051-1002 CREEK CHUB BAIT CO.
TOP-N-POP
IN   1955   3 IN
#500P SERIES $30

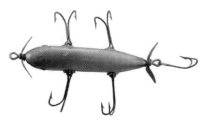

051-0906 CREEK CHUB BAIT CO.
UNDERWATER SPINNER
IN   1924   3 3/4 IN   3/4 OZ
#1800 SERIES $1500

051-1000 CREEK CHUB BAIT CO.
VIPER
IN
#8800 SERIES $30

051-0900 CREEK CHUB BAIT CO.
WAGTAIL
IN   1920   2 3/4 IN
#800 SERIES, OLD $300

051-0901 CREEK CHUB BAIT CO.
WAGTAIL
IN   1926   2 3/4 IN   1/2 OZ
#800 SERIES, NO EYES $200

051-0902 CREEK CHUB BAIT CO.
WAGTAIL
IN
#800 SERIES, GLASS EYES $200

051-0903 CREEK CHUB BAIT CO.
WAGTAIL
IN   1920   2 3/4 IN   1/2 OZ
#800 SERIES, NEWER $150

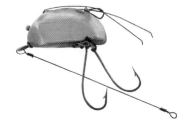

051-0948 CREEK CHUB BAIT CO.
WEED BUG
IN
#2800 SERIES $500

051-0949 CREEK CHUB BAIT CO.
WEED BUG
IN   1927   2 IN   3/4 OZ
#2800 SERIES $400

051-0952 CREEK CHUB BAIT CO.
WEE-DEE
IN
#200 SERIES, PLASTIC $20

051-0954 CREEK CHUB BAIT CO.
WEE-DEE
IN   1936   2 1/2 ON   5/8 OZ
#4800 SERIES $500

FISHING PLUGS

052-0933 CREEK CHUB BAIT CO.
WIGGLE FISH SPECIAL
IN   3 1/2 IN
   $200

052-0961 CREEK CHUB BAIT CO.
WIGGLE WIZARD
IN   1934   2 1/2 IN   1/2 OZ
#4500 SERIES $300

052-1015 CREEK CHUB BAIT CO.
WIGGLEDIVER, SALTWATER
IN
#5000 SERIES, SMALL $40

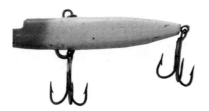

052-1016 CREEK CHUB BAIT CO.
WIGGLEDIVER, SALTWATER
IN
MEDIUM $40

052-1017 CREEK CHUB BAIT CO.
WIGGLEDIVER, SALTWATER
IN
#1800 SERIES, LARGE $40

052-0939 CREEK CHUB BAIT CO.
WIGGLEFISH
IN   1925   3 1/2 IN   3/4 OZ
#2400 SERIES, OLD STYLE $300

052-0932 CREEK CHUB BAIT CO.
WIGGLEFISH, BABY
IN   1925   2 1/2 IN   1/2 OZ
#2500 SERIES $200

052-0938 CREEK CHUB BAIT CO.
WIGGLEFISH, DEEP DIVE
IN   3 1/2 IN
#2400D SERIES $200

052-0928 CREEK CHUB BAIT CO.
WIGGLEFISH, MUSKY
IN   1926   5 IN
   $900

052-0820 CREEK CHUB BAIT CO.
WIGGLER
IN
#100, EARLY $1000

052-0822 CREEK CHUB BAIT CO.
WIGGLER
IN
#100, EARLY $1000

052-0850 CREEK CHUB BAIT CO.
WIGGLER
IN
#100, LATER $100

052-0851 CREEK CHUB BAIT CO.
WIGGLER
IN
#100, EARLY $200

052-0852 CREEK CHUB BAIT CO.
WIGGLER
IN   1906   3 1/2 IN   1 OZ
#100, EARLIEST $300

052-0854 CREEK CHUB BAIT CO.
WIGGLER
IN   1926   3 1/2 IN   1 OZ
#100, NO EYE $300

053-0853 CREEK CHUB BAIT CO.
WIGGLER 1918
IN   1918
#100 $400

053-0855 CREEK CHUB BAIT CO.
WIGGLER, BABY
IN
#200, EARLY $400

053-0856 CREEK CHUB BAIT CO.
WIGGLER, BABY
IN   1917   2 3/4 IN   1/2 OZ
#200 $300

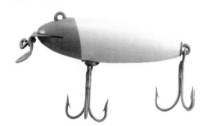

053-0857 CREEK CHUB BAIT CO.
WIGGLER, BABY
IN   1926   2 3/4 IN   1/2 OZ
#200, NO EYES $200

053-0858 CREEK CHUB BAIT CO.
WIGGLER, BABY
IN   1/2 OZ
#200, LATER $200

053-7011 CREEK KING LURES
DIVER, CREEK KING
AR   1965
    $20

053-7010 CREEK KING LURES
INJURED MINNOW, CREEK KING
AR   1965
    $20

053-0791 CREME, NICK
DU DAD
TX   1960   2 IN
    $40

053-7055 CREME, NICK
FLAPTAIL WORM
TX   1965
    $10

053-0780 CREME, NICK
LOLLIPOP
TX   1960   2 IN
    $40

053-0788 CREME, NICK
MAD DAD
TX   1960   3 3/4 IN
    $40

053-0789 CREME, NICK
MAD DAD
TX   1960   3 IN
JR SIZE $40

053-7054 CREME, NICK
WORM, CRÈME
TX   1962
    $10

053-7056 CREME, NICK
WORM, CRÈME
TX   1958
    $10

053-7057 CREME, NICK
WORM, CRÈME
TX   1960
    $10

FISHING PLUGS

054-0622 CROWDER, BILL
BIG JERK
IL   1960   2 IN
  $30

054-0620 CROWDER, BILL
DO WEE GEE
IL   1960
  $30

054-0623 CROWDER, BILL
LOUD MOUTH
IL   1960
  $30

054-0619 CROWDER, BILL
PLASTERED MINNOW
IL   1960
  $30

054-0621 CROWDER, BILL
WOBBLING WILLIE
IL   1960   1 3/4 IN
  $30

054-0714 CRUTCHO
LIZARD,   CRUTCHO

  $100

054-0567 CUMINGS, ED INC.
ED'S HULA HULA BAIT
MI   1936   3 3/4 IN
  $150

054-1070 CUMMINGS BAIT CO
CUMMINGS BAIT
NJ
  $500

054-1072 CUMMINGS BAIT CO
CUMMINGS BAIT
NJ
  $500

054-1073 CUMMINGS BAIT CO
CUMMINGS BAIT
NJ
  $500

054-1075 CUMMINGS BAIT CO
CUMMINGS BAIT
NJ
  $300

054-1077 CUMMINGS BAIT CO
CUMMINGS BAIT
NJ
  $500

054-1078 CUMMINGS BAIT CO
CUMMINGS BAIT
NJ
  $500

054-1081 CUMMINGS BAIT CO
CUMMINGS BAIT
NJ
  $500

054-1083 CUMMINGS BAIT CO
CUMMINGS BAIT
NJ
  $500

055-1085 CUMMINGS BAIT CO
CUMMINGS BAIT
NJ
$500

055-1087 CUMMINGS BAIT CO.
CUMMINGS BAIT, UNKNOWN
NJ
$500

055-5273 CUMMINGS BAIT CO.
CUMMINGS BAIT, UNKNOWN
NJ
$300

055-5274 CUMMINGS BAIT CO.
CUMMINGS BAIT, UNKNOWN
NJ
$300

055-5275 CUMMINGS BAIT CO.
CUMMINGS BAIT, UNKNOWN
NJ
$300

055-5276 CUMMINGS BAIT CO.
CUMMINGS BAIT, UNKNOWN
NJ
$300

055-5277 CUMMINGS BAIT CO.
CUMMINGS BAIT, UNKNOWN
NJ
$300

055-5278 CUMMINGS BAIT CO.
CUMMINGS BAIT, UNKNOWN
NJ
$300

055-5279 CUMMINGS BAIT CO.
CUMMINGS BAIT, UNKNOWN
NJ
$300

055-5280 CUMMINGS BAIT CO.
CUMMINGS BAIT, UNKNOWN
NJ
$300

055-5281 CUMMINGS BAIT CO.
CUMMINGS BAIT, UNKNOWN
NJ
$300

055-5282 CUMMINGS BAIT CO.
CUMMINGS BAIT, UNKNOWN
NJ
$300

055-5283 CUMMINGS BAIT CO.
CUMMINGS BAIT, UNKNOWN
NJ
$300

055-5284 CUMMINGS BAIT CO.
CUMMINGS BAIT, UNKNOWN
NJ
$300

055-5285 CUMMINGS BAIT CO.
CUMMINGS BAIT, UNKNOWN
NJ
$300

056-5286 CUMMINGS BAIT CO.
CUMMINGS BAIT, UNKNOWN
NJ
 $300

056-5287 CUMMINGS BAIT CO.
CUMMINGS BAIT, UNKNOWN
NJ
 $300

056-5288 CUMMINGS BAIT CO.
CUMMINGS BAIT, UNKNOWN
NJ
 $300

056-5289 CUMMINGS BAIT CO.
CUMMINGS BAIT, UNKNOWN
NJ
 $300

056-5290 CUMMINGS BAIT CO.
CUMMINGS BAIT, UNKNOWN
NJ
 $300

056-5291 CUMMINGS BAIT CO.
CUMMINGS BAIT, UNKNOWN
NJ
 $300

056-5292 CUMMINGS BAIT CO.
CUMMINGS BAIT, UNKNOWN
NJ
 $300

056-5293 CUMMINGS BAIT CO.
CUMMINGS BAIT, UNKNOWN
NJ
 $300

056-5294 CUMMINGS BAIT CO.
CUMMINGS BAIT, UNKNOWN
NJ
 $300

056-5295 CUMMINGS BAIT CO.
CUMMINGS BAIT, UNKNOWN
NJ
 $300

056-5296 CUMMINGS BAIT CO.
CUMMINGS BAIT, UNKNOWN
NJ
 $300

056-5297 CUMMINGS BAIT CO.
CUMMINGS BAIT, UNKNOWN
NJ
 $300

056-5298 CUMMINGS BAIT CO.
CUMMINGS BAIT, UNKNOWN
NJ
 $300

056-5299 CUMMINGS BAIT CO.
CUMMINGS BAIT, UNKNOWN
NJ
 $300

056-5300 CUMMINGS BAIT CO.
CUMMINGS BAIT, UNKNOWN
NJ
 $300

FISHING PLUGS

057-5301 CUMMINGS BAIT CO.
CUMMINGS BAIT, UNKNOWN
NJ
  $300

057-5302 CUMMINGS BAIT CO.
CUMMINGS BAIT, UNKNOWN
NJ
  $300

057-5303 CUMMINGS BAIT CO.
CUMMINGS BAIT, UNKNOWN
NJ
  $300

057-0568 CUMMINGS BAIT CO.
CUMMINGS BASS BAIT
NJ   1918   3 1/2 IN
  $300

057-5393 CY'S DECOYS
DECOY, PERCH, CY'S
MN   1950
  $200

057-5427 CY'S DECOYS
DECOY, PERCH, CY'S
MN   1950
  $200

057-5446 CY'S DECOYS
DECOY, PIKE, CY'S
MN
  $200

057-5414 CY'S DECOYS
FISH DECOY,
MN
  $100

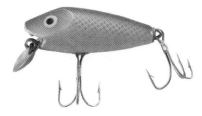

057-1100 D' ANNA LURES
BAYOU BOOGIE
LA   1952
  $20

057-0719 D.A.M.
BLEEDER BAIT
GER
GERMANY $40

057-1061 D.A.M.
D.A.M BLEEDER BAIT
GER   1950   3 IN
GERMAN, BLOOD TABLET $40

057-2469 D.A.M.
D.A.M. BAIT
GER
GERMAN $40

057-2470 D.A.M.
D.A.M. BAIT
GER
GERMAN $40

057-1058 D.A.M.
D.A.M. MINNOW
GER   1952
JOINTED, GERMAN $150

057-1059 D.A.M.
D.A.M. MINNOW
GER   1952
JOINTED, GERMAN $150

058-1079 D.A.M.
D.A.M. MINNOW
GER
GERMAN $40

058-1069 D.A.M.
D.A.M. MINNOW, JOINTED
GER   1958
JOINTED, GERMAN $90

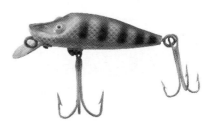

058-1074 D.A..M..
RIVER RUNT TYPE
GER
GERMANY $400

058-1065 D.A.M.
PIKE TYPE, D.A.M., JOINTED,
GER   1940   4 3/4 IN
GERMANY $100

058-1063 DALBERG.
BONZO,
GER
GERMANY, SMALL $60

058-1064 DALBERG
RIVER RUNT MINOR
GER
GERMANY $60

058-1258 DANDY LURES
DANGLE BACK
FL   1940'S
FLORIDA FISHING TACKLE $60

058-1429 DANDY LURES
DANGLE BACK
FL   1940's   4 1/4 IN
FLORIDA FISHING TACKLE $60

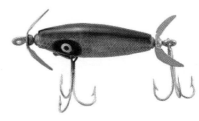

058-1215 DANDY LURES
FLORIDA PEE WEE
FL   3 IN   1/2 OZ
$40

058-1091 DANIELSON, RUBIN
DANIELSON WEEDLESS
IL   4 1/4 IN
$400

058-1103 DARBY, TIM.
DARBY LURE
IN   1932   4 IN
SPRING-LOADED $400

058-1088 DAVIS LURE CO.
LECTRO-LURE
IL   1931   4 1/4 IN
$400

058-1099 DAVIS TACKLE MFG. GO.
TRIGGER FISH
MI   1947   3 3/8 IN
$120

058-1095 DAVIS, JOHN
SALTWATER MINNOW, DAVIS
WA   1948   8 IN
$90

058-1102 DAVIS, WM .E.
JERSEY EXPERT
NJ   1909   3 1/2 IN
$4500

059-1094 DAYTON BAIT CO.
WIGGLE WONDER
OH 1949 2 1/4 IN
$30

059-1090 DEAN, POP
MASTER MINNOW
1956 10 IN
$450

059-1042 DECKER, ANS B.
DECKER BAIT
NJ 1909 2 3/4 IN 5/8 OZ
BABY SIZE $300

059-1043 DECKER, ANS B.
DECKER BAIT
NJ 1910 4 1/4 IN
MUSKY SIZE $1000

059-1044 DECKER, ANS B.
DECKER BAIT
NJ 1908 3 1/2 IN
$200

059-1097 DECKER, ANS B.
DECKER BAIT
NJ 1910 2 1/2 IN
BABY SIZE $1000

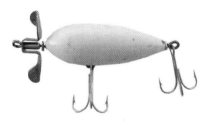

059-1047 DECKER, ANS B.
DECKER UNDERWATER BAIT
NJ 1910
$1500

059-1053 DECKER, ANS B.
DECKER UNDERWATER BAIT
NJ 1910 2 1/4 IN
$1500

059-1086 DECKER, ANS. B.?
UNKNOWN DECKER?
NJ
$500

059-1089 DECOY MFG.
CANADIAN DECOY
CAN
WITH CHEATER HOOKS $100

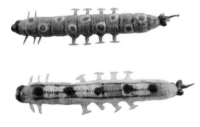

059-7063 DELONG
CATALPA WORM
TX 1969
$10

059-7077 DELONG
CRAWFISH
TX 1969
$20

059-7079 DELONG
EEK
TX 1969
$10

059-7064 DELONG
EEL, DELONG
TX 1969
$10

059-7039 DELONG
FROG, DELONG
TX 1963
$10

FISHING PLUGS

060-7075 DELONG
FROG, DELONG
TX   1969
  $10

060-7076 DELONG
FROGGIE, DELONG
TX   1969
  $10

060-7073 DELONG
GRASSHOPPER, DELONG
TX   1969
  $10

060-7068 DELONG
MUD PUPPY, DELONG
TX   1969
  $10

060-7071 DELONG
MUD PUPPY, DELONG
TX   1969
  $10

060-7072 DELONG
NEWT
TX   1969
  $10

060-7067 DELONG
RIVER SHINER
TX   1969
  $10

060-7080 DELONG
SEGMENTED EEL
TX   1969
  $10

060-7058 DELONG
SHAD
TX   1962
  $10

060-7065 DELONG
SHINER
TX   1969
  $10

060-7078 DELONG
SNAKE
TX   1969
  $10

060-7074 DELONG
SPIDER
TX   1969
  $10

060-7069 DELONG
SUCKER CARP
TX   1969
  $10

060-7066 DELONG
SUCKER, DELONG
TX   1969
  $10

060-7070 DELONG
TAD POLLY
TX   1969
  $10

061-7062 DELONG
TADPOLE
TX   1968
  $10

061-7061 DELONG
WORM, DELONG
TX   1968
  $10

061-1106 DEMON LURE CO.
SAIL SHARK
TX   1960
  $10

061-1116 DETROIT BAIT CO.
BASS CALLER
MI   1937   3 1/2 IN
  $200

061-3167 DETROIT BAIT MFG. CO.
NORTH CHANNEL MINNOW
MI   1910
3-HOOK, SMALL $1200

061-3168 DETROIT BAIT MFG. CO.
NORTH CHANNEL MINNOW
MI   1907   3 3/4 IN
5-HOOK,   LARGE, OLD $1500

061-3169 DETROIT BAIT MFG. CO.
NORTH CHANNEL MINNOW
MI   1912   3 3/4 IN
5-HOOK,   MEDIUM, NEW $1200

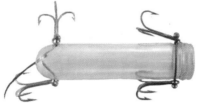

061-1122 DETROIT GLASS MINN. TUBE CO
DETROIT LIVE MINNOW TUBE
MI   1914   3 1/2 IN
  $1500

061-1123 DETROIT WEEDLESS MFG.
DETROIT WEEDLESS
MI   1929
  $900

061-2695 DEUSTER, E.J.
GOPHER
WI   1957   6 IN
  $100

061-1120 DEWITT, BILL, BAITS
DUCKBILL
NY
  $300

061-1110 DEWITT, BILL, BAITS
NATURAL MINNOW
NY   1936   4 3/4 IN
  $40

061-1115 DEWITT, BILL, BAITS
NATURAL MINNOW
NY   1936   3 3/8 IN
  $50

061-1124 DEWITT, BILL, BAITS
NATURAL MINNOW
NY   1936   3 3/8 IN
  $50

061-7131 DICKENS BAIT CO., THE
DICKENS, UNKNOWN
IN
  $600

FISHING PLUGS

062-1108 DICKENS BAIT CO., THE
LIAR CONVERTIBLE MINNOW
IN   1918   3 1/2 IN
CLIP IN HOOK $400

062-1105 DICKENS BAIT CO., THE
WEEDLESS WONDER
IN   1920   1 3/4 IN
  $300

062-1113 DILLON-BECK MFG. CO
DILLONBECK MINNOW
NJ   1960's
  $50

062-1107 DILLON-BECK MFG. CO
KILLER DILLER
NJ
  $50

062-1127 DOANE, EDWARD
DOANE'S MINNOW
FL   1928   3 1/4 IN
  $600

062-1050 DONALY, JIM
JERSEY WOW
NJ   1936   3 IN
LARGE $400

062-1051 DONALY, JIM
JERSEY WOW
NJ   1936   2 3/4 IN
SMALL $400

062-1046 DONALY, JIM
REDFIN COLLAR BAIT
NJ   1915   4 IN
'CATCHUMBIG' $3000

062-1054 DONALY, JIM
REDFIN FLOATING BAIT
NJ   1925   2 3/4 IN
  $600

062-1049 DONALY, JIM
REDFIN MINNOW
NJ   1908   3 1/2 IN
  $2500

062-1052 DONALY, JIM
REDFIN MINNOW
NJ
  $2000

062-1048 DONALY, JIM
REDFIN WEEDLESS BAIT
NJ   1915   3 1/4 IN
  $3500

062-1080 DONALY, JIM
UNKNOWN NAME
NJ
QUESTIONABLE $1500

062-7134 DONALY, JIM
WOW
NJ   1936
  $300

062-7141 DONALY, JIM
WOW
NJ
BELLY-HOOK $300

FISHING PLUGS

063-7142 DONALY, JIM
WOW
NJ   1935   2 3/4 IN
SIDE-HOOK, SMALL $300

063-1096 DRAG-IT BAIT CO.
DRAG-IT BAIT

$10

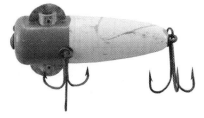

063-1126 DRAKE, HARRY F.
SEA BAT
WI   1932   3 1/4 IN
$100

063-1150 DRIESEL, FRED
DRIESEL BAIT
OK   1957
$60

063-1153 DRIESEL, FRED
DRIESEL BAIT
OK   1958
$60

063-1154 DRIESEL, FRED
DRIESEL BAIT
OK   1957
$60

063-1155 DRIESEL, FRED
DRIESEL BAIT
OK   1957
$60

063-1156 DRIESEL, FRED
DRIESEL BAIT
OK   1957
$60

063-1157 DRIESEL, FRED
DRIESEL BAIT
OK   1957
$60

063-1163 DRIESEL, FRED
DRIESEL BAIT
OK   1957
$60

063-1164 DRIESEL, FRED
DRIESEL BAIT
OK   1957
$60

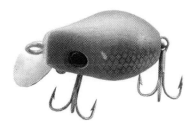

063-1148 DRIESEL, FRED
MOUSE, DRIESEL
OK   1958
$60

063-1149 DRIESEL, FRED
TOPWATER BAIT, DRIESEL
OK   1957
$60

063-1131 DRULEY'S RESEARCH PRODS
MINNIE THE SWIMMER
WI   1936   3 1/4 IN
MEDIUM, RUBBER $100

063-1132 DRULEY'S RESEARCH PRODS
MINNIE THE SWIMMER
WI   1939   4 1/2 IN
MUSKY $150

Page 63

FISHING PLUGS

064-1142 DURA-FLOTE
OLD TIMER NIPPLE-DIPPER
  1949   2 1/4 IN
RUBBER $90

064-1152 DYNA TACKLE
DYNA-MITE
TX   1952   1 3/4 IN
  $15

064-1207 E&E TACKLE
BLUE POPPER

  $60

064-1203 E&E TACKLE
BLUE STREAK

  $60

064-2761 EARL, MICHAEL
SIDE-FLOATING MINNOW
FL   1930   4 IN
GLASS EYES $800

064-1201 ECKFIELD BAIT CO
SNEAK-BAC

  $500

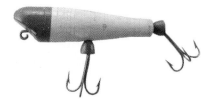

064-3935 EDON BAIT CO.
STRAUSBORGER MINNOW
OH   1932   3 1/4 IN
STRAUSBORGER, O.C. $400

064-5707 EDON BAIT CO.
STRAUSBORGER POPPER
OH   1932
STRAUSBORGER, O.C. $80

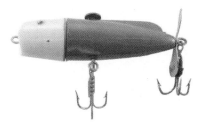

064-1200 ELECTROLURE CO
ELECTROLURE
IL
  $90

064-1194 ELECTRONIC UNITS INC.
JUMPING JO
OH
  $60

064-1195 ELKAY BAIT CO
PADDLE JUMPER

  $100

064-0015 ELKO TACKLE
FREAKFISH
NY   1958   2 1/2 IN
  $30

064-3954 ENGLISH, DOUG
BINGO
TX
SMALL $20

064-3948 ENGLISH, DOUG
FISHERMAN'S FAVORITE
TX   1940's
SMALL $20

064-3951 ENGLISH, DOUG
FISHERMAN'S FAVORITE
TX   1949   3 IN
LARGE $30

FISHING PLUGS

065-3941 ENGLISH, DOUG
HUMPY
TX   1940   2 1/2 IN
LARGE $20

065-3942 ENGLISH, DOUG
HUMPY
TX   1940   2 1/4 IN
SMALL $20

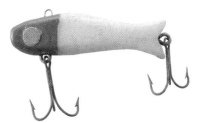

065-3945 ENGLISH, DOUG
WIGGLING MINNOW
TX   1939   3 IN
    $20

065-1165 EPPINGER, LOU J.
OSPREY WOBBLER
MI   1948   2 1/2 IN
BABY SIZE $40

065-1168 EPPINGER, LOU J.
OSPREY WOBBLER
MI   1946   5 IN
    $40

065-1171 EPPINGER, LOU J.
OSPREY WOBBLER
MI   1946   4 IN
SMALL $40

065-1197 ETCHEN TACKLE CO
HELGA-DEVIL
MI
    $60

065-1196 ETCHEN TACKLE CO
HELGA-LURE
MI
    $90

065-0767 EUREKA BAIT CO.
EUREKA WIGGLER
MI   1912   4 3/4 IN
OLD $300

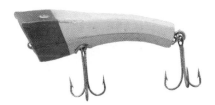

065-1192 EVANS, GLEN L.
BLURPER
ID
    $100

065-1191 EVANS, GLEN L.
UNDERTAKER
ID
    $100

065-1187 EVANS-CASE CO.
JIFFY PLUG
MA
ECCO LURES $75

065-1186 EVANS-CASE CO.
TIN SQUID
MA
ECCO LURES $75

065-1204 EXCEL LURE CO
SILVER MINNOW
IL
    $200

065-1205 EXCEL LURE CO
SILVER STREAK
IL
    $200

FISHING PLUGS

066-1283 FAIR PLAY IND
BUBBLE MINNIE
MI   1948
PLASTIC/METAL $60

066-2157 FAIR PLAY INDUSTRIES
BUBBLE SALLY
MI   1948
  $30

066-2652 FALLS BAIT CO
FISH'N FOOL
WI   1950   1 3/4 IN
  $40

066-1290 FALLS BAIT CO
INCH MINNOW
WI   1960   1 IN
  $40

066-1289 FALLS BAIT CO
INCH MINNOW, BIG
WI   1960
  $40

066-1291 FALLS BAIT CO
INCH MINNOW, LITTLE
WI   1960
  $40

066-1297 FALLS CITY BAIT CO.
DEEP SIX
MI
WOOD $40

066-1296 FALLS CITY BAIT CO.
MICHIGAN TIPPER
MI
WOOD, SMALL $40

066-1301 FALLS CITY BAIT CO.
MICHIGAN TIPPER
MI
WOOD,   LARGE $40

066-1294 FENNER WEEDLESS BAIT CO
W.A.B. BAIT
WI
'WEEDLESS AUTOMATIC BAIT' $150

066-1356 FERRIS BAIT CO
GREEN SIREN

  $200

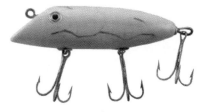

066-1357 FERRIS BAIT CO
GREEN SIREN

JR SIZE $200

066-5517 FETCHI LURE CO.
POPEYE
MO   1954
  $50

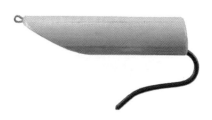

066-1295 FETCH-IT CO
FETCH-IT LURE
ID
  $50

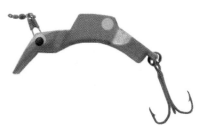

066-2705 FINLEY BAIT & TACKLE SHOP
FINLEY SPECIAL
IN   1963
  $10

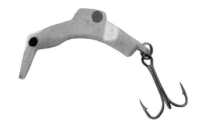

067-2706 FINLEY BAIT & TACKLE SHOP
FINLEY SPECIAL
IN   1963
$10

067-1265 FISCHER-SHUBERTH
CHICAGO CAPTOR
IL
MUSKY $1000

067-1276 FISCHER-SHUBERTH
CHICAGO CAPTOR
IL
$750

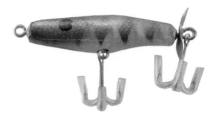

067-1246 FISH-A-LURE PRODUCTS
FISH-A-LURE
FL
JOE REE $40

067-1383 FISHATHON BAIT CO.
DIZZY DIVER
OK
$40

067-1387 FISHATHON BAIT CO.
DIZZY DIVER CRAWLER
OK   1947   3 IN   5/8 OZ
$60

067-1384 FISHATHON BAIT CO.
DIZZY FLOATER
OK
OLD $40

067-1385 FISHATHON BAIT CO.
DIZZY FLOATER
OK   1957   4 IN   1/2 OZ
NEW $40

067-1377 FISHMASTER SPORT GOODS
FISHMASTER LURE
MA
SMALL $20

067-1380 FISHMASTER SPORT GOODS
FISHMASTER LURE
MA
LARGE $20

067-1378 FISHMASTER SPORT GOODS
FISHMASTER WOBBLER
MA
SMALL $20

067-1379 FISHMASTER SPORT GOODS
FISHMASTER WOBBLER
MA
LARGE $30

067-5352 FLANNIGAN, W.
DECOY PIKE, FLANNIGAN
NY   1938
HOMEMADE FOLKART $200

067-5394 FLANNIGAN, W.
FISH DECOY, FLANNIGAN
NY
$200

067-5420 FLANNIGAN, W.
FISH DECOY, FLANNIGAN
NY
$200

068-1369 FLEEME BAIT CO
FLEEME POPPER FISH
  1960
  $40

068-5737 FLEEME BAIT CO.
FLEEME BAIT

  $50

068-5744 FLEEME BAIT CO.
FLEEME BAIT

  $40

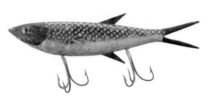

068-5745 FLEEME BAIT CO.
FLEEME BAIT

  $40

068-5754 FLEEME BAIT CO.
FLEEME BAIT

  $30

068-1359 FLOOD, F.L.B.
FLOOD MINNOW
FL 1929
FLORIDA SHINNER BAIT CO. $600

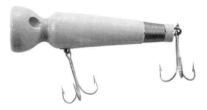

068-1365 FLORIDA ARTIFICAL BAIT CO
BUSY BODY
FL 1930's
  $250

068-1213 FLORIDA ARTIFICAL BAIT CO
FLORIDA MINNOW
FL 1930's
  $500

068-1366 FLORIDA ARTIFICAL BAIT CO
FLORIDA POPPER
FL 1930's
  $400

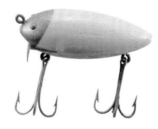

068-5536 FLORIDA ARTIFICAL BAIT CO
MOUSE, PEMBERTON
FL 1932
  $500

068-1364 FLORIDA ARTIFICAL BAIT CO
PEMBERTON FLAPPER
FL 1930's
  $250

068-1362 FLORIDA ARTIFICAL BAIT CO
SHRIMP, FLORIDA ARTICIAL BAIT
FL 1930
  $400

068-1358 FLORIDA ARTIFICAL BAIT CO
SUPERSTRIKE
FL 1929
  $300

068-7005 FLORIDA FISH TACKLE (EGER)
BUG WOBBLER
FL 1936
  $200

068-5763 FLORIDA FISHING TACKLE
UNKNOWN NAME
FL
100

069-7006 FLORIDA FISH TACKLE (EGER)
BUG, EGER
FL   1936
  $200

069-1242 FLORIDA FISH TACKLE (EGER)
BULL NOSE FROG
FL   1940's   3 IN   3/8 OZ
FROGSKIN COVERED $150

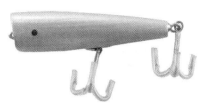

069-1243 FLORIDA FISH TACKLE (EGER)
CHUGGER TYPE
FL
  $50

069-1273 FLORIDA FISH TACKLE (EGER)
CHUNKER, EGER
FL
  $50

069-1260 FLORIDA FISH TACKLE (EGER)
DILLINGER
FL   1940's   2 1/2 IN   1/2 OZ
BABY $60

069-1261 FLORIDA FISH TACKLE (EGER)
DILLINGER, JUNIOR
FL   1940's   3 3/8 IN   5/8 OZ
  $60

069-1263 FLORIDA FISH TACKLE (EGER)
DILLINGER, WEEDLESS
FL   1940's   3 3/4 IN   5/8 OZ
  $60

069-1241 FLORIDA FISH TACKLE (EGER)
FLORIDA SHAD
FL
  $60

069-1257 FLORIDA FISH TACKLE (EGER)
FROG PAPPY
FL   1940's   3 7/8 IN   5/8 OZ
FROGSKIN COVERED $100

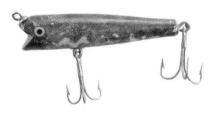

069-1253 FLORIDA FISH TACKLE (EGER)
FROGGIE, EGER
FL   1940's   3 1/8 IN   3/8 OZ
JR. $100

069-1209 FLORIDA FISH TACKLE (EGER)
MASTER DILLINGER
FL   1940's   3 7/8 IN   3/4 OZ
  $50

069-1264 FLORIDA FISH TACKLE (EGER)
PLUNKER, EGER
FL
  $150

069-5621 FLORIDA FISH TACKLE (EGER)
SARGEANT SEA DIVER
FL   1951
  $40

069-1262 FLORIDA FISH TACKLE (EGER)
SEA DILLINGER
FL   1940's   3 7/8 IN   3/4 OZ
  $60

069-1256 FLORIDA FISH TACKLE (EGER)
STUMP KNOCKER, SPINNING
FL   1948   3 1/8 IN   1/2 OZ
  $60

FISHING PLUGS

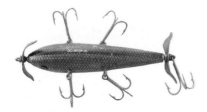

070-1235 FLORIDA FISH TACKLE (EGER)
SUICIDE
FL
  $100

070-1239 FLORIDA FISH TACKLE (EGER)
TOPPER, EGER
FL
  $60

070-1274 FLORIDA FISH TACKLE (EGER)
WIGGLE TAIL
FL
  $20

070-1225 FLORIDA FISHING TACKLE CO.
999 CONVICT
FL   1950's   4 1/4 IN   5/8 OZ
  $100

070-1224 FLORIDA FISHING TACKLE CO.
BULGE EYE FROG
FL   1950's   4 IN   3/4 OZ
  $100

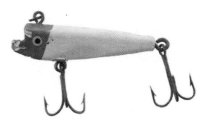

070-1217 FLORIDA FISHING TACKLE CO.
CLOTHES PIN BAIT, FLA FISH TACK
FL
  $40

070-1233 FLORIDA FISHING TACKLE CO.
CLOTHES PIN BAIT, FLA FISH TACK
FL
DANDY $40

070-1268 FLORIDA FISHING TACKLE CO.
DALTON SPECIAL
FL
JR SIZE, PLASTIC $20

070-1269 FLORIDA FISHING TACKLE CO.
DALTON SPECIAL
FL
PLASTIC $20

070-1270 FLORIDA FISHING TACKLE CO.
DALTON SPECIAL
FL
SMALL $40

070-1271 FLORIDA FISHING TACKLE CO.
DALTON SPECIAL
FL
LG $40

070-1272 FLORIDA FISHING TACKLE CO.
DALTON SPECIAL
FL   1958
SPINNING $50

070-1267 FLORIDA FISHING TACKLE CO.
DALTON TWIST
FL
  $40

070-1251 FLORIDA FISHING TACKLE CO.
EGER DARTER
FL
  $40

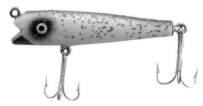

070-1255 FLORIDA FISHING TACKLE CO.
EGER DARTER
FL
JR SIZE $40

071-1211 FLORIDA FISHING TACKLE CO.
FLORIDA FISHING TACKLE BAIT
FL
  $40

071-1228 FLORIDA FISHING TACKLE CO.
FLORIDA FISHING TACKLE BAIT
FL
  $100

071-1230 FLORIDA FISHING TACKLE CO.
FLORIDA FISHING TACKLE BAIT
FL
  $200

071-1237 FLORIDA FISHING TACKLE CO.
FLORIDA SHAD
FL
DANDY $60

071-1238 FLORIDA FISHING TACKLE CO.
FLORIDA SHAD
FL   1950's   5 IN
2 SIZES $60

071-1212 FLORIDA FISHING TACKLE CO.
FLORIDA SHINER
FL
  $60

071-1249 FLORIDA FISHING TACKLE CO.
FLORIDA SHINER
FL
  $60

071-1250 FLORIDA FISHING TACKLE CO.
FLORIDA SHINER
FL
JR SIZE $60

071-1240 FLORIDA FISHING TACKLE CO.
GAR MINNOW, FLA FISH TACKLE
FL
  $75

071-1232 FLORIDA FISHING TACKLE CO.
MASTER DILLINGER
FL
DANDY $60

071-1248 FLORIDA FISHING TACKLE CO.
MASTER FLORIDA SHINER
FL
  $40

071-1227 FLORIDA FISHING TACKLE CO.
MAY WES
FL   1950's
2 SIZES $30

071-1214 FLORIDA FISHING TACKLE CO.
OLE ALBERT
FL
  $150

071-1216 FLORIDA FISHING TACKLE CO.
PEE WEE
FL
  $50

071-1231 FLORIDA FISHING TACKLE CO.
REYHU
FL   1950's   3 IN   11/16 OZ
GLASS EYES $150

FISHING PLUGS

072-1234 FLORIDA FISHING TACKLE CO.
REYHU
FL
DANDY $50

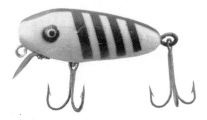

072-1275 FLORIDA FISHING TACKLE CO.
SCO-BO
FL   1950's   3 1/4 IN   9/16 OZ
PLASTIC $60

072-1210 FLORIDA FISHING TACKLE CO.
SEA DILLINGER
FL
DANDY $40

072-1247 FLORIDA FISHING TACKLE CO.
SEA SHINER
FL
  $60

072-1236 FLORIDA FISHING TACKLE CO.
SUICIDE
FL
  $100

072-1223 FLORIDA FISHING TACKLE CO.
TIPSY CUDA
FL   1950's   4 1/2 IN   13/16 OZ
  $50

072-1226 FLORIDA FISHING TACKLE CO.
TORPECUDA
FL   1950's   5 1/2 IN   5/8 OZ
  $100

072-1254 FLORIDA FISHING TACKLE CO.
TWITCHIN' CUDA
FL
  $40

072-1252 FLORIDA FISHING TACKLE CO.
TWITCHIN' CUDA, SPINNING
FL   1950
  $40

072-1428 FORTY-NINER BAIT CO
FORTY-NINER BAIT
MN   1949   3 IN
  $40

072-2524 FOSTER ENTERPRISES
ROCKET RACER
MI   1959
  $10

072-2525 FOSTER ENTERPRISES
ROCKET RACER
MI   1959
  $10

072-0342 FOX, CHARLES
POCONO BAIT

  $50

072-2458 FRIEND-PARDEE
KENT 3-HOOK MINNOW
OH   1900   3 1/2 IN
  $10000

072-2457 FRIEND-PARDEE
KENT 5-HOOK MINNOW
OH   1900   4 IN
  $10000

FISHING PLUGS

073-2460 FRIEND-PARDEE
KENT FROG
OH   1907   2 3/8 IN
    $6000

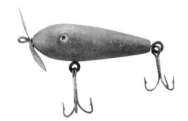

073-2459 FRIEND-PARDEE
KENT TOPWATER
OH   1907
    $1500

073-1355 FROST, H.J. & CO
SENATE WOOD MINNOW
NY   1914
    $900

073-1368 FUELSCH,   DON J. & CO
SHORE PATROL
AR
    $20

073-1370 FURY MFG CO
CHARMER
MI
    $30

073-1372 FURY MFG CO
FURY SET
MI
    $200

073-1371 FURY MFG CO
GO GETTUM
MI
    $30

073-1367 FURY MFG CO
PUP, FURY
MI
    $30

073-1424 G. G. BAIT CO.
GENE'S GEM
MN   1949   3 1/2 IN
    $40

073-1466 GABBARD TACKLE
GAB-LUR
MI   1948   4 IN
    $50

073-1487 GAIDE, CARL
GAIDE BAIT, THE
IN
    $4000

073-1421 GAME GUIDE PRODUCTS
PHANTOM FLATTIE
WA   1937
WOOD $60

073-1404 GARCIA, CHARLES (ABU)
EELETTEY
NY   1957   4 IN
SWEDEN $20

073-1392 GARCIA, CHARLES (ABU)
HI-LO
NY   1957   2 IN
SWEDEN $20

073-1396 GARCIA, CHARLES (ABU)
HI-LO
NY   1957
LARGE, SWEDEN $20

074-1405 GARCIA, CHARLES (ABU)
MINNOW, ABU
NY 1957
SWEDEN $10

074-1397 GARCIA, CHARLES (ABU)
PLUNKY
NY 1957 4 1/4 IN
LARGE, SWEDEN $10

074-1399 GARCIA, CHARLES (ABU)
PLUNKY
NY 1957 2 3/4 IN
SMALL, SWEDEN $10

074-1398 GARCIA, CHARLES (ABU)
PLUNKY
SWE 1957 2 /4 IN
MEDIUM, SWEDEN $10

074-1431 GARCIA, CHARLES (ABU)
GUPPY,
FR 1964
$10

074-1419 GARDNER SPORTS MFG.
TWIN-DANCER
MA 1948 2 1/2 IN
SMALL $20

074-1423 GARDNER SPORTS MFG.
TWIN-DANCER
MA 1948 3 IN
$20

074-1432 GARLAND BROTHERS
CORK-HEAD DARTER
FL
$300

074-1420 GARLAND BROTHERS
CORK-HEAD MINNOW
FL 1936 3 3/4 IN 5/8 OZ
$300

074-1430 GARLAND BROTHERS
INJURED MINNOW, GARLAND
FL 1946 3 3/4 IN
$30

074-2677 GARLAND BROTHERS
INJURED MINNOW, GARLAND
FL (POSSIBLY SOUTH BEND)
$100

074-1435 GARLAND BROTHERS
PIKE, GARLAND
FL 1938
$300

074-1440 GARLAND BROTHERS
PLUNKER, GARLAND BROTHERS
FL
$40

074-1413 GARRETT BAIT CO.
SUR-LUR

$10

074-1414 GARRETT BAIT CO.
SUR-LUR

$10

FISHING PLUGS

075-1415 GARRETT BAIT CO.
SUR-LUR

$10

075-1416 GARRETT BAIT CO.
SUR-LUR

$10

075-1417 GARRETT BAIT CO.
SUR-LUR

$10

075-1418 GARRETT BAIT CO.
SUR-LUR

$10

075-2283 GAVIAN CORP
SHAD QUACK
MN   1980
   $10

075-1442 GAYLE, GEORGE, W.
GAYLE DIVER
KY
   $100

075-1441 GAYLE, GEORGE, W.
GAYLE UNDERWATER BAIT
KY   1935   2 1/4 IN
   $100

075-1438 GAYLE, GEORGE, W.
GAYLE SURFACE BAIT
KY   1936   5 IN
   $100

075-1450 GEEN BAIT CO.
GEEN BAIT
ENG   1890   5 1/2 IN
ENGLAND $350

075-1443 GENERAL TOOL CO.
MAGNETIC WEEDLESS
MN   1947   3 IN
   $60

075-1437 GEN-SHAW BAIT CO.
GEN-SHAW BAIT
IL   1953   3 1/4 IN
   $20

075-1472 GIBBS, STAN
PENCIL POPPER
MA   1946   4 IN
   $30

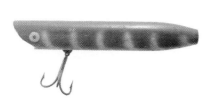

075-5198 GIBBS, STAN
POPPER, GIBBS
MA
   $50

075-5112 GI-GI LURE CO.
PADDLE POPPER
TX   1947
   $100

075-1461 GILL, J.J.
BASS BIRD
CA
   $60

076-1425 GILMORE MFG. CO.
GILMORE BAIT
AR   1959
  $20

076-1426 GILMORE MFG. CO.
HOODLER
AR   1958
  $20

076-22748 GILMORE MFG. CO.
HOODLER JR.
AR   1958
  $20

076-1407 GLENWILLOW PRODUCTS
SAFE-T-LURE
OH   1946
  $40

076-3828 GLENWILLOW PRODUCTS
SAFE-T-LURE
OH   1947   2 1/4 IN
  $60

076-1456 GLO BOY BAIT CO.
GLO BOY BAIT
  1941   3 1/4 IN
  $150

076-1076 GOBLE, B.C.
GOBLE MINNOW
OK   1936
  $300

076-1062 GOBLE, B.C.
PUNKINSEED, EVERREADY
OK   1929   4 1/2 IN
EVERREADY $300

076-1068 GOBLE, B.C.
PUNKINSEED, JOINTED, EVERREADY
OK   1927   3 3/4 IN
EVERREADY $300

076-1066 GOBLE, B.C.
TULSA WIGGLER
OK   1927   4 IN
SMALL $800

076-1067 GOBLE, B.C.
TULSA WIGGLER
OK   1926   5 1/2 IN
LARGE $800

076-1454 GOOD LUCK MFG. CO.
LITTLE IMP
OK   1949   2 IN
LARGE $10

076-1455 GOOD LUCK MFG. CO.
LITTLE IMP
OK   1949   1 3/4 IN
SMALL $10

076-5124 GOWEN MFG.
BUMBLE BUG

  $40

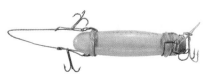

076-1484 GRAVES, CALVIN V.
WELSH & GRAVES MINNOW TUBE
NY   1893   5 IN
SMALL $1500

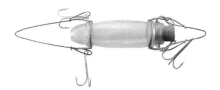

077-1485 GRAVES, CALVIN V.
WELSH & GRAVES MINNOW TUBE
NY   1893   4 1/4 IN
LARGE $1500

077-1406 GREAT LAKES BAIT CO
WE-D-FYER,   DIVING
MI
   $40

077-1410 GREAT LAKES BAIT CO
WE-D-FYER,   SURFACE
MI
   $40

077-1467 GREEN-WYLE CO
KILPON MINNOW
NY   1930
   $300

077-1468 GREEN-WYLE CO
KILPON MINNOW
NY   1930
   $300

077-1469 GREEN-WYLE CO
KILPON MINNOW
NY   1930
   $300

077-1470 GREEN-WYLE CO
KILPON MINNOW
NY   1930   5 1/4 IN
   $300

077-1471 GREEN-WYLE CO
KILPON MINNOW
NY   1930   3 IN
   $300

077-1477 GREIDER, J.A.
RETREATING MINNOW
IN   1933   3 1/4 IN
   $500

077-1422 GROUIX, J.E.
SOCK-IT
   1962
   $10

077-1493 GRUBE, W.J.
CRAW, GRUBE
OH   1910   3 3/4 IN
   $40

077-1497 GRUBE, W.J.
MINNOW, GRUBE
OH   1910
   $100

077-1498 GRUBE, W.J.
MINNOW, GRUBE
OH   1910
   $100

077-1496 GRUBE, W.J.
MOUSE, GRUBE
OH   1910   2 3/4 IN
   $40

077-1434 GUDEBROD BROS
GUDEBROD DARTER
PA   1960   3 IN
   $20

FISHING PLUGS

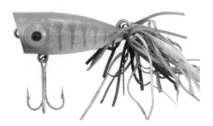

078-1458 GUDEBROD BROS
GUDEBROD DEEPSTER
PA   1960   3 IN
SMALL $30

078-1460 GUDEBROD BROS
GUDEBROD DEEPSTER
PA   1960   4 IN
LARGE $30

078-1459 GUDEBROD BROS
GUDEBROD POPPER
PA   1960   2 IN
  $30

078-1457 GUDEBROD BROS
GUDEBROD TOPPER
PA
  $60

078-1463 GUSICK, HENRY
BONANZA
WI   1959
  $90

078-0708 H & H PLUG CO.
12-IN-1 STRIP TEASER BAIT
IA
WITH 2 EXTRA BODIES $150

078-0713 H & H PLUG CO.
12-IN-1 STRIP TEASER BAIT
IA
WITH 2 EXTRA BODIES $80

078-1753 HAAS TACKLE CO.
LIV-MINNO
OK   1933   3 IN
  $600

078-1755 HAAS TACKLE CO.
LIV-MINNO
OK   1938
  $500

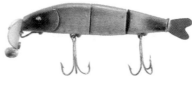

078-1757 HAAS TACKLE CO.
LIV-MINNO
OK
MUSKY $1000

078-1758 HAAS TACKLE CO.
LIV-MINNO
OK   1928   4 IN   5/8 OZ
GLASS EYES $600

078-1759 HAAS TACKLE CO.
LIV-MINNO
OK   1938   4 IN   5/8 OZ
PAINTED EYES $500

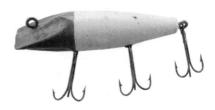

078-1744 HALIK CO., THE
HALIK FROG
MN   1955   4 3/8 IN
  $50

078-1743 HALIK CO., THE
HALIK FROG JR.
MN   1955   3 1/2 IN
  $50

078-1531 HALL, FLOYD R.
HALL'S WOBBLER
MI   1936
LARGE $300

FISHING PLUGS

079-1752 HALL, FLOYD R.
HALL'S WOBBLER
MI   1936
SMALL $300

079-1745 HALL, WM C.
HALL- LURE
VA   1951
  $40

079-01740 HAMILTON, F.B.
MEDLEY'S WIGGLY CRAWFISH
CA   1920   2 1/4 IN
SMALL $300

079-1741 HAMILTON, F.B.
MEDLEY'S WIGGLY CRAWFISH
CA   1920
  $350

079-1706 HAN-CRAFT MFG. CO.
PLUNK-O-LURE
OH   1939   3 1/4 IN
GLASS EYES $300

079-5554 HAND-FEL PRODUCTS
HAND-FEL LURE
AL   1969
  $300

079-1739 HANSEN
SUBMASTER
KS   1954   1 3/4 IN
  $50

079-0166 HANSEN, JACOB
LIFE LIKE SURFACE
MI   1910   4 1/4 IN
(ADOLPH ARNTZ) $2500

079-0165 HANSEN, JACOB
LIFE LIKE WOBBLER
MI   1910   4 1/4 IN
1 OF 3 KNOWN (ADOLPH ARNTZ) $2500

079-0163 HANSEN, JACOB
MICHIGAN LIFE LIKE
MI   1908   3 3/4 IN
WOOD, 5-HK (ADOLPH ARNTZ) $2500

079-0164 HANSEN, JACOB
MICHIGAN LIFE LIKE
MI   1908   3 IN
WOOD, 3-HK (ADOLPH ARNTZ) $2500

079-0167 HANSEN, JACOB
PULL ME SLOW
MI   1918   4 3/4 IN
WOOD $1000

079-0169 HANSEN, JACOB
PULL ME SLOW
MI   1925   3 1/4 IN
WOOD $1000

079-0168 HANSEN, JACOB
SPOON JACK
MI   1920   4 IN
WOOD $1000

079-0172 HANSEN, JACOB
SPOON JACK
MI   1918   4 1/2 IN
WOOD $1000

FISHING PLUGS

080-1698 HANSON, WM. B.
IRRESISTABLE MINNOW
PA   1919   3 3/4 IN
   $1200

080-1700 HANSON, WM. B.
IRRESISTABLE MINNOW
PA   1917   4 1/4 IN
MUSKY SIZE $1200

080-5684 HARDY BROS
FEATHERED MINNOW, HARDY
UK
ENGLISH $30

080-5551 HARDY BROS
HARDY LURE
UK
ENGLISH $100

080-1714 HARDY, J.A.
KROU MINNOW
IN   1917   4 IN
   $1500

080-1715 HARDY, W.A.
INTERCHANGEABLE MINNOW
IN   1907   2 3/4 IN
   $5000

080-1725 HARGRETT
CAT'S PAW
MI   1946   3 1/2 IN
   $150

080-6991 HARLOW & STEINBAUGH
E-Z WAY
OH   1915
   $500

080-1692 HARMON, JACK
3-IN-1 JACK HARMON POPPER
OK   1948   2 3/4 IN
   $100

080-1708 HARMON, JACK
HARMON BAIT
OK   1948   2 1/2 IN
   $100

080-1709 HARMON, JACK
HARMON BAIT
OK
   $100

080-1687 HARMON, JACK
JACK HARMON BAIT
OK
   $100

080-1688 HARMON, JACK
JACK HARMON BAIT
OK
   $100

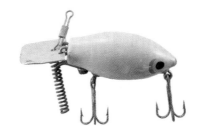

080-1695 HARMON, JACK
JACK HARMON BAIT
OK   1949   2 1/2 IN
   $100

080-1696 HARMON, JACK
JACK HARMON BAIT
OK
   $100

Page 80

FISHING PLUGS

081-1697 HARMON, JACK
JACK HARMON BAIT
OK
$100

081-5709 HARP, MARVIN
HARP'S DUNK
OK   1939
$30

081-1717 HARRIS , C.R.
FLOATING FROG
MI   1897   3 1/4 IN
CORK $1500

081-2767 HARRIS , C.R.
MANISTEE BAIT
MI   1899   3 1/2 IN
EARLY $8000

081-2759 HARRIS , C.R.
MANISTEE MINNOW
MI   1909   4 1/4 IN
SMALL $4000

081-1718 HARRIS , C.R.
SUBMERSIBLE FROG, HARRIS
MI   1897   3 1/4 IN
$1500

081-1719 HARTMAN, LEN
GUIDED MISSILE LURE
1960   2 3/4 IN
$20

081-4734 HARVEY, JIM
SHINNER MINNOW, HARVEY
CT   1949
$30

081-1724 HASKELL, RILEY
HASKELL FISH HOOK
OH   1859   4 1/2 IN
$15000

081-1704 HASTINGS SPORTING GOOD
FROG, HASTINGS
MI   1895   3 1/2 IN   1/2 OZ
WILSON $200

081-1736 HAWK FISH LURE CO.
BASS HAWK
MO   1953   2 IN
$30

081-1735 HAWK FISH LURE CO.
BASS HAWK CRAW
MO
$40

081-1737 HAWK FISH LURE CO.
HAWK DIVER
MO   1953   2 1/2 IN
$30

081-1738 HAWK, DAVE LURE CO.
LUCKYBUG
AR   1952
$30

081-1732 HAYNES, W.B.
HAYNES MAGNET
OH   1908   5 IN
$1500

FISHING PLUGS

082-1839 HEDDON, JAMES & SONS CO.
ARTISTIC MINNOW   #50
MI
  $600

082-1838 HEDDON, JAMES & SONS CO.
ARTISTIC MINNOW   #51
MI
  $500

082-1912 HEDDON, JAMES & SONS CO.
BASSER
MI   1922   4 IN
NEW, SALTWATER $200

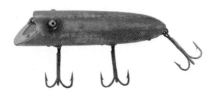

082-1918 HEDDON, JAMES & SONS CO.
BASSER
MI
SALTWATER $200

082-1917 HEDDON, JAMES & SONS CO.
BASSER #8500
MI
  $100

082-1919 HEDDON, JAMES & SONS CO.
BASSER #8500
MI
  $100

082-1913 HEDDON, JAMES & SONS CO.
BASSER , PLUNKING JR #8400.
MI   1926   3 IN   5/8 OZ
  $500

082-1910 HEDDON, JAMES & SONS CO.
BASSER, DELUXE #8520
MI   1936   4 IN   7/8 OZ
  $250

082-1916 HEDDON, JAMES & SONS CO.
BASSER, HEAD-ON #8500
MI
  $150

082-1920 HEDDON, JAMES & SONS CO.
BASSER, HEAD-ON #8500
MI
  $150

082-1911 HEDDON, JAMES & SONS CO.
BASSER, HEAD-ON #8500
MI
  $200

082-1904 HEDDON, JAMES & SONS CO.
BASSER, KING #8550
MI   1937   5 IN
  $400

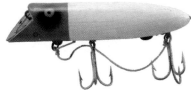

082-1902 HEDDON, JAMES & SONS CO.
BASSER, KING #8560
MI
  $400

082-1899 HEDDON, JAMES & SONS CO.
BASSER, KING #8540
MI   1920   4 1/4 IN   3/4 OZ
  $400

082-1909 HEDDON, JAMES & SONS CO.
BASSER, SALMON
MI   1925   4 IN
1st SALMON PLUG $450

083-2109 HEDDON, JAMES & SONS CO.
BIG BUD
MI
  $50

083-1985 HEDDON, JAMES & SONS CO.
BIG JOE, #600
MI   1924   3 5/8 IN   3/4 OZ
  $300

083-1834 HEDDON, JAMES & SONS CO.
BLACK SUCKER #1300
MI   1911   5 3/4 IN   2 1/2 OZ
UNDERWATER $4500

083-1766 HEDDON, JAMES & SONS CO.
BOB
MI   1903   2 IN
  $7000

083-1837 HEDDON, JAMES & SONS CO.
CASTING WEIGHT, HEDDON
MI
  $400

083-1946 HEDDON, JAMES & SONS CO.
CHUGGER SPECIAL #9540
MI
  $500

083-1949 HEDDON, JAMES & SONS CO.
CHUGGER SPECIAL, BABY #9520
MI
  $300

083-1947 HEDDON, JAMES & SONS CO.
CHUGGER, #9540
MI
FLAP-RIG $60

083-1948 HEDDON, JAMES & SONS CO.
CHUGGER, TINY #335
MI   1955   2 IN
  $50

083-1991 HEDDON, JAMES & SONS CO.
COAST MINNOW #640
MI   1914   5 IN
LARGE $1500

083-1996 HEDDON, JAMES & SONS CO.
COAST MINNOW #610
MI   1914   2 3/4 IN
SMALL $1200

083-1995 HEDDON, JAMES & SONS CO.
COAST MINNOW #630
MI   1914   4 1/2 IN
MEDIUM $1500

083-2096 HEDDON, JAMES & SONS CO.
COBRA , SPARKLE FINISH, #9930
MI
LARGE $30

083-2097 HEDDON, JAMES & SONS CO.
COBRA , SPARKLE FINISH, #9970
MI
LARGE, TOPWATER $30

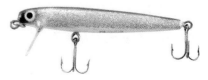

083-2100 HEDDON, JAMES & SONS CO.
COBRA,   SPARKLE FINISH, #9905
MI
SMALL $30

084-2094 HEDDON, JAMES & SONS CO.
COBRA,   SPARKLE FINISH, #9920
MI
MEDIUM $30

084-2099 HEDDON, JAMES & SONS CO.
COBRA,   SPARKLE FINISH, #9960
MI
SMALL, TOPWATER $30

084-2104 HEDDON, JAMES & SONS CO.
COBRA, #9910
MI
MEDIUM $30

084-2073 HEDDON, JAMES & SONS CO.
COBRA, #9920
MI
  $50

084-2095 HEDDON, JAMES & SONS CO.
COBRA, #9940
MI
LARGE $30

084-2093 HEDDON, JAMES & SONS CO.
COMMANDO
MI
  $30

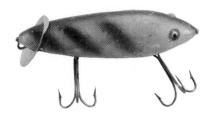

084-2140 HEDDON, JAMES & SONS CO.
COUSINS II
MI
  $50

084-1866 HEDDON, JAMES & SONS CO.
CRAB WIGGLER,
MI   1914   4/1/4 IN
NO EYES $1500

084-1868 HEDDON, JAMES & SONS CO.
CRAB WIGGLER, #1800
MI   1920   4 IN
NEW $200

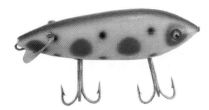

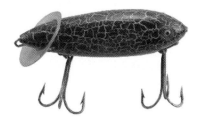

084-1869 HEDDON, JAMES & SONS CO.
CRAB WIGGLER, #1800
MI   1920   4 IN
  $150

084-1870 HEDDON, JAMES & SONS CO.
CRAB WIGGLER, BABY #1900
MI   1920   3 1/8 IN
  $200

084-1871 HEDDON, JAMES & SONS CO.
CRAB WIGGLER, BABY #1900
MI   1920
FLAP-RIG $200

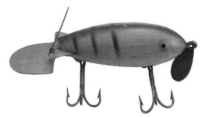

084-1867 HEDDON, JAMES & SONS CO.
CRAB WIGGLER, BABY #1900
MI   1916   3 1/8 IN   5/8 OZ
OLD $200

084-1876 HEDDON, JAMES & SONS CO.
CRAB, GO DEEPER #1900
MI   1948   3 1/2 IN   1/2 OZ
  $60

084-1874 HEDDON, JAMES & SONS CO.
CRAB, MIDGET #1950
MI
  $200

085-1875 HEDDON, JAMES & SONS CO.
CRAB, MIDGET #1950
MI   1930   2 1/2 IN   3/7 OZ
FLAP-RIG $300

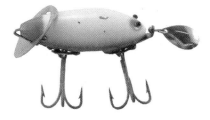

085-1872 HEDDON, JAMES & SONS CO.
CRAB-SPOOK #9900
MI   1950   2 1/2 IN
SMALL $100

085-1873 HEDDON, JAMES & SONS CO.
CRAB-SPOOK #9900
MI   1936   3 IN   3/4 OZ
$100

085-6925 HEDDON, JAMES & SONS CO.
CRAZY CRAWLER
MI
PLASTIC $30

085-1964 HEDDON, JAMES & SONS CO.
CRAZY CRAWLER   #2100
MI
$90

085-1965 HEDDON, JAMES & SONS CO.
CRAZY CRAWLER   #2100
MI
$90

085-1966 HEDDON, JAMES & SONS CO.
CRAZY CRAWLER   #2100
MI
$120

085-1960 HEDDON, JAMES & SONS CO.
CRAZY CRAWLER CHIPMUNK #2100
MI   1941   3 IN
$500

085-1963 HEDDON, JAMES & SONS CO.
CRAZY CRAWLER, MUSKY #2150
MI   1941   3 1/2 IN   1 OZ
$150

085-1967 HEDDON, JAMES & SONS CO.
CRAZY CRAWLER, BABY #2120
MI   1946   2 1/2 IN
$90

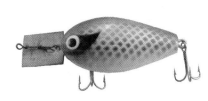

085-7000 HEDDON, JAMES & SONS CO.
SIDE SHAD, HEDDON
MI   1965
SMALL $40

085-1957 HEDDON, JAMES & SONS CO.
DARTING ZARA, #6600
MI   1936   4 IN
NEW $300

085-1958 HEDDON, JAMES & SONS CO.
DARTING ZARA, #6600
MI   1934   4 IN   5/8 OZ
OLD $600

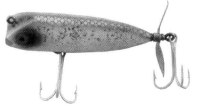

085-1951 HEDDON, JAMES & SONS CO.
DARTING ZARA-SPOOK, #9200
MI   1948   3 1/4 IN   4/5 OZ
$60

085-1775 HEDDON, JAMES & SONS CO.
DECOY, BATWING, #400
MI   1910   4 3/8 IN
$3000

086-1774 HEDDON, JAMES & SONS CO.
DECOY, HEDDON, #400
MI   1920   8 1/2 IN
$2500

086-1776 HEDDON, JAMES & SONS CO.
DECOY-SPOOK
MI   1930   5 IN
$1500

086-2075 HEDDON, JAMES & SONS CO.
DEEP 6   #345
MI
$10

086-1853 HEDDON, JAMES & SONS CO.
DEEP DIVING WIGGLER #1600
MI   1916   4 1/4 IN
NEW $400

086-1864 HEDDON, JAMES & SONS CO.
DEEP DIVING WIGGLER #1600
MI
$500

086-1865 HEDDON, JAMES & SONS CO.
DEEP DIVING WIGGLER #1600
MI   1915   4 3/4 IN   3/4 OZ
CUP- RIG, OLD $600

086-1877 HEDDON, JAMES & SONS CO.
DEEP-O-DIVER #7000
MI   1919   2 1/2 IN   2/3 OZ
$225

086-1786 HEDDON, JAMES & SONS CO.
SURFACE MINNOW #200
MI   1930   4 3/4 IN
GLASS EYES $500

086-1789 HEDDON, JAMES & SONS CO.
DOWAGIAC KILLER #400
MI
EARLY $1500

086-1791 HEDDON, JAMES & SONS CO.
DOWAGIAC KILLER #400
MI
LATER $700

086-1792 HEDDON, JAMES & SONS CO.
DOWAGIAC KILLER #400
MI
1 GILL MARK $1000

086-5306 HEDDON, JAMES & SONS CO.
DOWAGIAC KILLER #400
MI
$600

086-1790 HEDDON, JAMES & SONS CO.
DOWAGIAC KILLER #450
MI   1905   3 IN
$1500

086-1793 HEDDON, JAMES & SONS CO.
DOWAGIAC KILLER #450
MI
LATER, SPRAYED GILLS $700

086-1794 HEDDON, JAMES & SONS CO.
DOWAGIAC KILLER #450
MI
2 GILL MARKS $1000

FISHING PLUGS

087-1795 HEDDON, JAMES & SONS CO.
DOWAGIAC MINNOW #100
MI   1907
2 WEIGHTS, SLOPE $1000

087-1796 HEDDON, JAMES & SONS CO.
DOWAGIAC MINNOW #100
MI   1905   2 3/4 IN
OLD, 3 BELLY WEIGHTS $1200

087-1797 HEDDON, JAMES & SONS CO.
DOWAGIAC MINNOW #100
MI   1917   3 IN
$400

087-1798 HEDDON, JAMES & SONS CO.
DOWAGIAC MINNOW #100
MI   1920
$400

087-1799 HEDDON, JAMES & SONS CO.
DOWAGIAC MINNOW #100
MI   1930
LATER $400

087-1807 HEDDON, JAMES & SONS CO.
DOWAGIAC MINNOW #100
MI
SURFACE RIG, LATEST $150

087-1783 HEDDON, JAMES & SONS CO.
DOWAGIAC MINNOW #150
MI
$1500

087-1801 HEDDON, JAMES & SONS CO.
DOWAGIAC MINNOW #150
MI   1905   4 IN
3 WEIGHTS $10000

087-1802 HEDDON, JAMES & SONS CO.
DOWAGIAC MINNOW #150
MI   1907   3 3/4 IN
SLOPED, 2 BELLY WEIGHTS $1500

087-1803 HEDDON, JAMES & SONS CO.
DOWAGIAC MINNOW #150
MI   1912
CUP RIG $800

087-1804 HEDDON, JAMES & SONS CO.
DOWAGIAC MINNOW #150
MI   1928
TOILET SEAT RIG $800

087-1805 HEDDON, JAMES & SONS CO.
DOWAGIAC MINNOW #150
MI   1917   4 IN
L-RIG $400

087-1806 HEDDON, JAMES & SONS CO.
DOWAGIAC MINNOW #150
MI   1930
FLAP RIG $800

087-1849 HEDDON, JAMES & SONS CO.
DOWAGIAC MINNOW #20
MI   1905   2 1/4 IN
BABY $500

087-1850 HEDDON, JAMES & SONS CO.
DOWAGIAC MINNOW #20
MI
BABY, TACK EYES $75

FISHING PLUGS

088-1968 HEDDON, JAMES & SONS CO.
DREWCO #72
MI
  $200

088-1817 HEDDON, JAMES & SONS CO.
DUMMY- DOUBLE #1500
MI
SMALL $2500

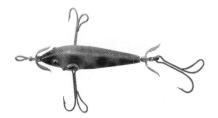

088-1818 HEDDON, JAMES & SONS CO.
DUMMY- DOUBLE #1500
MI
SMALL, MODIFIED L-RIG $1500

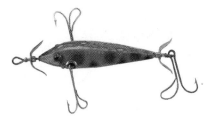

088-1819 HEDDON, JAMES & SONS CO.
DUMMY- DOUBLE #1500
MI
LARGE, MODIFIED L-RIG $1500

088-2101 HEDDON, JAMES & SONS CO.
DYING FLUTTER #9205
MI   1959   4 IN
  $30

088-2098 HEDDON, JAMES & SONS CO.
DYING QUIVER #9200
MI   1959   4 IN
  $30

088-1986 HEDDON, JAMES & SONS CO.
EMMA DEAR #500
MI
  $400

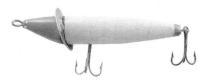

088-1779 HEDDON, JAMES & SONS CO.
EXPERT DOWAGIAC
MI
  $1000

088-1780 HEDDON, JAMES & SONS CO.
EXPERT DOWAGIAC
MI
  $1000

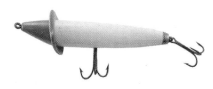

088-1778 HEDDON, JAMES & SONS CO.
EXPERT TOPWATER, HEDDON
MI   1902   4 1/2 IN
1st COMMERCIAL $1500

088-2113 HEDDON, JAMES & SONS CO.
FIDGET #400
MI   1955   2 1/8 IN   3/8 OZ
  $30

088-2112 HEDDON, JAMES & SONS CO.
FIDGET, FLASHER   #400
MI   1956   2 1/8 IN   3/8 OZ
  $30

088-2147 HEDDON, JAMES & SONS CO.
FIDGET, FLASHER #400
MI   1955   2 1/8 IN   3/8 OZ
  $30

088-2008 HEDDON, JAMES & SONS CO.
FLAPTAI, #7110L
MI   1935   4 IN
1 HOOK, JR $225

088-2009 HEDDON, JAMES & SONS CO.
FLAPTAIL
MI   1935   4 IN
2 HOOK, JR $150

FISHING PLUGS

089-2013 HEDDON, JAMES & SONS CO.
FLAPTAIL #7000
MI   1935   4 1/2 IN
  $100

089-2014 HEDDON, JAMES & SONS CO.
FLAPTAIL #7000
MI
  $75

089-2015 HEDDON, JAMES & SONS CO.
FLAPTAIL #7000
MI
  $60

089-2010 HEDDON, JAMES & SONS CO.
FLAPTAIL, HUSKY #7400
MI   1937   7 IN   1 OZ
  $300

089-2011 HEDDON, JAMES & SONS CO.
FLAPTAIL, HUSKY #7400
MI
  $150

089-2012 HEDDON, JAMES & SONS CO.
FLAPTAIL, MUSKY #7040
MI   1940   5 1/2 IN
  $300

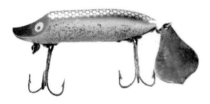

089-2007 HEDDON, JAMES & SONS CO.
FLAPTAIL-SPOOK #9700
MI   1948   3 3/8 IN
  $50

089-1847 HEDDON, JAMES & SONS CO.
FLIPPER #142
MI   1927   3 3/4 IN
  $900

089-1887 HEDDON, JAMES & SONS CO.
FLORIDA SPECIAL #10B
MI   1922   2 1/2 IN   3/4 OZ
LARGE $1200

089-1886 HEDDON, JAMES & SONS CO.
FLORIDA SPECIAL #10S
MI   1922   2 3/4 IN   1/2 OZ
SMALL $1200

089-1763 HEDDON, JAMES & SONS CO.
FROG, HEDDON
MI   1896   4 1/4 IN
1st SOLD $30000

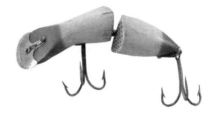

089-1857 HEDDON, JAMES & SONS CO.
GAME FISHER #5400
MI   1925   4 IN   1/2 OZ
BABY, 2-PC $200

089-1858 HEDDON, JAMES & SONS CO.
GAME FISHER #5400
MI   1925   4 IN   1/2 OZ
BABY $120

089-1855 HEDDON, JAMES & SONS CO.
GAME FISHER #5500
MI   1923   4 3/4 IN   3/4 OZ
2 PIECE $200

089-1856 HEDDON, JAMES & SONS CO.
GAME FISHER #5500
MI   1923   4 3/4 IN   3/4 OZ
  $100

090-1773 HEDDON, JAMES & SONS CO.
GLOBE TYPE, HEDDON
MI
  $1000

090-1829 HEDDON, JAMES & SONS CO.
HEAVY CASTING MINNOW #175
MI   1911   3 3/4 IN
  $2250

090-4080 HEDDON, JAMES & SONS CO.
HEDDON MINNOW #150
MI   1912
  $300

090-2076 HEDDON, JAMES & SONS CO.
HI-TAIL   #305
MI
  $30

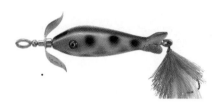

090-1816 HEDDON, JAMES & SONS CO.
LIGHT CASTING MINNOW, #11
MI   1922   2 1/2 IN
  $1200

090-1987 HEDDON, JAMES & SONS CO.
LITTLE MARY, #850
MI   1924   3 IN   1/2 OZ
  $450

090-1922 HEDDON, JAMES & SONS CO.
LUCKY 13 BABY, #2400
MI
NEWER $30

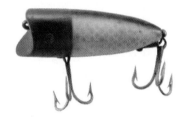

090-1923 HEDDON, JAMES & SONS CO.
LUCKY 13 BABY, #2400
MI
  $40

090-1924 HEDDON, JAMES & SONS CO.
LUCKY 13 JR, #2400
MI   1921   3 1/8 IN   1/2 OZ
OLDER $300

090-1921 HEDDON, JAMES & SONS CO.
LUCKY 13, #2500
MI
NEWER $40

090-1935 HEDDON, JAMES & SONS CO.
LUCKY 13, #2500
MI
  $200

090-1936 HEDDON, JAMES & SONS CO.
LUCKY 13, #2500
MI   1920   3 7/8 IN   5/8 OZ
OLD $225

090-1937 HEDDON, JAMES & SONS CO.
LUCKY 13, #2500
MI
  $150

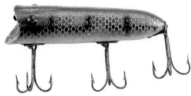

090-1938 HEDDON, JAMES & SONS CO.
LUCKY 13, #2500
MI   1940   3 3/4 IN
NEW $150

090-1939 HEDDON, JAMES & SONS CO.
LUCKY 13, #2500
MI
  $100

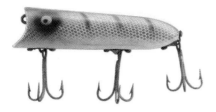

091-1940 HEDDON, JAMES & SONS CO.
LUCKY 13, #2500
MI
  $50

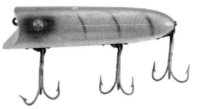

091-1941 HEDDON, JAMES & SONS CO.
LUCKY 13, #2500
MI
  $50

091-1925 HEDDON, JAMES & SONS CO.
LUCKY 13, BABY, #2400
MI   1919   2 1/2 IN
NO EYE $300

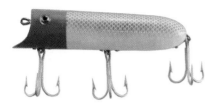

091-1934 HEDDON, JAMES & SONS CO.
LUCKY 13, MUSKY
MI   1958   5 3/4 IN
  $500

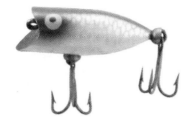

091-1930 HEDDON, JAMES & SONS CO.
LUCKY 13, TINY #370
MI   1955   1 7/8 IN   1/5 OZ
  $30

091-1983 HEDDON, JAMES & SONS CO.
LUNY FROG #3500
MI   1926   4 1/4 IN   7/8 OZ
  $400

091-1984 HEDDON, JAMES & SONS CO.
LUNY FROG #3500
MI   1926   4 1/4 IN   7/8 OZ
SPECIAL ORDER $1200

091-1982 HEDDON, JAMES & SONS CO.
LUNY FROG, LITTLE #3400
MI   1926   3 3/4 IN   2/3 OZ
  $400

091-1897 HEDDON, JAMES & SONS CO.
MEADOW MOUSE #4000
MI
  $120

091-1898 HEDDON, JAMES & SONS CO.
MEADOW MOUSE #4000
MI   1929   2 3/4 IN
  $200

091-1905 HEDDON, JAMES & SONS CO.
MEADOW MOUSE #4000
MI   CUP RIG
  $200

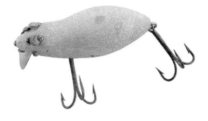

091-1906 HEDDON, JAMES & SONS CO.
MEADOW MOUSE #4000
MI   1955   3 IN
NEWER $120

091-1907 HEDDON, JAMES & SONS CO.
MEADOW MOUSE #4000
MI
  $40

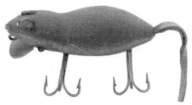

091-1908 HEDDON, JAMES & SONS CO.
MEADOW MOUSE #4000
MI   1939
  $40

091-1820 HEDDON, JAMES & SONS CO.
MUSKALLONGE MINNOW #700
MI
  $3000

FISHING PLUGS

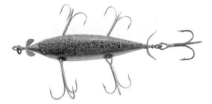

092-1821 HEDDON, JAMES & SONS CO.
MUSKALLONGE MINNOW #700
MI
 $8000

092-1851 HEDDON, JAMES & SONS CO.
NEAR SURFACE WIGGLER
MI   1917   3 IN
BABY $4000

092-1852 HEDDON, JAMES & SONS CO.
NEAR SURFACE WIGGLER #1700
MI
 $400

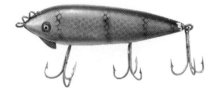

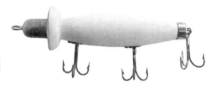

092-1854 HEDDON, JAMES & SONS CO.
NEAR SURFACE WIGGLER #1700
MI   1915   4 1/4 IN   3/4 OZ
 $400

092-1815 HEDDON, JAMES & SONS CO.
NEW SURFACE MINNOW #402
MI   1907   4 3/4 IN
 $2000

092-1760 HEDDON, JAMES & SONS CO.
NIGHT BAIT
MI   1890   2 3/4 IN
 $1000

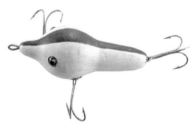

092-1761 HEDDON, JAMES & SONS CO.
NIGHT BAIT
MI   1912   5 IN
 $1000

092-1762 HEDDON, JAMES & SONS CO.
NIGHT- RADIANT
MI
BABY $5000

092-1764 HEDDON, JAMES & SONS CO.
NIGHT- RADIANT BAIT
MI   1912   3 3/4 IN
BABY $10000

092-1824 HEDDON, JAMES & SONS CO.
O MINNOW
MI
SMALL $600

092-1825 HEDDON, JAMES & SONS CO.
O MINNOW
MI
LARGE $600

092-1826 HEDDON, JAMES & SONS CO.
O MINNOW
MI
LARGE $600

092-1827 HEDDON, JAMES & SONS CO.
OO MINNOW
MI
 $700

092-1828 HEDDON, JAMES & SONS CO.
OO MINNOW
MI
 $700

092-2089 HEDDON, JAMES & SONS CO.
PROWLER, #7050
MI
 $50

093-1945 HEDDON, JAMES & SONS CO.
PUNKIE-SPOOK #380
MI   1960   1 5/8 IN   1/20 OZ
  $60

093-22569 HEDDON, JAMES & SONS CO.
PUNKINSEED
MI   1940
  $100

093-1943 HEDDON, JAMES & SONS CO.
PUNKINSEED #730
MI   1940   2 IN
SINKER $300

093-1942 HEDDON, JAMES & SONS CO.
PUNKINSEED #740
MI
  $300

093-1944 HEDDON, JAMES & SONS CO.
PUNKINSEED-SPOOK #9630
MI
  $100

093-2085 HEDDON, JAMES & SONS CO.
RESEARCH DEEP-DIVE
MI   1950   5 IN
  $100

093-2088 HEDDON, JAMES & SONS CO.
RESEARCH PROTOTYPE, HEDDON
MI
  $100

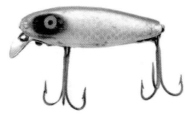

093-2028 HEDDON, JAMES & SONS CO.
RIVER RUNT #110, HEDDON
MI
LATE $90

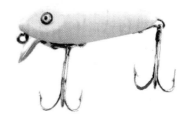

093-2029 HEDDON, JAMES & SONS CO.
RIVER RUNT #110, HEDDON
MI   1939
  $200

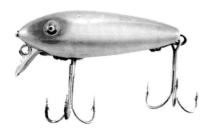

093-2030 HEDDON, JAMES & SONS CO.
RIVER RUNT #110, HEDDON
MI   1939   2 5/8 IN   1/2 OZ
  $200

093-2027 HEDDON, JAMES & SONS CO.
RIVER RUNT DEEP DIVING, JTD. #9430
MI   1946   3 1/8 IN
  $30

093-2037 HEDDON, JAMES & SONS CO.
RIVER RUNT SEA RUNT #610
MI   1939   2 5/8 IN   5/8 OZ
  $400

093-2038 HEDDON, JAMES & SONS CO.
RIVER RUNT SEA RUNT #610
MI
LATER $150

093-24678 HEDDON, JAMES & SONS CO.
RIVER RUNT, FIRE FINISH, HEDDON
MI
SHUR-STRIKE $40

093-2031 HEDDON, JAMES & SONS CO.
RIVER RUNT, GIANT #7510
MI   1940   3 1/4 IN   1 OZ
  $1200

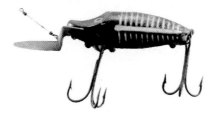

094-2044 HEDDON, JAMES & SONS CO.
RIVER RUNT, GO DEEPER #D-9110
MI 1924
LARGE $30

094-2024 HEDDON, JAMES & SONS CO.
RIVER RUNT, HI-LO
MI 1959 3 1/4 IN
$40

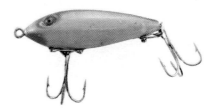

094-2033 HEDDON, JAMES & SONS CO.
RIVER RUNT, LAGUNA #L-10
MI
$450

094-2047 HEDDON, JAMES & SONS CO.
RIVER RUNT, MIDGET #9010
MI 1938 2 1/8 IN
$30

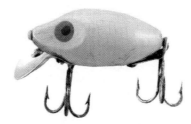

094-2036 HEDDON, JAMES & SONS CO.
RIVER RUNT, MIDGET DIGIT #920
MI 1941 1 1/2 IN 2/5 OZ
$75

094-2035 HEDDON, JAMES & SONS CO.
RIVER RUNT, MIDGET-DIGIT SPOOK
MI 1946 1 5/8 IN 5.8 OZ
#9020 $60

094-2032 HEDDON, JAMES & SONS CO.
RIVER RUNT, SALMON #8850
MI 1941 5 IN 1/25 OZ
$600

094-2034 HEDDON, JAMES & SONS CO.
RIVER RUNT, SURFACE #100
MI
$1000

094-2048 HEDDON, JAMES & SONS CO.
RIVER RUNT, TINY FLOATING #340
MI 1952 2 3/8 IN 1/4 OZ
$30

094-2043 HEDDON, JAMES & SONS CO.
RIVER RUNT, TINY GO DEEPER
MI 1952 2 IN
#D-350 $40

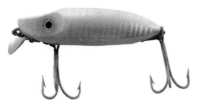

094-2046 HEDDON, JAMES & SONS CO.
RIVER RUNT, FLOATING #9400
MI 1937 3 IN
$30

094-2040 HEDDON, JAMES & SONS CO.
RIVER RUNT, GO DEEPER #D-9110
MI 1939 2 1/4 IN 3/7 OZ
SMALL $60

094-2041 HEDDON, JAMES & SONS CO.
RIVER RUNT, GO DEEPER #D-9110
MI 1939 2 1/2 IN 5/8 OZ
LARGE $60

094-2042 HEDDON, JAMES & SONS CO.
RIVER RUNT, GO DEEPER #D-9110
MI 1946 2 1/4 IN
SMALL, SPECIAL COLOR $40

094-2049 HEDDON, JAMES & SONS CO.
RIVER-RUNT-SPOOK #9110
MI 1936 2 1/2 IN
$30

095-2045 HEDDON, JAMES & SONS CO.
RIVER-RUNT-SPOOK, NO-SNAG
MI   1941   2 1/2 IN   5/8 OZ
#N-9110 $90

095-2026 HEDDON, JAMES & SONS CO.
RIVER-RUNT-SPOOK, JTD #9330
MI   1946   3 IN
SINKER $30

095-2025 HEDDON, JAMES & SONS CO.
RIVER-RUNT-SPOOK, JTD #9340
MI   1946   4 IN   3/4 OZ
FLOATING $30

095-1832 HEDDON, JAMES & SONS CO.
S.O.S MINNOW #160
MI
   $200

095-1833 HEDDON, JAMES & SONS CO.
S.O.S MINNOW #170
MI   1928   4 1/2 IN
3 HK $300

095-1841 HEDDON, JAMES & SONS CO.
S.O.S. MINNOW #140
MI
   $70

095-1842 HEDDON, JAMES & SONS CO.
S.O.S. MINNOW #140
MI   1937   3 IN   1/2 OZ
GLASS EYES $200

095-1835 HEDDON, JAMES & SONS CO.
S.O.S. MINNOW #160
MI   1928   4 1/2 IN
2 HK $200

095-1831 HEDDON, JAMES & SONS CO.
S.O.S. MINNOW #370
MI   1928   4 3/4 IN
MUSKY $1200

095-1836 HEDDON, JAMES & SONS CO.
S.O.S. MINNOW #170
MI
   $300

095-1989 HEDDON, JAMES & SONS CO.
SALT-SPOOK #9600
MI   1924   2 3/4 IN   1/2 OZ
   $400

095-1970 HEDDON, JAMES & SONS CO.
SALTWATER HEDDON
MI   1926   3 5/8 IN
   $600

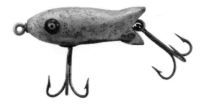

095-1990 HEDDON, JAMES & SONS CO.
SALTWATER SPECIAL #800
MI
   $400

095-1988 HEDDON, JAMES & SONS CO.
SALTWATER SPECIAL #850
MI   1924   3 IN   1/2 OZ
   $400

095-1971 HEDDON, JAMES & SONS CO.
SALTWATER SPECIAL, HEDDON
MI
   $300

FISHING PLUGS

096-1823 HEDDON, JAMES & SONS CO.
SALTWATER TORPEDO   #30
MI
  $150

096-2023 HEDDON, JAMES & SONS CO.
SCISSORTAIL-SPOOK, #9830
MI   1948   3 1/4 IN
  $50

096-1973 HEDDON, JAMES & SONS CO.
SEA-SPOOK #9800
MI   1929   3 3/4 IN
  $400

096-1969 HEDDON, JAMES & SONS CO.
SHARK-MOUTH MINNIE, #520
MI   1935   3 IN   3/4 OZ
  $1000

096-2134 HEDDON, JAMES & SONS CO.
SHRIMPY #375
MI
  $40

096-1972 HEDDON, JAMES & SONS CO.
SHRIMPY-SPOOK #9000
MI   1930   4 IN   1 OZ
  $400

096-2074 HEDDON, JAMES & SONS CO.
SIDE SHAD
MI
LARGE $30

096-2087 HEDDON, JAMES & SONS CO.
SONAR #433
MI   1958   1 3/4 IN
BABY $30

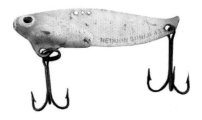

096-2086 HEDDON, JAMES & SONS CO.
SONAR #435
MI   1958   2 1/2 IN
  $30

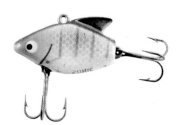

096-2081 HEDDON, JAMES & SONS CO.
SONIC #395
MI
  $30

096-2082 HEDDON, JAMES & SONS CO.
SONIC, CHROME
MI
  $30

096-2079 HEDDON, JAMES & SONS CO.
SONIC, FIRETAIL
MI
  $30

096-2078 HEDDON, JAMES & SONS CO.
SONIC, SUPER #9385
MI
  $30

096-2077 HEDDON, JAMES & SONS CO.
SONIC, SUPER, FIREFINISH, #9385
MI
  $30

096-2080 HEDDON, JAMES & SONS CO.
SONIC, ULTRA
MI
  $30

FISHING PLUGS

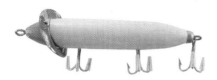

097-1784 HEDDON, JAMES & SONS CO.
SPECIAL #200
MI   1912   4 3/4 IN   4/5 OZ
   $1200

097-1785 HEDDON, JAMES & SONS CO.
SPECIAL #200
MI
   $1200

097-1787 HEDDON, JAMES & SONS CO.
SPECIAL #200
MI
   $1500

097-1863 HEDDON, JAMES & SONS CO.
SPIN-DIVER #3000
MI   1919
   $1500

097-1896 HEDDON, JAMES & SONS CO.
STANLEY PORK RIND BAIT #70
MI   1923   2 1/4 IN   5/8 OZ
   $300

097-2083 HEDDON, JAMES & SONS CO.
STINGAREE #9930
MI
   $30

097-2084 HEDDON, JAMES & SONS CO.
STINGAREE, TINY #330
MI   1948   1 1/2 IN
   $30

097-1974 HEDDON, JAMES & SONS CO.
SUPER DOWAGIAC #9100
MI   1930   3 3/4 IN   1 OZ
   $150

097-1975 HEDDON, JAMES & SONS CO.
SUPER DOWAGIAC #9100
MI   1931   3 1/2 IN
BABY $150

097-1976 HEDDON, JAMES & SONS CO.
SUPER DOWAGIAC #9100
MI
LATER $70

097-1977 HEDDON, JAMES & SONS CO.
SUPER DOWAGIAC SPECIAL
MI   1936   2 1/4 IN
   $900

097-5307 HEDDON, JAMES & SONS CO.
SURFUSSER, #300
MI
   $600

097-1781 HEDDON, JAMES & SONS CO.
SURFACE MINNOW #200
MI
   $500

097-1782 HEDDON, JAMES & SONS CO.
SURFACE MINNOW #200
MI
   $750

097-1767 HEDDON, JAMES & SONS CO.
SURFACE MINNOW #210
MI
GLASS EYES $150

FISHING PLUGS

098-1769 HEDDON, JAMES & SONS CO.
SURFACE MINNOW #210
MI   1920   3 1/2 IN   3/8 OZ
  $150

098-1770 HEDDON, JAMES & SONS CO.
SURFACE MINNOW #210
MI   1930   3 1/2 IN
  $175

098-1771 HEDDON, JAMES & SONS CO.
SURFACE MINNOW #210
MI
NEW STYLE $50

098-1772 HEDDON, JAMES & SONS CO.
SURFACE MINNOW #210
MI
NO EYE $200

098-1848 HEDDON, JAMES & SONS CO.
SURFACE MINNY, #260
MI   1934   3 3/4 IN
  $1200

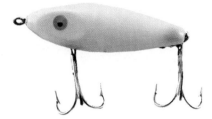

098-2039 HEDDON, JAMES & SONS CO.
SURFACE RUNT
MI
LATER $100

098-1809 HEDDON, JAMES & SONS CO.
SURFUSSER #300
MI   1907   4 IN
OLD $1500

098-1810 HEDDON, JAMES & SONS CO.
SURFUSSER #300
MI   1911   4 IN
  $1000

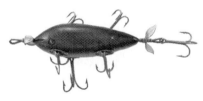

098-1811 HEDDON, JAMES & SONS CO.
SURFUSSER #300
MI   1930   3 3/4 IN
  $1500

098-1812 HEDDON, JAMES & SONS CO.
SURFUSSER #300
MI
  $500

098-1813 HEDDON, JAMES & SONS CO.
SURFUSSER #300
MI
  $1200

098-1814 HEDDON, JAMES & SONS CO.
SURFUSSER #300
MI
TACK-THROUGH $500

098-1822 HEDDON, JAMES & SONS CO.
SURFUSSER #300
MI
  $500

098-1808 HEDDON, JAMES & SONS CO.
SURFUSSER #350
MI   1936   4 IN   1 OZ
MUSKY $1500

098-1860 HEDDON, JAMES & SONS CO.
SWIMMING MINNOW #800, HEDDON
MI   1910   3 IN
BABY $1500

FISHING PLUGS

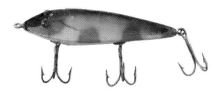

099-1861 HEDDON, JAMES & SONS CO.
SWIMMING MINNOW #900, HEDDON
MI
  $1500

099-1862 HEDDON, JAMES & SONS CO.
SWIMMING MINNOW #900, HEDDON
MI   1910   4 1/2 IN
  $1200

099-1880 HEDDON, JAMES & SONS CO.
TAD-POLLY #5000
MI
BABY $250

099-1881 HEDDON, JAMES & SONS CO.
TAD-POLLY #5000
MI   1923   3 7/8 IN   5/8 OZ
FLAP-RIG, BABY $200

099-1879 HEDDON, JAMES & SONS CO.
TAD-POLLY #6000
MI   1925   4 5/8 IN   3/4 OZ
LARGE $250

099-1885 HEDDON, JAMES & SONS CO.
TAD-POLLY MAGNUM
MI
  $40

099-1883 HEDDON, JAMES & SONS CO.
TAD-POLLY RUNT #5100
MI   1936   3 IN   1/2 OZ
  $1500

099-6928 HEDDON, JAMES & SONS CO.
TAD-POLLY SANTA LURE
MI
  $100

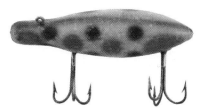

099-1878 HEDDON, JAMES & SONS CO.
TAD-POLLY, NO LIP
MI   1919   4 IN
  $1500

099-1882 HEDDON, JAMES & SONS CO.
TAD-POLLY-SPOOK #9000
MI   1948   3 IN   3/8 OZ
  $40

099-2106 HEDDON, JAMES & SONS CO.
TIGER #1010
MI
SMALL $40

099-2102 HEDDON, JAMES & SONS CO.
TIGER #1020
MI
LARGE $40

099-2107 HEDDON, JAMES & SONS CO.
TIGER, DEEP DIV #D1020
MI
LARGE $40

099-2103 HEDDON, JAMES & SONS CO.
TIGER, DEEP DIVE #D1010
MI
SMALL $40

099-2108 HEDDON, JAMES & SONS CO.
TIGER, SALTWATER #1020
MI
CHROME FINISH $40

100-2105 HEDDON, JAMES & SONS CO.
TIGER, SALTWATER #1030
MI
$40

100-6926 HEDDON, JAMES & SONS CO.
TINY LUCKY 13 #370
MI
$10

100-1884 HEDDON, JAMES & SONS CO.
TINY TAD, #390
MI 1955 2 1/8 IN 1/5 OZ
$40

100-2155 HEDDON, JAMES & SONS CO.
TINY-SPOOK, #310
MI 1955 1 7/8 IN 1/4 OZ
$60

100-1843 HEDDON, JAMES & SONS CO.
TORPEDO #120
MI 1925 4 4/8 IN 7/8 OZ
SMALL $300

100-1844 HEDDON, JAMES & SONS CO.
TORPEDO #130
MI
DECAL EYES $100

100-1845 HEDDON, JAMES & SONS CO.
TORPEDO #130
MI
LARGE $300

100-1846 HEDDON, JAMES & SONS CO.
TORPEDO #130
MI
$400

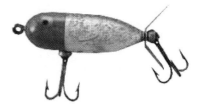

100-1997 HEDDON, JAMES & SONS CO.
TORPEDO, TINY SPOOK #360
MI 1955 2 IN
$15

100-1840 HEDDON, JAMES & SONS CO.
TORPEDO-SPOOK, #130
MI 1933 4 3/4 IN 3.4 OZ
$300

100-1765 HEDDON, JAMES & SONS CO.
UNDERWATER EXPERT
MI 1904 2 1/2 IN
1st UNDERWATER $7000

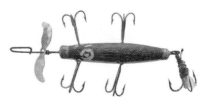

100-1788 HEDDON, JAMES & SONS CO.
UNDERWATER EXPERT, 1st MADE
MI 1890 4 1/4 IN
1st BAIT $9000

100-2002 HEDDON, JAMES & SONS CO.
VAMP #7300
MI 1931 3 1/2 IN 1/2 OZ
BABY $120

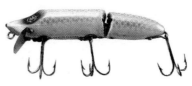

100-2003 HEDDON, JAMES & SONS CO.
VAMP #7300
MI 1925 4 3/4 IN 3/4 OZ
$120

100-2001 HEDDON, JAMES & SONS CO.
VAMP #7400
MI
BABY $120

FISHING PLUGS

101-2019 HEDDON, JAMES & SONS CO.
VAMP #7500
MI
LATE $60

101-2021 HEDDON, JAMES & SONS CO.
VAMP #7500
MI
 $150

101-2022 HEDDON, JAMES & SONS CO.
VAMP #7500
MI
 $90

101-1999 HEDDON, JAMES & SONS CO.
VAMP #7550
MI
ALLEN STRIPEY, SALTWATER $600

101-2020 HEDDON, JAMES & SONS CO.
VAMP LUNY, #7500
MI
 $400

101-2004 HEDDON, JAMES & SONS CO.
VAMP, BABY, SURFACE
MI   1930   3 1/2 IN
 $400

101-1998 HEDDON, JAMES & SONS CO.
VAMP, GREAT #7540
MI   1928   5 IN
 $900

101-1994 HEDDON, JAMES & SONS CO.
VAMP, JOINTED #7300
MI
OLD $100

101-1992 HEDDON, JAMES & SONS CO.
VAMP, JOINTED #7300
MI
2 PIECE $100

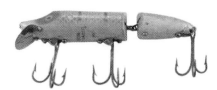

101-1993 HEDDON, JAMES & SONS CO.
VAMP, JOINTED #7300
MI
NEWER $40

101-2005 HEDDON, JAMES & SONS CO.
VAMP, JOINTED MUSKY #7350
MI   1948   4 3/4 IN   3/4 OZ
 $300

101-2000 HEDDON, JAMES & SONS CO.
VAMP, MUSKY #7550
MI   1927   6 IN
 $600

101-2006 HEDDON, JAMES & SONS CO.
VAMP, MUSKY #7600
MI   1925   8 IN
 $900

101-2016 HEDDON, JAMES & SONS CO.
VAMP-SPOOK #9750
MI
LATE $30

101-2017 HEDDON, JAMES & SONS CO.
VAMP-SPOOK #9750
MI   1935   4 1/2 IN   3/4 OZ
2 PIECE $60

FISHING PLUGS

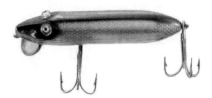

102-2018 HEDDON, JAMES & SONS CO.
VAMP-SPOOK, FLOATING, #9500
MI   1931   3 3/4 IN   3/4 OZ
  $300

102-1892 HEDDON, JAMES & SONS CO.
WALTON FEATHER TAIL   #40
MI   1922   3 IN   1/2 OZ
OLD, NO-EYE $1200

102-1893 HEDDON, JAMES & SONS CO.
WALTON FEATHER TAIL   #40
MI   1924   3 IN   1/2 OZ
  $450

102-1888 HEDDON, JAMES & SONS CO.
WEEDLESS WIDOW #220
MI
L-RIG, EARLY $120

102-1889 HEDDON, JAMES & SONS CO.
WEEDLESS WIDOW #220
MI
FLAP-RIG $100

102-1890 HEDDON, JAMES & SONS CO.
WEEDLESS WIDOW #220
MI
FLAP-RIG $90

102-1891 HEDDON, JAMES & SONS CO.
WEEDLESS WIDOW #220
MI   1939   2 1/4 IN
LATER $75

102-1914 HEDDON, JAMES & SONS CO.
WIGGLE KING, #2000
MI
  $300

102-1915 HEDDON, JAMES & SONS CO.
WIGGLE KING, 1ST
MI   1918   4 1/4 IN
PROTOTYPE $900

102-7059 HEDDON, JAMES & SONS CO.
WORM, HEDDON
MI   1969
  $10

102-2111 HEDDON, JAMES & SONS CO.
WOUNDED-SPOOK, #9160
MI
  $40

102-1950 HEDDON, JAMES & SONS CO.
ZARAGOSSA
MI   1932
MUSKY $1000

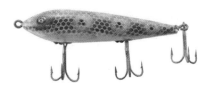

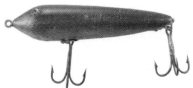

102-1952 HEDDON, JAMES & SONS CO.
ZARAGOSSA #6500
MI   1922   4 1/2 IN   3/4 OZ
  $600

102-1953 HEDDON, JAMES & SONS CO.
ZARAGOSSA #6500
MI   1919   4 1/4 IN
OLD $800

102-1955 HEDDON, JAMES & SONS CO.
ZARAGOSSA #6500
MI
LATER $90

Page 102

FISHING PLUGS

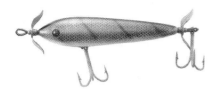

103-1959 HEDDON, JAMES & SONS CO.
ZARAGOSSA SPECIAL, W. HARDEN
MI   1936   4 1/4 IN
WALTER HARDEN $600

103-1954 HEDDON, JAMES & SONS CO.
ZARAGOSSA, #6500
MI
   $400

103-1956 HEDDON, JAMES & SONS CO.
ZARAGOSSA-SPOOK
MI   1939   4 1/4 IN
   $450

103-1961 HEDDON, JAMES & SONS CO.
ZARA-SPOOK, #9260
MI   1948   4 1/4 IN   4/5 OZ
   $50

103-1962 HEDDON, JAMES & SONS CO.
ZARA-SPOOK, #9260
MI   1948   2 7/8 IN   5/8 OZ
JR $20

103-1931 HEDDON, JAMES & SONS CO.
ZIG-WAG #8300
MI
   $200

103-1932 HEDDON, JAMES & SONS CO.
ZIG-WAG #8300
MI   1927   4 1/2 IN   3/4 OZ
   $200

103-1933 HEDDON, JAMES & SONS CO.
ZIG-WAG #8300
MI
   $200

103-1926 HEDDON, JAMES & SONS CO.
ZIG-WAG JR. #8340
MI   1929   3 1/4 IN   1/2 OZ
   $200

103-1927 HEDDON, JAMES & SONS CO.
ZIG-WAG JR. #8340
MI
NEW $60

103-1928 HEDDON, JAMES & SONS CO.
ZIG-WAG JR. #8340
MI
   $200

103-1929 HEDDON, JAMES & SONS CO.
ZIG-WAG JR, SALMON
MI   1930   3 1/4 IN
   $900

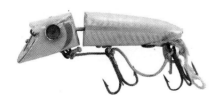

103-1900 HEDDON, JAMES & SONS CO.
ZIG-WAG, KING #8350
MI   1939   5 IN   1 1/8 OZ
   $225

103-1901 HEDDON, JAMES & SONS CO.
ZIG-WAG, KING #8350
MI   1948   4 1/2 IN   3/4 OZ
   $225

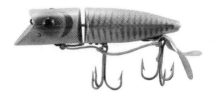

103-1903 HEDDON, JAMES & SONS CO.
ZIG-WAG, KING #8360
MI   1939   6 IN   1 1/2 OZ
   $225

104-1733 HELENA BAIT CO.
HELENA MINNOW
OK   1950   5 IN
  $50

104-1606 HELIN TACKLE CO.
FISHCAKE
MI   1957   3 IN
LARGE $50

104-1607 HELIN TACKLE CO.
FISHCAKE
MI
MEDIUM $50

104-1627 HELIN TACKLE CO.
FISHCAKE
MI
SMALL $50

104-1621 HELIN TACKLE CO.
FLATFISH
MI
MEDIUM $25

104-1622 HELIN TACKLE CO.
FLATFISH
MI   1933   4 IN
LARGE $25

104-1626 HELIN TACKLE CO.
FLATFISH
MI
VERY LARGE, LAKE TROUT $25

104-1628 HELIN TACKLE CO.
FLATFISH
MI
SMALL $25

104-1629 HELIN TACKLE CO.
FLATFISH
MI
MEDIUM $25

104-1608 HELIN TACKLE CO.
SWIMMERSPOON
MI   1960
MEDIUM $30

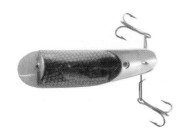

104-1609 HELIN TACKLE CO.
SWIMMERSPOON
MI   1960
SMALL $30

104-1535 HENDRYX, A.B.
CORK BAIT
CT   1910   1 IN
  $150

104-1553 HENDRYX, A.B.
HENDRYX PLUG BAIT
CT   1906
  $1000

104-1537 HENDRYX, A.B.
SNAKEBAIT
CT   1900   3 1/4 IN
  $1500

104-1669 HENKENIUS,.J./KANE, PETER
HENKENIUS/KANE BAIT
IN   1900   4 1/2 IN
  $4000

FISHING PLUGS

105-1693 HENNING, C.E.
HENNING MINNOW TUBE
OH   1911
  $3000

105-1199 HENRY, BUCK, BAIT CO.
BUCK-A-NEER

  $300

105-1703 HENZEL, J.G.
BOOSTER BAIT
IL   1907   2 3/4 IN
  $500

105-1671 HEP BAIT CO.
BLOOY LOOY
MN   1958
  $40

105-1690 HERINGTON, BILL
BAG-O-MAD
MO   1933
GLASS EYES $120

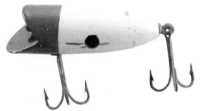

105-1691 HERINGTON, BILL
BAG-O-MAD
MO   1934   2 3/4 IN
JR SIZE $100

105-1673 HERTER INC.
HERTER BAIT
MN
  $20

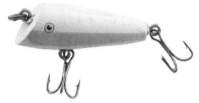

105-1674 HERTER INC.
HERTER BAIT
MN
  $20

105-1675 HERTER INC.
HERTER BAIT
MN
  $20

105-1679 HERTER INC.
HERTER BAIT
MN   1954   3 IN
  $30

105-1680 HERTER INC.
HERTER BAIT
MN   1960
  $20

105-1681 HERTER INC.
HERTER BAIT
MN
  $30

105-1682 HERTER INC.
HERTER BAIT
MN   1954   2 1/2 IN
  $30

105-1684 HERTER INC.
HERTER BAIT
MN   1960
  $30

105-1685 HERTER INC.
HERTER BAIT
MN   1960
  $30

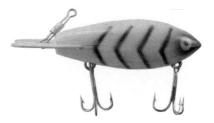

106-1686 HERTER INC.
HERTER BAIT
MN   1960
  $30

106-1672 HERTER INC.
LAZY IVER
MN
  $30

106-7050 HERTER INC.
LIL' CAT
MN   1965
  $10

106-7051 HERTER INC.
MUD PUPPY, HERTER
MN   1965
  $10

106-1657 HETZEL
HETZEL MINNOW
  1946   4 1/4 IN
  $70

106-1662 HIBBARD, C.B.
HIBBARD MINNOW
MI   1890
HOLLOW ALUMINUM BODY $1000

106-5199 HICKY-DO PLUG CO.
BEACHCOMBER
MA   1948
  $50

106-5184 HICKY-DO PLUG CO.
HICKY-DO PLUG
MA   1949
  $50

106-1510 HIGGINS, J.C
LUCKY 13 TYPE
MI   1952   4 IN
SEARS $20

106-1505 HIGGINS, J.C.
BABE-ORENO TYPE
MI
SEARS $20

106-1506 HIGGINS, J.C.
BASS-ORENO TYPE, HIGGINS
MI
SEARS $20

106-1514 HIGGINS, J.C.
DARTER TYPE
MI   1952   4 IN
SEARS $20

106-1516 HIGGINS, J.C.
INJURED MINNOW TYPE
MI   1952   2 1/4 IN
SEARS $20

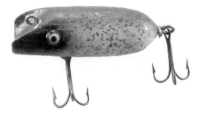

106-1511 HIGGINS, J.C.
MIDGE-ORENO TYPE
MI   1952   3 IN
SEARS $60

106-1517 HIGGINS, J.C.
MIDGET DIGIT TYPE
MI
SEARS $20

FISHING PLUGS

107-1513 HIGGINS, J.C.
MIDGET RUNT TYPE
MI
SEARS $20

107-1515 HIGGINS, J.C.
PIKIE TYPE
MI   1952   2 1/2 IN
SEARS $20

107-1519 HIGGINS, J.C.
PIKIE, JOINTED, HIGGINS
MI   1952   2 1/2 IN
SEARS, SMALL $20

107-1508 HIGGINS, J.C.
PIKIE, JOINTED TYPE
MI
SEARS $20

107-1512 HIGGINS, J.C.
RIVER RUNT DEEP DIVE
MI
SEARS $20

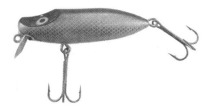

107-1507 HIGGINS, J.C.
RIVER RUNT TYPE
MI
SEARS $20

107-1509 HIGGINS, J.C.
RUNT TYPE, FLOATING, HIGGINS
MI   1952   2 1/2 IN
SEARS $20

107-1518 HIGGINS, J.C.
SLIM JIM TYPE
MI
SEARS $20

107-1520 HIGGINS, J.C.
SLIM JIM TYPE
MI   1952   4 IN
SEARS, LARGE $20

107-1572 HILDEBRANDT, J.J. & CO.
GO-GETTER, HILDEBRANDT
IN   1928
WOOD $300

107-1617 HILDRETH, MIKE
WONDER BUG
CO   1960   2 1/2 IN
 $40

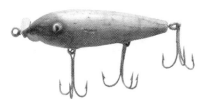

107-5456 HILL, ED
SPIN-O-BAIT
 1946
$100

107-5476 HILL, ED
SPIN-O-BAIT
 1946
$20

107-1650 HINCKLEY, LIVINGSTON S.
FISH PHANTOM
NJ
BABY $200

107-1651 HINCKLEY, LIVINGSTON S.
FISH PHANTOM
NJ   1898   4 1/4 IN
MUSKY $500

FISHING PLUGS

108-1649 HINCKLEY, LIVINGSTON S.
YELLOW BIRD
NJ   1898   3 1/4 IN
  $300

108-1658 HINKLE, JOE B.
HINKLE LIZARD
KY   1946   6 IN
  $200

108-1723 HOAGE, CLYDE
SPOON-FIN MINNOW
MN   1938
LARGE $800

108-1501 HOBBS BROS
GLITTERFISH
CA   1948
  $30

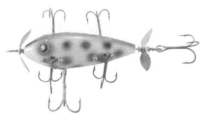

108-0324 HOBBS, W.H. SUPPLY CO
BON-NET MUSKY BAIT
WI   1952   4 IN
WOOD, 6-HK $100

108-3429 HOEGEE, WM & CO.
NORTH COAST MINNOW
OH   1925   4 IN
(PFLUEGER) $900

108-3430 HOEGEE, WM & CO.
NORTH COAST MINNOW
OH   1925   2 1/2 IN
(PFLUEGER) $900

108-1521 HOFSCHNEIDER CORP.
RED EYE WIGGLER
NY   1948   3 IN
WOOD $50

108-1523 HOFSCHNEIDER CORP.
RED EYE WIGGLER
NY
PLASTIC $20

108-1663 HOLZAPFEL
MUSHROOM BASS BAIT
MI   1919   3 1/4 IN
SMALL, NEW $800

108-1664 HOLZAPFEL
MUSHROOM BASS BAIT
MI   1917   4 1/2 IN
  $1000

108-1665 HOLZAPFEL
MUSHROOM BASS BAIT
MI   1917   4 1/4 IN
OLD $1000

108-1666 HOLZAPFEL
MUSHROOM BASS BAIT
MI   1919   4 1/2 IN
NEW, LARGE $800

108-1653 HOLZWARTH, J.C.
EXPERT MINNOW, HOLZWARTH
OH   1904   3 3/4 IN
  $1000

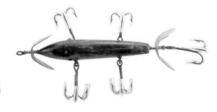

108-1654 HOLZWARTH, J.C.
EXPERT MINNOW, HOLZWARTH
OH   1904   3 1/4 IN
  $800

FISHING PLUGS

109-1655 HOLZWARTH, J.C.
EXPERT MINNOW, HOLZWARTH
OH 1904 3 1/2 IN
$800

109-1620 HOM-ARTS BAIT CO.
DIPPER
OH 1949 2 1/2 IN
$30

109-1751 HOM-ARTS BAIT CO.
ROTOLADY
OH 1949
$30

109-1614 HOM-ARTS BAIT CO.
SKIPPER, HOM-ARTS
OH 1949 2 1/2 IN
$30

109-1462 HOOKZEM BAIT CO.
HOOKZEM
IL 1921 3 IN
GOTTSCHAK $600

109-0042 HORROCKS-IBBOTSON CO.
ADJUSTABLE METAL WIGGLER
NY 1947
$100

109-0008 HORROCKS-IBBOTSON CO.
BABE-ORENO
NY 1958 3 IN
$30

109-0052 HORROCKS-IBBOTSON CO.
BASS-ORENO TYPE, HICO
NY 1958
$30

109-0029 HORROCKS-IBBOTSON CO.
BIG BROTHER MUSKY LURE
NY 1958
$50

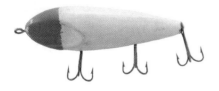

109-0030 HORROCKS-IBBOTSON CO.
BIG BROTHER MUSKY LURE
NY 1958
$50

109-0048 HORROCKS-IBBOTSON CO.
BIG BROTHER MUSKY LURE
NY 1958
$50

109-0049 HORROCKS-IBBOTSON CO.
BIG BROTHER MUSKY LURE
NY 1958
$50

109-0014 HORROCKS-IBBOTSON CO.
BIG BROTHER TEASER
NY 1958
$50

109-0001 HORROCKS-IBBOTSON CO.
BIG FISH LURE
NY 1957 4 IN
$30

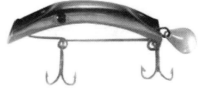

109-0002 HORROCKS-IBBOTSON CO.
BIG FISH LURE
NY 1958 3 IN
SMALL $30

110-0045 HORROCKS-IBBOTSON CO.
CRAB, HORROCKS-IBBOTSON
NY   1947
$50

110-0046 HORROCKS-IBBOTSON CO.
CRAZY CRAB, HORROCKS-IBBOT.
NY   1958
$50

110-24685 HORROCKS-IBBOTSON CO.
FROG, HORROCKS-IBBOTSON
NY
$50

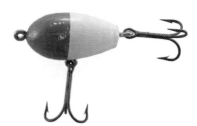

110-0018 HORROCKS-IBBOTSON CO.
HICO LURE
NY   1948   3 1/2 IN
$40

110-0019 HORROCKS-IBBOTSON CO.
HICO LURE
NY   1938   3 1/4 IN
$30

110-0020 HORROCKS-IBBOTSON CO.
HICO LURE
NY   1947   1 3/4 IN
$30

110-0021 HORROCKS-IBBOTSON CO.
HICO LURE
NY   1947   3 IN
$30

110-0023 HORROCKS-IBBOTSON CO.
HICO LURE
NY   1947
$30

110-0026 HORROCKS-IBBOTSON CO.
HICO LURE
NY   1947
$30

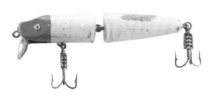

110-0041 HORROCKS-IBBOTSON CO.
HICO LURE
NY   1958
$30

110-0054 HORROCKS-IBBOTSON CO.
HICO LURE
NY   1958
$30

110-0055 HORROCKS-IBBOTSON CO.
HICO LURE
NY   1958
$30

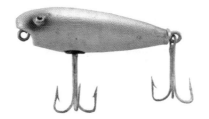

110-0056 HORROCKS-IBBOTSON CO.
HICO LURE
NY   1958
$30

110-0060 HORROCKS-IBBOTSON CO.
HICO LURE
NY   1958
$30

110-0047 HORROCKS-IBBOTSON CO.
MOUSE, HICO
NY   1947
$50

111-24639 HORROCKS-IBBOTSON CO.
MUSKY BAIT, HORROCK-IBBOTSON
NY
  $30

111-0012 HORROCKS-IBBOTSON CO.
PIKE TYPE, HORROCKS-IBBOTSON, JTD
NY   1958
  $30

111-0005 HORROCKS-IBBOTSON CO.
RUNT TYPE, H-I
NY   1958   1 3/4 IN
  $30

111-0004 HORROCKS-IBBOTSON CO.
SHMOO
NY   1947   3 IN
  $300

111-0034 HORROCKS-IBBOTSON CO.
TANGO TYPE, HICO
NY   1958
  $30

111-0035 HORROCKS-IBBOTSON CO.
TANGO TYPE, HICO
NY   1958
  $30

111-0033 HORROCKS-IBBOTSON CO.
TROUT TANGO TYPE, HICO
NY   1958
  $30

111-1660 HORVATH, F.H.
TWIGGLER
VT   1954   3 IN
  $300

111-1636 HOUSER FLY CO.
BLABBERMOUTH
MO   1955   4 IN
  $30

111-1656 HOWE'S VACUUM BAIT CO.
HOWE'S VACUUM BAIT
IN   1909   2 1/2 IN
  $600

111-1644 HUB MFG. CO.
MUK-KA-CHOC FROG
MI   1938   2 1/4 IN
  $100

111-1613 HUMPY BAIT CO.
HUMPY PLUG
IA   1950   4 1/2 IN
  $30

111-1638 HUMPY BAIT CO.
HUMPY PLUG
IA   1950
  $30

111-1637 HUNT LURE CO.
HOOKER, THE
TN   1957   3 IN   1/2 OZ
  $30

111-2165 IDEEL FISH LURES
WEEDER
IL   1952
  $60

FISHING PLUGS

112-2159 IMMELL BAIT CO
CHIPPEWA BASS BAIT
WI 1913 3 IN
SINKER $750

112-2161 IMMELL BAIT CO
CHIPPEWA BASS BAIT
WI 1913
FLOATER $1000

112-2162 IMMELL BAIT CO
CHIPPEWA MUSKY BAIT
WI 1913 5 IN
SINKER $1500

112-2160 IMMELL BAIT CO
CHIPPEWA PIKE BAIT
WI 1913 4 IN
SINKER $1000

112-2163 IMMELL BAIT CO
CHIPPEWA SKIPPER
WI 1915 4 1/2 IN
(C.J. FROST) $2500

112-1532 INSTANT BASS PLUG CO.
INSTANT BASS BAIT
OK 1959 3 3/4 IN
LARGE $30

112-1533 INSTANT BASS PLUG CO.
INSTANT BASS BAIT
OK
JR SIZE $30

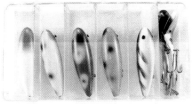

112-2156 INTERCHANGEABLE BAIT CO.
QUICKIE, THE
MI
$200

112-5452 INTERNATION HARVESTER
FISH DECOY, COPPER

$1500

112-2164 ISLE ROYALE BAITS
CHUB, ISLE ROYALE
MI 1948 3 1/4 IN
BASS SIZE $60

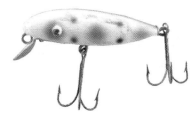

112-2170 ISLE ROYALE BAITS
CHUB, ISLE ROYALE
MI 1948 2 3/4 IN
PIKE SIZE $50

112-2166 ISLE ROYALE BAITS
INJURED CHUB. ISLE ROYALE
MI
$100

112-2172 ISLE ROYALE BAITS
MOUSE, ISLE ROYALE
MI 1947
$100

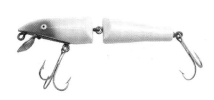

112-24638 ISLE ROYALE BAITS
PIKIE, JOINTED, ISLE ROYALE
MI 1940's
$30

112-2177 ISLE ROYALE BAITS
PLUNKER, ISLE ROYALE
MI 1947
$50

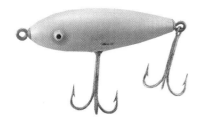

113-2171 ISLE ROYALE BAITS
TOPWATER BAIT, ISLE ROYALE
MI   1947   2 3/4 IN
  $50

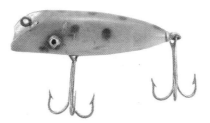

113-2174 ISLE ROYALE BAITS
UNKNOWN NAME
MI   1947
  $50

113-2168 ISLE ROYALE BAITS
WOBBLIT
MI   1948   2 5/8 IN
  $50

113-2308 J & R TACKLE
JIM BO
FL   1954   3 IN
  $20

113-2183 JACK'S TACKLE MFG. CO
J.T.'S SHINER
OK   1947   2 5/8 IN
LARGE $50

113-2196 JACK'S TACKLE MFG. CO
J.T.'S SHINER
OK   1948   2 IN
BABY SIZE $50

113-2192 JACK'S TACKLE MFG. CO
JACK'S BASS BAIT
OK   1960
  $30

113-2190 JACK'S TACKLE MFG. CO
JACK'S DIVER
OK   1958   4 IN
LARGE $30

113-2193 JACK'S TACKLE MFG. CO
JACK'S DIVER
OK   1959   2 1/4 IN
SMALL $30

113-2197 JACK'S TACKLE MFG. CO
JACK'S WOBBLER
OK
  $40

113-2180 JACK'S TACKLE MFG. CO
LASSITER BAIT
OK   1941   1 1/2 IN
  $500

113-2188 JACK'S TACKLE MFG. CO
POGO STICK, JACK'S TACKLE
OK   1958   4 IN
LARGE $30

113-2194 JACK'S TACKLE MFG. CO
POGO STICK, JACK'S TACKLE
OK
MEDIUM $30

113-2195 JACK'S TACKLE MFG. CO
POGO STICK, JACK'S TACKLE
OK
SMALL $30

113-2185 JACK'S TACKLE MFG. CO
RIP-L-LURE
OK   1948   3 3/4 IN
  $100

FISHING PLUGS

114-2186 JACK'S TACKLE MFG. CO
RIP-L-LURE
OK
DIVER $100

114-2184 JACK'S TACKLE MFG. CO
RIP-L-LURE,   JOINTED
OK   1948
   $100

114-0515 JACK'S TACKLE MFG. CO.
SHARKIE
OK
   $20

114-2313 JACOBS NOVELTY CO.
FISH NIPPLE, JACOBS
MN   1902   2 IN
SMALL $600

114-2314 JACOBS NOVELTY CO.
FISH NIPPLE, JACOBS
MN   1902   2 IN
LARGE $600

114-2312 JACOBS, EDWARD L.
JACOBS BUCKTAIL BAIT
MI   1942   3 IN
   $150

114-2311 JACOBS, EDWARD L.
JACOBS HORSE FLY BAIT
MI   1942
   $1500

114-2310 JACOBS, EDWARD L.
JACOBS POLLYWOG
MI   1942
   $200

114-2309 JACOBS, EDWARD L.
JACOBS POLLYWOG POPPER
MI   1942
   $200

114-2242 JAMISON, WM. J.
BEETLE-PLOP
IL   1941   2 IN   1/2 OZ
   $75

114-2230 JAMISON, WM. J.
BILL'S BASS GETTER
IL
   $650

114-2246 JAMISON, WM. J.
BOTTLE BASS POPPER
IL   1946   3 1/4 IN
BLATZ $200

114-2247 JAMISON, WM. J.
BOTTLE BASS POPPER
IL   1946   3 1/4 IN
MILLER HIGH LIFE $200

114-2248 JAMISON, WM. J.
BOTTLE BASS POPPER
IL   1946
   $200

114-2224 JAMISON, WM. J.
CHICAGO WOBBLER
IL   1917   4 IN
   $600

FISHING PLUGS

115-2201 JAMISON, WM. J.
COAXER
IL
SMALL, WEEDLESS $150

115-2204 JAMISON, WM. J.
COAXER
IL 1905 2 1/8 IN
MUSKY $300

115-2213 JAMISON, WM. J.
COAXER
IL
FIRST COAXER $400

115-2205 JAMISON, WM. J.
COAXER #1
IL 1904 1 5/8 IN
$150

115-2209 JAMISON, WM. J.
COAXER #2
IL
$150

115-2206 JAMISON, WM. J.
COAXER TEASER
IL 2 1/2 IN
$400

115-2207 JAMISON, WM. J.
COAXER, BUCKTAIL #1
IL
$150

115-2208 JAMISON, WM. J.
COAXER, BUCKTAIL #2
IL
$150

115-2200 JAMISON, WM. J.
COAXER, BUCKTAIL, LUMINOUS
IL
WEEDLESS $150

115-2203 JAMISON, WM. J.
COAXER, CONVERTIBLE
IL 4 1/4 IN
$150

115-2211 JAMISON, WM. J.
COAXER, UNDERWATER
IL 2 IN
$150

115-2202 JAMISON, WM. J.
COAXER, LUMINOUS
IL
LARGE, WEEDLESS $150

115-2216 JAMISON, WM. J.
FROG, SOFT RUBBER, HOLLOW
IL
WEEDLESS /JAMISON-HASTINGS $250

115-2231 JAMISON, WM. J.
HUMDINGER DE LUXE
IL 1916 3 1/4 IN
$1000

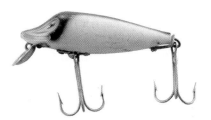

115-2243 JAMISON, WM. J.
JAMISON #1500
IL 1941 3 1/4 IN 5/8 OZ
$300

Page 115

FISHING PLUGS

116-2251 JAMISON, WM. J.
JAMISON #1501, JOINTED
IL   1941   2/12 IN   1/2 OZ
  $150

116-2244 JAMISON, WM. J.
LUR-O-LITE
IL   1941   4 IN   3 OZ
  $150

116-2226 JAMISON, WM. J.
MASCOT
IL   1916   4 IN
  $500

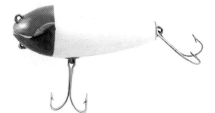

116-2225 JAMISON, WM. J.
MASCOT, WINGED
IL   1916   2 3/4 IN
BABY SIZE $450

116-2233 JAMISON, WM. J.
MASCOT, WINGED
IL   1916   4 IN
  $700

116-2227 JAMISON, WM. J.
MASCOT, WINGED MUSKY
IL   1920   5 1/4 IN
  $1000

116-2228 JAMISON, WM. J.
MASCOT, WINGED MUSKY
IL   1916   5 IN
  $1000

116-2222 JAMISON, WM. J.
NEMO BASS BAIT
IL   1911   2 1/4 IN
  $2000

116-2223 JAMISON, WM. J.
NEMO MUSKY BAIT
IL   1911   4 1/4 IN
  $3000

116-2249 JAMISON, WM. J.
QUIVERLURE BASS
IL   1940   4 3/4 IN   1 OZ
  $90

116-2252 JAMISON, WM. J.
QUIVERLURE BASS
IL   1940   3 1/4 IN   5/8 OZ
  $90

116-2232 JAMISON, WM. J.
STRUGGLING MOUSE
IL   1919   2 1/4 IN
  $400

116-2229 JAMISON, WM. J.
SURFACE WIGGLER
IL   1928   2 3/4 IN
  $1000

116-2245 JAMISON, WM. J.
TORPEDO, JAMISON
IL   1940   3 3/4 IN
  $60

116-2253 JAMISON, WM. J.
WEIGHTED TRAILER
IL   1929
  $30

FISHING PLUGS

117-2254   JAMISON, WM. J.
WEIGHTED TRAILER
IL   1929
  $30

117-2241   JAMISON, WM. J.
WIG-L-TAIL
IL   1941   2 1/4 IN
  $90

117-2250   JAMISON, WM. J.
WIG-L-TWIN
IL   1939   2 1/2 IN   5/8 OZ
  $90

117-2218   JAMISON, WM. J.
WIG-WAG GEP BAIT
IL   1938   4 1/2 IN
  $300

117-2219   JAMISON, WM. J.
WIG-WAG GEP, MUSKY
IL
  $300

117-2282   JEMCO BAIT CO.
JEMCO SONIC LURE
IN   1956
  $10

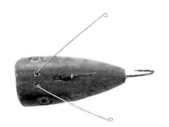

117-2318   JENNINGS FISHING TACKLE CO
JENNINGS BULL FROG PLUG
WA
  $300

117-2323   JENNINGS FISHING TACKLE CO
JENNINGS SURFACE MINNOW
WA
  $200

117-2320   JENSON DISTRIBUTING CO.
FLIPPER SHRIMP
TX   1960   2 1/2 IN
  $30

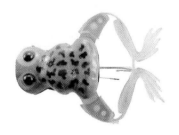

117-2322   JENSON DISTRIBUTING CO.
FROG POPPER
TX   1946   1 3/4 IN
  $50

117-2324   JENSON DISTRIBUTING CO.
FROG, JENSON
TX
SURFACE $50

117-2321   JENSON DISTRIBUTING CO.
FROGLEG KICKER
TX   1946   1 3/4 IN
PLASTIC $50

117-2326   JENSON DISTRIBUTING CO.
FROGLEGS
TX   1950   1 1/2 IN
BABY $50

117-2319   JENSON SPORTING GOODS
ZIPPER, JENSON
TX   2 3/4 IN
  $30

117-2307   JET LURES
JET WIGGLER
NY   1947   3 IN
  $75

118-2306 JOE BOB MFG
CRIPPLE CRITTER CRAWFISH
OK
PLASTIC $150

118-2305 JOE BOB MFG
CRIPPLE CRITTER DIVER
OK
PLASTIC $60

118-2303 JOHN L. BAIT CO
WORM, JOHN L.
OK
  $10

118-2299 JOHNSON
DART-O
WI
IMPROVED $100

118-2302 JOHNSON
DART-O
WI   1947   3 1/4 IN
  $100

118-2300 JOHNSON
WEED-O
WI   1947   3 IN
  $100

118-5242 JOHNSON LURES
MULLET JIG
NY   1955
  $30

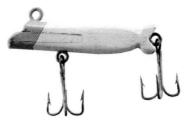

118-2301 JOHNSON, ERNEST
CLOTHES PIN BAIT MINNOW
FL   1930   3 IN
  $60

118-2327 JOHNSON, CARL A.
AUTOMATIC STRIKER BAIT
IL   1936   3 IN
MED $900

118-2328 JOHNSON, CARL A.
AUTOMATIC STRIKER BAIT
IL   1935   6 1/2 IN
LARGE $1200

118-2329 JOHNSON, CARL A.
AUTOMATIC STRIKER BAIT
IL   1939   1 3/4 IN
SMALL $500

118-2334 JOS. TACKLE SHOP
JOS. DOODLE BUG
IN
  $300

118-2342 JOY'S BAIT CO.
JOY'S PLUG
MI   1934
LARGE $300

118-2341 JOY'S BAIT CO.
JOY'S WATER NEMESIS
MI   1934   3 5/8 IN
  $300

118-5558 JOY'S BAIT CO.
JOY'S WATER NEMESIS
MI   1928
SMALL $200

FISHING PLUGS

119-2335 JUDGES BAIT CO.
JAW BREAKER
MO   1956   3 1/2 IN
  $30

119-2538 JUMPING JACK LURES
JUMPING JACK
FL   1948
  $50

119-2539 JUMPING JACK LURES
JUMPING JACK
FL   1948
  $50

119-2398 K & K MFG. CO.
GHOST, THE
OH   1908   2 3/4 IN
  $2500

119-2395 K & K MFG. CO.
K & K ANIMATED MINNOW
OH   1908   4 1/2 IN
MEDIUM $1200

119-2396 K & K MFG. CO.
K & K ANIMATED MINNOW
OH   1908   5 1/2 IN
LARGE $1200

119-2397 K & K MFG. CO.
K & K ANIMATED MINNOW
OH   1908   4 IN
SMALL $1200

119-2394 K & K MFG. CO.
K & K ANIMATED MINNOW, DIVER
OH   1908   4 IN
  $1500

119-2424 K & M TACKLE CO.
K & M JET
NH
  $20

119-24714 K. M. TACKLE CO.
SHRIMP, K.M. TACKLE
TX
  $10

119-2348 KALA LURES
SPLASH KING
MI   1947
PLASTIC/WOOD $40

119-2422 KALVIG, L.J. & CO.
K-LURE
MN   1954   3 1/4 IN
  $60

119-2452 KATCHALL BAIT CO
KATCHALL WOBBLER
  1936
  $300

119-2421 KATCHMORE BAIT CO.
BASS CHARGER
IN   1955   2 1/4 IN
  $40

119-24732 KAUTH, BILL.
STREAMLINE, JOINTED MINNOW.
IN   1932
  $100

120-5500 KAUTH, BILL.
STREAMLINE JOINTED MINNOW
IN   1939
   $100

120-2343 KAUFMAN, A.H..
NAPPANEE YPSI BAIT,
IN   1936   3 1/4 IN
   $90

120-2426 KAUFMAN, H.C.
HARKAUF TOPWATER MINNOW
PA
   $600

120-2427 KAUFMAN, H.C.
HARKAUF WOOD MINNOW
PA   1907   3 IN
GLASS EYES $1000

120-2428 KAUFMAN, H.C.
HARKAUF WOOD MINNOW
PA   1903   2 3/4 IN
PAINTED EYES $2000

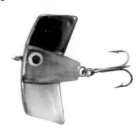

120-2406 KAUTSKY LAZY IKE CORP.
BAT IKE
IA   1960
   $20

120-2408 KAUTSKY LAZY IKE CORP.
CHUG IKE
IA   1949   2 3/4 IN
LARGE $15

120-2410 KAUTSKY LAZY IKE CORP.
CHUG IKE
IA   1949   2 1/4 IN
SMALL $15

120-2403 KAUTSKY LAZY IKE CORP.
DEEP IKE
IA   1949   2 3/4 IN
   $15

120-2405 KAUTSKY LAZY IKE CORP.
FLEX IKE
IA   1946   3 IN
   $20

120-2412 KAUTSKY LAZY IKE CORP.
LAZY IKE
IA   1946   3 1/2 IN   5/8 OZ
   $15

120-2417 KAUTSKY LAZY IKE CORP.
LAZY IKE #1
IA   1940   2 IN   1/8 OZ
   $15

120-2413 KAUTSKY LAZY IKE CORP.
LAZY IKE #2
IA
   $15

120-2415 KAUTSKY LAZY IKE CORP.
LAZY IKE #3
IA   1939   3 IN   1/2 OZ
   $15

120-2416 KAUTSKY LAZY IKE CORP.
LAZY IKE #5
IA
   $15

121-2414 KAUTSKY LAZY IKE CORP.
LAZY IKE #6
IA
  $15

121-2411 KAUTSKY LAZY IKE CORP.
MUSKY IKE
IA   1946   4 1/2 IN
  $20

121-2399 KAUTSKY LAZY IKE CORP.
SHARK IKE
IA   1960   1 1/2 IN
  $15

121-2404 KAUTSKY LAZY IKE CORP.
SKITTER IKE
IA   1960   3 IN
  $15

121-2401 KAUTSKY LAZY IKE CORP.
STINGEREE
IA   1960   2 1/2 IN
LARGE $15

121-2402 KAUTSKY LAZY IKE CORP.
STINGEREE
IA   1960   2 IN
SMALL $15

121-2407 KAUTSKY LAZY IKE CORP.
TOP IKE
IA   1950   2 3/4 IN   1/4 OZ
SMALL $20

121-2409 KAUTSKY LAZY IKE CORP.
TOP IKE
IA   1950   3 3/4 IN   5/8 OZ
LARGE $20

121-7053 KAUTSKY LAZY IKE CORP.
WIGGLY-JIG IKE
IA   1969
  $10

121-2362 KEELING, FRED C.
BEAR CAT
IL
  $200

121-2350 KEELING, FRED C.
CRAB, KEELING
IL   1923   2 1/2 IN
SMALL $400

121-2359 KEELING, FRED C.
CRAB, KEELING
IL   1933   3 1/4 IN
LARGE $400

121-2379 KEELING, FRED C.
EXPERT WOOD MINNOW, KEELING
IL   1912   3 1/4 IN
NO EYE $700

121-2380 KEELING, FRED C.
EXPERT WOOD MINNOW, KEELING
IL   1919   4 IN
5 TREBLE HOOKS $800

121-2381 KEELING, FRED C.
EXPERT WOOD MINNOW, KEELING
IL   1923   3 1/4 IN
3 HOOK $500

FISHING PLUGS

122-2371 KEELING, FRED C.
EXPERT, MUSKY
IL   1920   5 IN
  $1500

122-2376 KEELING, FRED C.
FLAPPER
IL   1918   4 1/2 IN
  $400

122-2352 KEELING, FRED C.
KEELING, UNKNOWN
IL
SMALL $400

122-2353 KEELING, FRED C.
KEELING, UNKNOWN
IL   1923   3 3/4 IN
  $400

122-2354 KEELING, FRED C.
KEELING, UNKNOWN
IL
  $200

122-2355 KEELING, FRED C.
KEELING, UNKNOWN
IL
  $400

122-2356 KEELING, FRED C.
KEELING, UNKNOWN
IL   1933   2 1/2 IN
  $300

122-2357 KEELING, FRED C.
KEELING, UNKNOWN
IL   1934   3 1/2 IN
  $400

122-2360 KEELING, FRED C.
KEELING, UNKNOWN
IL   1930-1939
  $400

122-2361 KEELING, FRED C.
KEELING, UNKNOWN
IL   1923   2 1/2 IN
  $400

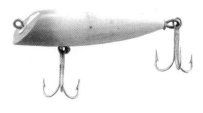

122-2363 KEELING, FRED C.
KEELING, UNKNOWN
IL   1923
  $400

122-2364 KEELING, FRED C.
KEELING, UNKNOWN
IL
  $300

122-2365 KEELING, FRED C.
KEELING, UNKNOWN
IL
  $400

122-2366 KEELING, FRED C.
KEELING, UNKNOWN
IL
  $400

122-2368 KEELING, FRED C.
KING-BEE
IL   1917   3 3/4 IN
  $600

FISHING PLUGS

123-2387 KEELING, FRED C.
LITTLE TOM WIGGLER
IL   1920   2 1/2 IN
  $200

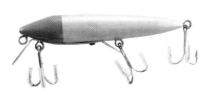

123-2375 KEELING, FRED C.
LONG TOM WIGGLER
IL   1923   4 1/2 IN
  $400

123-2351 KEELING, FRED C.
MOUSE, KEELING
IL   1923
  $400

123-2386 KEELING, FRED C.
PIKE TOM WIGGLER
IL   1920   2 3/4 IN
  $200

123-2385 KEELING, FRED C.
PIKE-KEE-WIG
IL   1923   3 1/2 IN
BABY $400

123-5657 KEELING, FRED C.
REVOLVING MINNO
IL   1920
  $150

123-2369 KEELING, FRED C.
ROUND EXPERT SURFACE MINNOW
IL   1920   2 5/8 IN
  $400

123-2377 KEELING, FRED C.
SCOUT, KEELING
IL   1920   3 3/4 IN
  $200

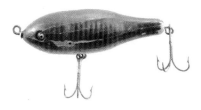

123-2372 KEELING, FRED C.
ST. JOHN'S WIGGLER
IL   1918   4 IN
  $400

123-2373 KEELING, FRED C.
SURFACE TOM WIGGLER
IL   1920   3 1/4 IN
  $400

123-2367 KEELING, FRED C.
SURF-KEE-WIG
IL   1923   3 1/4 IN
  $400

123-2358 KEELING, FRED C.
TIP-TOP
IL   1923   4 IN
OLD $400

123-2370 KEELING, FRED C.
TIP-TOP
IL
  $400

123-2389 KEELING, FRED C.
TOM THUMB WIGGLER
IL   1917   2 IN
  $300

123-2390 KEELING, FRED C.
TOM THUMB WIGGLER
IL   1915   2 IN
OLD $500

124-2388 KEELING, FRED C.
TOM WIGGLER
IL   1920   2 IN
BABY $200

124-2374 KEELING, FRED C.
TOM WIGGLER, MUSKY
IL   1920   3 5/8 IN
  $500

124-5513 KEELING, FRED C.
WOBBLE, KEELING
IL
  $200

124-2345 KEEN BAIT MFG.
FAST WATER WOBBLER
MI   1950
  $400

124-2346 KEEN BAIT MFG.
KEEN KNIGHT FROG
MI   1946
  $500

124-2420 KEISTER, A.J.
KEISTER PLUG
  1935   3 IN
$100

124-2819 KELLER
GETS-EM BAIT
IN   1916   3 3/4 IN
  $700

124-5802 KELLER, JIM
KELLER SURFACE BAIT
IL   1915
  $500

124-2419 KENTUCKY BAIT CO.
FLYING FISH BAIT
KY   1960   3 1/4 IN
  $40

124-2476 KETTLETY, E.A.
TUNAJIG
MA   1958   6 IN
  $30

124-2444 KEY, CLYDE E.
GLUTTON DIBBLER
MI   1950   3 IN
  $60

124-2451 KEYS & JONES CO. LTD.
FISH CALL
AR   1957   3 1/2 IN
  $150

124-2456 KIMMICH BAIT CO.
MOUSE, HAIRLESS KIMMICH
PA   1936   2 3/4 IN
  $600

124-2455 KIMMICH BAIT CO.
MOUSE, KIMMICH
PA   1929   2 1/2 IN
  $600

124-2454 KING BAIT CO.
KING WIGGLER, KING BAIT CO.
MN   1918   3 IN
  $400

FISHING PLUGS

125-2453 KING SPIRAL BAIT CO.
KING SPIRAL BAIT
MI   1947   2 3/4 IN
   $150

125-2474 KINGFISHER BAITS
KINGFISHER BAIT
PA
   $200

125-2475 KINGFISHER BAITS
KINGFISHER BAIT
PA
   $200

125-2440 KINNEY, H. A. & CO.
KINNEY BASS BAIT
MI   1919   3 1/4 IN
   $2500

125-5505 KINNEY, H. A. & CO.
SKIDDER
MI   1915
   $400

125-5516 KINNEY, H. A. & CO.
SKIDDER
MI   1912
   $400

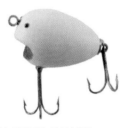

125-2441 KIRWIN, M.F. MFG.
KIRWAN'S BAD EGG
NE   1923   2 IN
   $400

125-2423 K-L COMPANY
MERCURY WORM
IN   1955   2 1/2 IN
   $40

125-2443 KNIGHT & WALL
ISTOKPOGA BAIT
FL   1930   4 1/2 IN
   $500

125-2446 KNIGHT TACKLE
KNIGHT WOBBLER
FL   1958
LARGE $100

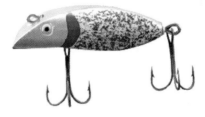

125-2447 KNIGHT TACKLE
KNIGHT WOBBLER
FL
SMALL $100

125-2477 KOEPKE, FRANK
KOEPKE BAIT
WA
   $300

125-2478 KOEPKE, FRANK
KOEPKE BAIT
WA   1922   4 1/2 IN
   $300

125-2442 KONO MFG. CO
MYOPIC MINNOW
SC
   $300

125-3997 KOSTIELNY BAIT CO.
CHRIS FLOATER
MI   1925   3 IN
   $300

126-2467 KOSTIELNY BAIT CO.
KOSTIELNY BUCKTAIL BAIT
MI   1929   2 1/2 IN
  $150

126-2468 KOSTIELNY BAIT CO.
KOSTIELNY TOPWATER BAIT
MI   1929   2 1/2 IN
  $150

126-0782 KRANTZ & SMITH
CHAUTAUQUA MINNOW
NY   1909   3 1/2 IN
WEEDLESS $12000

126-5424 KROAB, M.
FISH DECOY, KROAB

  $300

126-2463 KUMM, A.J.
FISH SPOTTER
MI   1935   3 1/4 IN
DIVER $300

126-2464 KUMM, A.J.
FISH SPOTTER
MI   1945   3 IN
TOPWATER $200

126-2461 KURZ BROS. CO.
BUCKSKIN BAIT
IL   1922   6 1/2 IN
MUSKY SIZE $150

126-2462 KURZ BROS. CO.
BUCKSKIN BAIT
IL   1922   3 1/4 IN
BASS SIZE $100

126-2576 L & L BAIT CO.
WIGGLEWORM
MI   1958
  $60

126-2519 L & S BAIT CO.
BABY CAT
IL   1946   3 1/4 IN
JOINTED $20

126-2518 L & S BAIT CO.
BASS MASTER
IL   3 1/4 IN
JOINTED $10

126-2521 L & S BAIT CO.
BASS MASTER
IL   1940   3 1/4 IN
LEMASTER, H.A. $40

126-5750 L & S BAIT CO.
MIRROLURE
FL
  $20

126-2522 L & S BAIT CO.
PIKE-MASTER
IL   1940   3 3/4 IN
LEMASTER, H.A. $40

126-2520 L & S BAIT CO.
SHINER MINNOW, JOINTED, L & S
IL   1933   3 1/4 IN
WOOD, LEMASTER, H.A $800

FISHING PLUGS

127-2510 LAKE GEORGE BAIT CO.
LAKE GEORGE FLOATER
MI   1913   3 IN
  $800

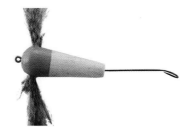

127-2569 LAKE O' WOODS
MUSKY CHIPPEWA BAIT
WI   1932   3 IN
  $500

127-3879 LAKESIDE LURE CO.
SASSY SUSIE
TX   1946
  $90

127-2511 LAMOTHE-STOKES
SWIVALURE
  1921
PLASTIC $100

127-2506 LANDEM LURE CO.
LANDEM LURE
IA   1938   4 3/4 IN
  $100

127-2554 LANE, CHAS. W.
AUTOMATIC WEEDLESS
NY   1912   2 1/2 IN
  $5000

127-2556 LANE, CHAS. W.
WONDER WAGTAIL WOBBLER
NY   1917   3 IN
  $1000

127-2565 LARSON
WEEDSPLITTER
OH   1940   3 1/4 IN
  $70

127-2543 LASSITER LURES
LUNKER-LOCATER
TX   1947   3 1/2 IN
  $60

127-2548 LAUBY BAIT CO.
CHUNK BAIT
WI   1930
  $500

127-2618 LAUBY BAIT CO.
LAUBY BASS BAIT
WI   1929   2 3/4 IN
  $400

127-2550 LAUBY BAIT CO.
LAUBY LURE
WI   1930   4 1/4 IN
MUSKY SIZE $500

127-2551 LAUBY BAIT CO.
LAUBY LURE
WI   1929   3 3/4 IN
PIKE SIZE $400

127-2544 LAUBY BAIT CO.
LAUBY MINNOW
WI   1934   2 3/4 IN
MED $150

127-2545 LAUBY BAIT CO.
LAUBY MINNOW
WI   1934   3 1/4 IN
LARGE $150

FISHING PLUGS

128-2546 LAUBY BAIT CO.
LAUBY MINNOW
WI
SMALL $150

128-2515 LAYFIELD, LESTER
SUPER MIDGET
TX
OLD $75

128-2517 LAYFIELD, LESTER
SUPER MIDGET
TX
 $75

128-2516 LAYFIELD, LESTER
SUPER MIDGET PORK RIND
TX   1948   2 IN
 $75

128-2540 LAZY DAZY LURE CO.
LAZY DAZY
MN   1952
MUSKY $30

128-2541 LAZY DAZY LURE CO.
LAZY DAZY
MN   1952
SMALL $30

128-2542 LAZY DAZY LURE CO.
LAZY DAZY
MN   1952
MEDIUM $30

128-5439 LEACH, LOUIE
DECOY, PIKE
MN   1938
 $200

128-2575 LeBLANK, HOMER
SWIM WHIZ

 $20

128-2526 LEBOUFF BAIT CO.
LEBOUFF CREEPER
PA   1946   4 IN
 $60

128-2527 LEBOUFF BAIT CO.
LEBOUFF MUSKY CREEPER
PA   1946
WOOD $80

128-6992 LAKE O WOODS
CHIPPEWA MUSKY BAIT
MI 1932
 200

128-2537 LEEPER, HENRY
LEEPER'S BASS BAIT
KY   1921   2 3/4 IN   3/4 OZ
 $800

128-5143 LEON TACKLE CO.
CHASE-A-BUG
MI   1956
 $30

128-2534 LEVAN INDUSTRIES
LIM-BO-LEGS
IL   1940   2 1/2 IN   1/2 OZ
 $300

FISHING PLUGS

129-2535 LEW-MAK 64 LURE MFG. CO.
LEW-MAK 66
TX   1964
   $10

129-2523 LEX BAITS
KENTUCKY LEADER LURE
KY   1955   2 1/2 IN
   $30

129-2158 LIE, CORNELIUS
CORNELIUS LIE BAIT
MI   1885   2 1/4 IN
NORWAY $1500

129-2577 LIESKE, J.J.
JOE'S PLUG
MI   1934
   $200

129-4093 LIESKE, J.J.
SOUTH HAVEN MOUSE
MI   1938
   $100

129-4089 LIESKE, J.J.
SOUTH HAVEN PLUG
MI   1938   2 3/4 IN
   $100

129-4096 LIESKE, J.J.
SOUTH HAVEN PLUG
MI   1938
LARGE $150

129-4092 LIESKE, J.J.
SOUTH HAVEN WOBBLER
MI   1938   3 IN
   $150

129-4094 LIESKE, J.J.
SOUTH HAVEN WOBBLER
MI   1938
   $100

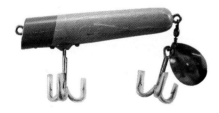

129-2533 LIKE LIVE BAIT CO.
LIKE LIVE MINNOW
FL   1932   4 IN
   $100

129-0604 LINDQUIST BROS BAIT CO.
CANADIAN WIGGLER
CAN   1952   3 3/4 IN
METAL $10

129-0605 LINDQUIST BROS BAIT CO.
CANADIAN WIGGLER
CAN   1952
   $10

129-0606 LINDQUIST BROS BAIT CO.
CANADIAN WIGGLER
CAN   1952   4 1/2 IN
METAL, JOINTED $10

129-2584 LLOYD & CO.
HUNGRY-JACK LURE
IL   1931   4 1/2 IN   3/4 OZ
   $1500

129-2582 LLOYD & CO.
LIGHTED PIRATE
IL   1940   4 IN
   $200

FISHING PLUGS

130-2583 LLOYD & CO.
LLOYD, UNKNOWN
IL   1938   2 1/2 IN
  $100

130-2589 LLOYD & CO.
TWIRL-BUG
IL   1938   2 IN
  $100

130-2581 LLOYD & CO.
WATER WITCH
IL   1940   4 IN
  $200

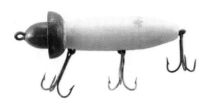

130-5508 LOCHER, WILLIAM
WHITE MILLER
MI   1910
  $300

130-2491 LOCKHART, E.J.
JERSEY SKEETER
MI   1914   2 1/2 IN
  $400

130-2492 LOCKHART, E.J.
LOCKHART WEEDLESS BAIT
MI   1920   4 IN
  $400

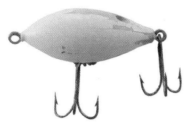

130-2490 LOCKHART, E.J.
POLYWOG BAIT
MI   1916   2 3/4 IN
  $400

130-2493 LOCKHART, E.J.
WAGTAIL WITCH
MI   1915   4 1/2 IN
  $400

130-2495 LOCKHART, E.J.
WATER WASP
MI
  $400

130-2494 LOCKHART, E.J.
WOBBLE WIZARD
MI   1916   4 1/2 IN
  $400

130-2531 LONG ISLAND MFG. CO.
FLASHER
NY   1934
LARGE $75

130-2532 LONG ISLAND MFG. CO.
FLASHER
NY   1934   3 1/2 IN
SMALL $75

130-2536 LONG ISLAND MFG. CO.
FLASH-O-LITE
NY   1939   3 1/2 IN
  $75

130-2794 LONGFELLOW PROD INC.
MERCURY MINNOW
MI   1947   4 IN   3/8 OZ
  $40

130-2793 LONGFELLOW PROD INC.
MERCURY MINNOW JR.
MI   1947   3 IN   5/8 OZ
  $40

FISHING PLUGS

131-2560 LUCKY DAY BAIT CO
DUBL-POP
MN   1948
LARGE $40

131-2562 LUCKY DAY BAIT CO
DUBL-POP
MN   1948
SMALL $40

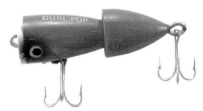

131-2564 LUCKY DAY BAIT CO
DUBL-POP
MN   1948
MEDIUM $40

131-2563 LUCKY DAY BAIT CO
DUBL-POP MINNOW
MN   1948
$40

131-2561 LUCKY DAY BAIT CO
DUBL-POP WOBBLER
MN   1948   4 IN
$40

131-2559 LUCKY DAY BAIT CO
LUCKY DUCK
MN   1948
$60

131-4885 LUCKY DAY BAIT CO
WIGGLE-TAIL
MN   1950's
$30

131-2557 LUCKY LURE BAIT CO
WATERLOU

$20

131-2579 LUCKY STRIKE BAIT CO.
LUCKY STRIKE JOINTED PIKE BAIT
CAN   1938   4 3/4 IN
$90

131-2580 LUCKY STRIKE BAIT CO.
LUCKY STRIKE PIKE BAIT
CAN   1938   4 1/2 IN
$90

131-2578 LUCKY STRIKE BAIT CO.
LUCKY STRIKE WOBBLER
CAN   1946   4 1/4 IN
$30

131-2572 LULU LURES
LULU LURE
OH
$30

131-0401 LUR-ALL
BEETLEBUG
MI   1941
LARGE $200

131-0403 LUR-ALL
BEETLEBUG
MI   1941   1 1/2 IN
WEEDLESS $100

131-2750 MACK'S TACKLE WORKSHOP
MOUSE, MACK'S
TX   1934   3 IN
$700

FISHING PLUGS

132-5202 MAC'S PLUGS
MAC'S SQUID PLUG
ID
  $20

132-2742 MAGIC MINNOW BAIT CO.
MAGIC MINNOW
MA   1946   2 1/2 IN
SMALL $75

132-2743 MAGIC MINNOW BAIT CO.
MAGIC MINNOW
MA   1939   3 1/2 IN   3/4 OZ
OLD $150

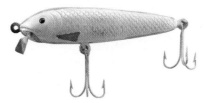

132-2744 MAGIC MINNOW BAIT CO.
MAGIC MINNOW
MA   1939   3 1/2 IN   3/4 OZ
NEW $100

132-2741 MAGIC MINNOW BAIT CO.
MAGIC MINNOW JIG
MA   1926   2 IN
  $100

132-2740 MAGIC MINNOW BAIT CO.
MAGIC MINNOW, SALTWATER
MA   1926   4 1/2 IN
  $300

132-2620 MAKINEN TACKLE CO.
HOLI-COMET
MI   1945   7 IN
MUSKY SIZE, WOOD $100

132-2625 MAKINEN TACKLE CO.
HOLI-COMET
MI   1945   4 IN   5/8 OZ
WOOD $50

132-2626 MAKINEN TACKLE CO.
HOLI-COMET
MI   1945
PLASTIC $50

132-2624 MAKINEN TACKLE CO.
MAKILURE
MI   1945   6 1/2 IN
MUSKY SIZE, WOOD $100

132-2630 MAKINEN TACKLE CO.
MAKILURE
MI   1945
WOOD $50

132-2632 MAKINEN TACKLE CO.
MAKILURE
MI   1945   3 3/4 IN
PLASTIC $50

132-2636 MAKINEN TACKLE CO.
MAKILURE
MI   1946
WOOD, SMALL $50

132-2628 MAKINEN TACKLE CO.
MERRY WIDOW
MI   1945   4 IN   5/8 OZ
WOOD $50

132-2629 MAKINEN TACKLE CO.
MERRY WIDOW
MI   1945
PLASTIC $50

FISHING PLUGS

133-2648 MAKINEN TACKLE CO.
RESEARCH PROTOTYPE, MAKINEN
MI
  $50

133-2622 MAKINEN TACKLE CO.
WADDLE BUG
MI   1945   3 IN
LARGE, TENITE $50

133-2627 MAKINEN TACKLE CO.
WADDLE BUG
MI   1945
WOOD $50

133-2631 MAKINEN TACKLE CO.
WADDLE BUG
MI   1945   2 1/2 IN
SMALL, TENITE $50

133-2651 MANHATTEN MINNOW CO
MANHATTEN MINNOW
NY
  $500

133-2656 MANHATTEN MINNOW CO
MANHATTEN MINNOW
NY
SMALL $500

133-2837 MANNING LURE CO
SHRIMP, MANNING
LA   1954
SMALL $100

133-2754 MANNING LURE CO.
SHRIMP, MANNING
LA   1954
  $100

133-2727 MARATHON BAIT CO.
BIG BILL
WI   1952   4 1/4 IN
  $75

133-2699 MARATHON BAIT CO.
EEL, MARATHON
WI
  $40

133-2731 MARATHON BAIT CO.
FEATHERED WOBBLER
WI   1948   2 IN
  $50

133-2723 MARATHON BAIT CO.
WORM SPINNER
WI   1950
  $40

133-2729 MARATHON BAIT CO.
MUSK-E-MONK
WI
NEW $75

133-2730 MARATHON BAIT CO.
MUSK-E-MONK
WI   1936   2 1/2 IN
GLASS EYES, OLD $150

133-2726 MARATHON BAIT CO.
MUSKIE HUSKIE
WI   1948   2 3/4 IN
DECAL EYES $100

FISHING PLUGS

134-2697 MARATHON BAIT CO.
MUSKRAT, MARATHON
WI   1960   4 IN
BABY $100

134-2698 MARATHON BAIT CO.
MUSKRAT, MARATHON
WI   1960   7 IN
  $100

134-2700 MARATHON BAIT CO.
OL' BUDDY
WI
  $40

134-5700 MARATHON BAIT CO.
SPOON TAIL MINNOW
WI
  $30

134-2782 MARS-HILLWOOD PRODUCTS
SKIPPER BILL
IN   1960
  $70

134-2672 MARTIN FISH LURE CO.
HOTTER 'N' HELL
WA
  $40

134-2667 MARTIN FISH LURE CO.
INJURED MINNOW , MARTIN
WA
  $150

134-2668 MARTIN FISH LURE CO.
SALMON DIVER
WA   1930's   4 1/4 IN
  $100

134-2673 MARTIN FISH LURE CO.
SALMON INJURED MINNOW
WA
OLD $200

134-2655 MARTIN FISH LURE CO.
SALMON PLUG, MARTIN
WA   1930's   7 IN
  $75

134-2657 MARTIN FISH LURE CO.
SALMON PLUG, MARTIN
WA   1930's   6 IN
  $75

134-2658 MARTIN FISH LURE CO.
SALMON PLUG, MARTIN
WA   1930's   5 IN
  $75

134-2659 MARTIN FISH LURE CO.
SALMON PLUG, MARTIN
WA   1930's   4 IN
  $75

134-2661 MARTIN FISH LURE CO.
SALMON PLUG, MARTIN
WA   1930's   5 IN
  $75

134-2662 MARTIN FISH LURE CO.
SALMON PLUG, MARTIN
WA   1930's   6 IN
  $75

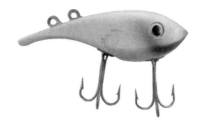

135-2663 MARTIN FISH LURE CO.
WESTERN BASS PLUG
WA   1946   3 1/2 IN
$200

135-2811 MARTIN, JACK
MARTIN LIZZARD
OK
NEW, PLASTIC $20

135-2812 MARTIN, JACK
MARTIN LIZZARD
OK
OLD $50

135-2753 MARTZ TACKLE CO.
VEE-BUG
MI   1948   3 3/4 IN   5/8 OZ
$40

135-2645 MARTZ, H.A.
LIVE BAIT FISHING PLUG, WEEDLESS
MN   1954
$100

135-2689 MAYGARD, ROY
SPARX-PLUG
WA   1946   4 1/2 IN
$75

135-2694 McCAGG, BARNEY
BARNEY GOOGLE
NY   1947
$70

135-2838 McCAGG, BARNEY
BARNEY GOOGLE
NY   1947
LARGE $60

135-2801 McDONALD
RUBBER CRAWFISH

$40

135-2643 McGUIRE-PHILLIPS
WEDGE LURE
RI   1947
$30

135-2787 MERMADE BAIT CO.
SCATBACK
WI
MUSKY $120

135-2788 MERMADE BAIT CO.
SCATBACK
WI   1949   2 3/4 IN
$60

135-2757 MICHIGAN TACKLE CO.
FLIPPER FISH, MICHIGAN TACKLE
MI   1950's   2 1/2 IN   3/8 OZ
$80

135-2760 MICHIGAN TACKLE CO.
MICHIGAN FIN WING
MI
$150

135-2781 MILES, WILLIAM C. BAIT CO
BILL'S PRIDE
NY   1928
$300

FISHING PLUGS

136-2646 MILLE-LACS MFG.
POKEY JOE
MN   1952
  $10

136-2805 MILLER LURES
TOP KICK
MO   1958   3 1/2 IN
LARGE $20

136-2806 MILLER LURES
TOP KICK
MO   1958   2 1/2 IN
SMALL $20

 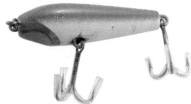 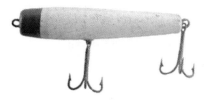

136-2796 MILLER, RALPH
LEAPING LENA
FL   1941   4 IN
LARGE $90

136-2797 MILLER, RALPH
LEAPING LENA
FL   1940   3 IN
SMALL $90

136-6147 MILLER, RALPH
LEAPING LENA #400
FL   1950's
  $30

 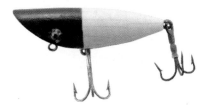 

136-2800 MILLER, RALPH
MILLER BAIT
FL
  $120

136-2780 MILLS, HERB FISHING TACKLE
ACROBAT SURFACE MINNOW
OH   1930   3 1/4 IN
  $300

136-2779 MILLS, HERB FISHING TACKLE
CHIEF TEAZUM
OH   1929   3 1/2 IN
  $400

  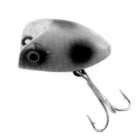

136-2778 MILLS, HERB FISHING TACKLE
CRAWDAD, MILLS
OH   1935   3 3/4 IN   5/8 OZ
  $400

136-2789 MILLS, HERB FISHING TACKLE
GOOF BALL
OH   1960   1 1/4 IN
  $60

136-2640 MILLSITE TACKLE CO.
BASSOR
MI   1946
SMALL $30

136-2641 MILLSITE TACKLE CO.
BASSOR
MI   1946   2 1/4 IN
FLOATER $30

136-2642 MILLSITE TACKLE CO.
BASSOR
MI   1946   2 IN
  $30

136-2676 MILLSITE TACKLE CO.
BASSOR
MI
LARGE $40

FISHING PLUGS

137-2639 MILLSITE TACKLE CO.
BEETLE BUG
MI   1946
SMALL $40

137-2644 MILLSITE TACKLE CO.
BEETLE BUG
MI   1938   1 IN   5/8 OZ
    $40

137-2650 MILLSITE TACKLE CO.
BEETLE BUG
MI   1946
FLOATER $300

137-2619 MILLSITE TACKLE CO.
DAILY DOUBLE
MI   1939
WOOD $500

137-2621 MILLSITE TACKLE CO.
DAILY DOUBLE
MI   1946   4 IN
LARGE, FLOATER, PLASTIC $50

137-2623 MILLSITE TACKLE CO.
DAILY DOUBLE
MI   1946   3 1/2 IN
LARGE, FLOATER, PLASTIC $50

137-2635 MILLSITE TACKLE CO.
DEEP CREEP
MI   1946   2 1/2 IN
    $30

137-2653 MILLSITE TACKLE CO.
PADDLE BUG
MI   1937   1 3/4 IN   1/2 OZ
    $40

137-2647 MILLSITE TACKLE CO.
RATTLE BUG
MI   1936   1 7/8 IN   5/8 OZ
    $40

137-2638 MILLSITE TACKLE CO.
WIG WAG
MI   1946   3 IN
    $30

137-2637 MILLSITE TACKLE CO.
WIG WAG SINKER
MI   1946   2 1/2 IN
    $30

137-2649 MILLSITE TACKLE CO.
WIG WAG FLOATER
MI   1946
    $30

137-5392 MINNETONKA BROS.
DECOY, TONKA FISH
MN
    $200

137-5639 MINNICK MFG.
PENCIL BAIT, MINNICK
MI   1946
    $30

137-2682 MINSER TACKLE CO
LUCKY LOUIE
WA   1935   5 IN
    $75

138-24687 MINSER TACKLE CO.
LUCKY LOUIE SALMON LURE
WA   1935
PLASTIC $30

138-5547 MIRACLE TACKLE CO.
ZARA TYPE
FL   1950's
   $20

138-6985 MIRACLE TACKLE CO.
MIRACLE FISH
FL   1950's
LARGE $20

138-6987 MIRACLE TACKLE CO.
MIRACLE FISH
FL   1950's
SMALL $20

138-2820 MIRR-O-LURE CO.
MIRR-O-LURE
FL   1959   3 IN
4 HEADS $75

138-0783 MITCHELL, JOHN
POOR MANS CHAUTAUQUA

   $500

138-2777 MITY ATOM BAIT CO.
MITY ATOM BAIT
TX   1947   2 1/2 IN
   $50

138-2818 MIZZOURI BAIT CO.
MIZZOURI BUG WOBBLER
MO   1916
   $1500

138-2839 MODERN SPORTING GOODS
FROGLEGS
TX
WOOD $200

138-2816 MOELLER MFG. CO.
MOELLER MINNOW
TX   1935
   $400

138-2798 MONTPELIER BAIT CO.
HOOTENANNA
OH   1939   2 3/4 IN
SMALL $90

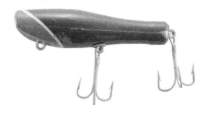

138-2799 MONTPELIER BAIT CO.
HOOTENANNA
OH   1939   3 1/4 IN
LARGE $100

138-2867 MOONLIGHT BAIT CO.
1913 SPECIAL
MI   1913
BABY SIZE $10000

138-2868 MOONLIGHT BAIT CO.
1913 SPECIAL
MI   1913
   $10000

138-2863 MOONLIGHT BAIT CO.
99% WEEDLESS BAIT
MI   1925   2 1/2 IN
   $300

FISHING PLUGS

139-2864 MOONLIGHT BAIT CO.
99% WEEDLESS BAIT
MI   1926   2 1/2 IN
   $300

139-2865 MOONLIGHT BAIT CO.
99% WEEDLESS BAIT,   BUCKTAIL
MI   1926   2 1/2 IN
   $300

139-2886 MOONLIGHT BAIT CO.
BASS SEEKER
MI   1921   3 1/2 IN
PAINTED EYES $900

139-2887 MOONLIGHT BAIT CO.
BASS SEEKER
MI   1921   3 1/2 IN
BABY, GLASS EYES $400

139-2888 MOONLIGHT BAIT CO.
BASS SEEKER
MI   1920   3 1/4 IN
   $400

139-2889 MOONLIGHT BAIT CO.
BRILLIANT BASS SEEKER
MI   1920   4 1/4 IN
TACK EYES $400

139-2869 MOONLIGHT BAIT CO.
BUCKTAIL BAIT, MOONLIGHT
MI
BABY $350

139-2870 MOONLIGHT BAIT CO.
BUCKTAIL BAIT, WEEDLESS
MI
   $350

139-2871 MOONLIGHT BAIT CO.
BUCKTAIL BAIT, WEIGHTED
MI   1930   1 1/4 IN
   $300

139-2892 MOONLIGHT BAIT CO.
BUG, THE, MOONLIGHT
MI   1916   3 IN   3/4 OZ
   $4000

139-2979 MOONLIGHT BAIT CO.
CRAWFISH, MOONLIGHT
MI   1929
   $1000

139-2952 MOONLIGHT BAIT CO.
DECOY, MOONLIGHT
MI
   $2000

139-2872 MOONLIGHT BAIT CO.
DREADNOUGHT, MOONLIGHT
MI   1918   4 IN
   $5000

139-2874 MOONLIGHT BAIT CO.
FEATHERED MINNOW   #1400, MOONLT
MI   1913   2 IN
   $600

139-2844 MOONLIGHT BAIT CO.
FISH NIPPLE, MOONLIGHT
MI
   $300

140-2934 MOONLIGHT BAIT CO.
FISH SPEAR
MI   1914   4 IN
  $2000

140-2890 MOONLIGHT BAIT CO.
FLASH-HEAD WOBBLER
MI   1929   3 1/2 IN   1 OZ
CUP-RIG $300

140-24591 MOONLIGHT BAIT CO.
GROOVED HEAD MOONLIGHT
MI   1922
  $300

140-2912 MOONLIGHT BAIT CO.
LADYBUG WIGGLER
MI
EARLY $1000

140-2905 MOONLIGHT BAIT CO.
LADYBUG WIGGLER
MI   1928   2 1/2 IN
NEW STYLE $2000

140-2906 MOONLIGHT BAIT CO.
LADYBUG WIGGLER
MI   1917   4 1/2 IN
OLD STYLE $2000

140-2945 MOONLIGHT BAIT CO.
LITTLE WONDER, MOONLIGHT
MI   1925   3 IN
  $450

140-2946 MOONLIGHT BAIT CO.
LITTLE WONDER, MOONLIGHT
MI   1923
LARGE $600

140-0434 MOONLIGHT BAIT CO.
MOONLIGHT BAIT
MI   1920's   4 IN
RIDGE FRONT $300

140-2859 MOONLIGHT BAIT CO.
MOONLIGHT BAIT #1
MI   1918   4 IN
  $400

140-2860 MOONLIGHT BAIT CO.
MOONLIGHT BAIT #1
MI
2ND OLDEST $450

140-2861 MOONLIGHT BAIT CO.
MOONLIGHT BAIT #1
MI
FAT BODY $300

140-2862 MOONLIGHT BAIT CO.
MOONLIGHT BAIT #1
MI   3 IN
POPPING $400

140-2853 MOONLIGHT BAIT CO.
MOONLIGHT BAIT #1 (OLDEST)
MI   1907   4 IN
  $2500

140-2858 MOONLIGHT BAIT CO.
MOONLIGHT BAIT #2
MI
  $450

FISHING PLUGS

141-2848 MOONLIGHT BAIT CO.
MOONLIGHT BAIT #2
MI
OLDEST $500

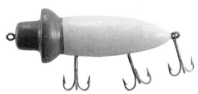

141-2849 MOONLIGHT BAIT CO.
MOONLIGHT BAIT #2
MI   1920   3 5/8 IN
3 HOOK $300

141-2851 MOONLIGHT BAIT CO.
MOONLIGHT BAIT #2
MI   1920   3 5/8 IN
SIDE-HOOK $300

141-2856 MOONLIGHT BAIT CO.
MOONLIGHT BAIT #2
MI   1910   3 3/4 IN
SMALL $900

141-2911 MOONLIGHT BAIT CO.
MOONLIGHT BAIT #1900
MI   1925   3 1/4 in
2 HOOK $450

141-2878 MOONLIGHT BAIT CO.
MOONLIGHT BAIT #2900
MI   1928   3 3/4 IN
$600

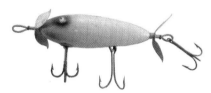

141-2873 MOONLIGHT BAIT CO.
MOONLIGHT BAIT #3000
MI   1924   3 1/4 IN
$600

141-2893 MOONLIGHT BAIT CO.
MOONLIGHT BAIT # 3350
MI   1925   3 3/4 IN
GLASS EYES $300

141-2894 MOONLIGHT BAIT CO.
MOONLIGHT BAIT # 3350
MI   1925   3 3/4 IN
PAINTED EYES $200

141-0435 MOONLIGHT BAIT CO.
MOONLIGHT BAIT JR
MI   1920's   3 IN
RIDGE FRONT $300

141-2854 MOONLIGHT BAIT CO.
MOONLIGHT BAIT, SPINNERED
MI   1915
BABY $1500

141-2884 MOONLIGHT BAIT CO.
MOONLIGHT CASTING MINNOW
MI
$900

141-2880 MOONLIGHT BAIT CO.
MOONLIGHT FLOATING 5-HOOK BAIT
MI   1910   3 3/4 IN
$600

141-2852 MOONLIGHT BAIT CO.
MOONLIGHT FLOATING BAIT
MI   1910   5 1/2 IN
LARGE $300

141-2855 MOONLIGHT BAIT CO.
MOONLIGHT NIGHT RADIANT BAIT
MI   1919
$900

FISHING PLUGS

142-2935 MOONLIGHT BAIT CO.
MOONLIGHT TOPWATER BAIT
MI
PAINTED EYES $300

142-2882 MOONLIGHT BAIT CO.
MOONLIGHT UNDERWATER 3-HOOK
MI   1910   3 IN
   $600

142-2883 MOONLIGHT BAIT CO.
MOONLIGHT UNDERWATER 3-HOOK
MI   1910   3 IN
SMALL $600

142-2881 MOONLIGHT BAIT CO.
MOONLIGHT UNDERWATER 5-HOOK
MI   1910   3 3/4 IN
   $600

142-2885 MOONLIGHT BAIT CO.
MOONLIGHT UNDERWATER BAIT
MI   1912   3 3/4 IN
   $900

142-2847 MOONLIGHT BAIT CO.
MOONLIGHT WEEDLESS BAIT #2
MI
   $350

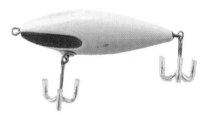

142-2948 MOONLIGHT BAIT CO.
MOONLIGHT WILSON WOBBLER
MI   1921   4 IN
   $225

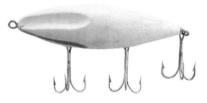

142-2949 MOONLIGHT BAIT CO.
MOONLIGHT WILSON WOBBLER
MI   1921
   $225

142-2845 MOONLIGHT BAIT CO.
MOONLIGHT WOBBLER
MI   12 IN
MUSKY $2000

142-2904 MOONLIGHT BAIT CO.
MOONLIGHT WOBBLER
MI
   $300

142-2875 MOONLIGHT BAIT CO.
MOONLIGHT, UNKNOWN
MI
   $300

142-2896 MOONLIGHT BAIT CO.
MOONLIGHT, UNKNOWN
MI   3 IN
   $200

142-2939 MOONLIGHT BAIT CO.
MOONLIGHT, UNKNOWN
MI   1919
   $400

142-2947 MOONLIGHT BAIT CO.
MOUSE, MOONLIGHT
MI   1930   2 1/2 IN
   $225

142-24734 MOONLIGHT BAIT CO.
MOUSE, MOONLIGHT
MI
LARGE $100

FISHING PLUGS

143-2897 MOONLIGHT BAIT CO.
MUSKY PIKAROON
MI   1923   5 1/2 IN
SCHOENFELD $900

143-2913 MOONLIGHT BAIT CO.
MUSKY PIKAROON,   JOINTED
MI   1924   5 3/4 IN
SCHOENFELD $1200

143-2915 MOONLIGHT BAIT CO.
PIKAROON
MI   1923   4 1/4 IN
SCHOENFELD $300

143-2916 MOONLIGHT BAIT CO.
PIKAROON
MI
BABY, JOINTED, SCHOENFELD $400

143-2933 MOONLIGHT BAIT CO.
PIKAROON
MI   1926
1 HOOK $1200

143-2914 MOONLIGHT BAIT CO.
PIKAROON, JOINTED
MI   1926   4 IN
SCHOENFELD $400

143-2895 MOONLIGHT BAIT CO.
POPPER, WEEDLESS
MI   2 3/4 IN
    $300

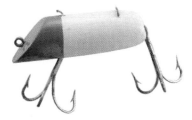

143-2902 MOONLIGHT BAIT CO.
PORK RIND PLUG
MI   4 IN
    $300

143-2903 MOONLIGHT BAIT CO.
PORK RIND PLUG
MI   1921   4 1/4 IN
3 HOOK, BABY $300

143-2917 MOONLIGHT BAIT CO.
SCHOENFELD, UNKNOWN
MI   3 IN
    $100

143-2918 MOONLIGHT BAIT CO.
SCHOENFELD, UNKNOWN
MI   3 IN
    $100

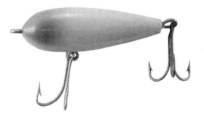

143-2919 MOONLIGHT BAIT CO.
SCHOENFELD, UNKNOWN
MI
    $100

143-2920 MOONLIGHT BAIT CO.
SCHOENFELD, UNKNOWN
MI
    $100

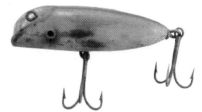

143-2921 MOONLIGHT BAIT CO.
SCHOENFELD, UNKNOWN
MI   3 IN
    $100

143-2899 MOONLIGHT BAIT CO.
SEA GULL
MI   1926   3 1/2 IN
BABY, SCHOENFELD $600

FISHING PLUGS

144-2900 MOONLIGHT BAIT CO.
SEA GULL
MI   1926   3 1/4 IN   BABY
SCHOENFELD, PAINTED EYES $500

144-2898 MOONLIGHT BAIT CO.
SEAGULL
MI   1925   4 IN
SCHOENFELD $600

144-2923 MOONLIGHT BAIT CO.
SEAGULL, JOINTED
MI   1926   3 1/2 IN
SCHOENFELD $600

144-2877 MOONLIGHT BAIT CO.
SURFACE MINNOW,   MOONLIGHT
MI   1922   3 IN
  $600

144-2879 MOONLIGHT BAIT CO.
TORPEDO, MOONLIGH
MI   1926
  $600

144-2876 MOONLIGHT BAIT CO.
WHIRLING CHUB
MI   1929   4 1/2 IN   1 OZ
  $500

144-2922 MOONLIGHT BAIT CO.
WOBBLER, MOONLIGHT
MI   2 3/4 IN
BABY $400

144-2926 MOONLIGHT BAIT CO.
WOBBLER, MOONLIGHT
MI   1927   4 IN
3 HOOK, SCHOENFELD $400

144-2907 MOONLIGHT BAIT CO.
ZIG-ZAG
MI   1913   3 3/4 IN
  $600

144-2908 MOONLIGHT BAIT CO.
ZIG-ZAG
MI   1914   3 IN
BABY $600

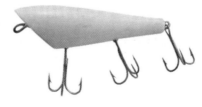

144-2901 MOONLIGHT BAIT CO.
ZIG-ZAG TOPPER
MI   1913   3 1/2 IN
  $600

144-2828 MOORE, JOE BAITS, INC.
MOORE'S YELLOW PLUG
TX   5 1/2 IN
  $200

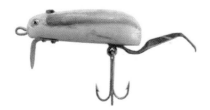

144-2831 MOUSE BAIT CO., THE
FT. WORTH MOUSE
TX   1926   2 3/4 IN
GLASS EYES $500

144-2833 MOUSE BAIT CO., THE
FT. WORTH MOUSE
TX
LATE $300

144-2704 MUSKY SUCKER BAIT MFG. CO.
MUSKY SUCKER BAIT
WI
BABY $75

FISHING PLUGS

145-2701 MUSKY SUCKER BAIT MFG. CO.
MUSKY SUCKER BAIT, DIVER
WI   1946   4 1/2 IN
3 SIZES $75

145-2703 MUSKY SUCKER BAIT MFG. CO.
MUSKY SUCKER BAIT, SURFACE
WI
 $75

145-2654 MY FAIR LADY PRODUCTS
MIKE, THE FISHERMAN'S LURE
CA   1960
 $40

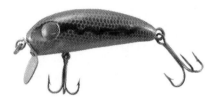

145-3115 N & N TACKLE
4-IN-1 BAIT
 1958   2 IN
 $30

145-1412 N. AMERICAN SPECIALTIES
GURGLING JOE
MI   1940
 $40

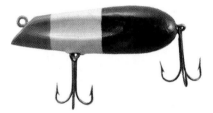

145-3121 NATIONAL BAIT CO.
BASS-KING
MN   1927   3 1/2 IN
LARGE $225

145-3122 NATIONAL BAIT CO.
BASS-KING
MN   1927   3 IN
SMALL $225

145-3267 NATIONAL DYNAMICS
COLORAMA

 $90

145-3778 NATIVE AMERICAN
POCAHONTAS
USA   7 IN
 $500

145-3114 NATURALURE BAIT CO.
QUEEN STRIKEE
CA   1950   7 IN   3 OZ
 $40

145-3112 NATURALURE BAIT CO.
STRIKEE MINNOW
CA   1950   3 7/8 IN   5/8 OZ
 $40

145-3113 NATURALURE BAIT CO.
TROPICAL STRIKEE
CA   1950   3 7/8 IN   5/8 OZ
 $40

145-3147 NEAL BAIT MFG CO.
NEAL SPINNER
IN   1940   2 IN   9/16 OZ
 $60

145-3148 NEAL BAIT MFG CO.
NEAL SPINNER
IN   1948   2 3/4 IN
 $60

145-3149 NEAL BAIT MFG CO.
NEAL SPINNER
IN   1948   2 3/4 IN
 $60

FISHING PLUGS

146-3130 NEON MICKEY BAIT CO.
NEON MICKEY
OR   1955   4 IN
  $30

146-3131 NESS, JOSEPH M.
NIFTY MINNIE
MN   1913   4 1/2 IN   1 OZ
  $2500

146-3137 NICHOLS LURE CO.
DIVING SHRIMP
TX
  $50

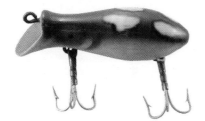

146-3146 NICHOLS LURE CO.
NICHOLS BOMBER
TX   1937   3 1/4 IN
  $50

146-3140 NICHOLS LURE CO.
NICHOLS PLUNKER
TX   1938   3 1/2 IN
  $50

146-3144 NICHOLS LURE CO.
NICHOLS POPPER
TX   1937   2 1/2 IN
  $40

146-3145 NICHOLS LURE CO.
NICHOLS RUNT
TX   1937   2 1/2 IN
  $40

146-3136 NICHOLS LURE CO.
NICHOLS SHRIMP
TX
FRED NICHOLS $40

146-3138 NICHOLS LURE CO.
NICHOLS SHRIMP
TX
OLD $50

146-3950 NICHOLS LURE CO.
NICHOLS SHRIMP
TX   1940's
LARGE $20

146-3139 NICHOLS LURE CO.
NICHOLS TOP PIKE
TX   1938   3 3/4 IN
TOP PIKE $50

146-3142 NICHOLS LURE CO.
NICHOLS WOBBLER
TX
  $50

146-3143 NICHOLS LURE CO.
NICHOLS WOBBLER
TX   1937   4 IN
  $50

146-3141 NICHOLS LURE CO.
NICHOLS, UNKNOWN
TX   1938   3 IN
  $50

146-5650 NICHOLS LURE CO.
POPPER KILLER
TX   1947
  $20

FISHING PLUGS

147-3129 NIXON, FRANK T.
NIXON IVORY MINNOW
MI   1914   3 3/4 IN
  $2000

147-3170 NORRIS, BRAD
SQUID
RI   1947   7 1/2 IN
  $300

147-5453 NORTHERN PUMP
FISH DECOY, COPPER

  $1500

147-1734 NORTHERN TACKLE CO.
TORPEDO RAY
MI   1948   4 IN
  $100

147-3116 NORTHWOOD BAIT CO.
CURVE-A-LURE
MI   1958   3 IN
  $60

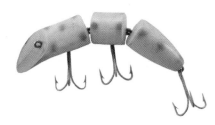

147-3120 NORTHWOOD BAIT CO.
NORTHWOOD BAIT, JOINTED
MI

  $60

147-3135 NORWICH FLORIDA CORP.
SHRIMP, JOINTED, NORWICH
FL   1938   4 IN
  $100

147-5110 NOVELTY CO.
KITCHEN SINK LURE

  $100

147-3109 NOVELTY LURE CO.
SAM-BO
NE   1952   3 IN
  $150

147-3171 O.M. BAIT CO.
UNNER-FLASH
MI   1938   1/2 OZ
TENITE $200

147-6138 O'BRIEN, A.F.
O'BRIEN MINNOW
  1915
  $1000

147-5115 ODON BAIT CO.
DRAGONFLY, ODON

  $40

147-3166 O'GENE CO.
GLITTER BUG
TX   1944   2 IN
  $40

147-3179 OLIVER & GRUBER
GLOWURM
WA   1920   4 3/4 IN
WOOD $500

147-5681 ORAVEC, STEVE
ORAVEC LURE
MI
  $40

FISHING PLUGS

148-3190 ORCHARD IND. INC.
BOTTOM-SCRATCHER
MI   1946   2 1/2 IN   9/16 OZ
PLASTIC $50

148-3189 ORCHARD IND. INC.
KICK-N-KACKLE
MI   1946   2 5/8 IN   9/16 OZ
PLASTIC $40

148-3191 ORCHARD IND. INC.
SLIPPERY SAM
MI   1946
    $40

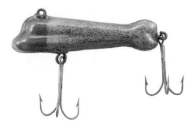

148-1363 ORLANDO BAIT CO
MASTER MINNOW
FL   1932
PLASTIC $400

148-3178 ORLUCK BAIT CO.
CRAZY GEORGE
MN   1945   5 1/2 IN
WOOD WITH METAL $40

148-5495 OUSLEY BAIT CO.
SNOOK MAGICIAN
FL
    $50

148-3195 OUTING MFG. CO.
BASSY GETUM
IN   1923   3 7/8 IN   5/8 OZ
    $400

148-3184 OUTING MFG. CO.
BUCKY GETUM
IN   1923   2 IN
LARGE $200

148-3185 OUTING MFG. CO.
BUCKY GETUM
IN   1923   1 3/4 IN
SMALL $200

148-3180 OUTING MFG. CO.
DU-GETUM
IN   1925   3 IN   3/4 OZ
LARGE $400

148-3181 OUTING MFG. CO.
DU-GETUM
IN   1925   2 3/4 IN   5/8 OZ
SMALL $400

148-3186 OUTING MFG. CO.
FEATHER GETUM
IN   1923   1 3/4 IN
    $200

148-3183 OUTING MFG. CO.
GETUM, FLOATER
IN   1923   4 1/4 IN   3/4 OZ
    $600

148-3196 OUTING MFG. CO.
PIKY GETUM
IN   1923   3 5/8 IN   1/2 OZ
    $400

148-3187 OUTING MFG. CO.
PORKY GETUM
IN   1 3/4 IN
    $200

FISHING PLUGS

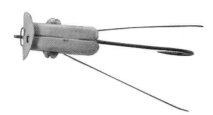

149-3188 OUTING MFG. CO.
PORKY GETUM
IN   1923   1 1/2 IN
SMALL $200

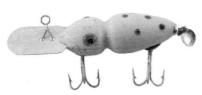

149-3150 OZARK LURE CO., THE
LIT'L LIZARD
OK   1948   2 1/4 IN
  $40

149-3159 OZARK LURE CO., THE
LIT'L LIZARD
OK   1950
  $40

149-3162 OZARK LURE CO., THE
OZARK LIZARD
OK   1948   4 1/4 IN
  $40

149-3163 OZARK LURE CO., THE
OZARK LIZARD WOBBLER
OK
  $40

149-3160 OZARK LURE CO., THE
TOP LIZARD
OK   1958   2 1/2 IN
LARGE $40

149-3161 OZARK LURE CO., THE
TOP LIZARD
OK   1960   2 1/4 IN
SMALL $40

149-3165 OZARK LURE CO., THE
TOP LIZARD
OK
  $50

149-5155 OZARK MOUNTAIN TACKLE CO.
WOODWALKER
  1946
  $50

149-3213 PACHNER & KOLLER (P&K)
AMAZIN' MAIZIE
IL   1946   2 1/4 IN   5/8 OZ
TENITE $40

149-3219 PACHNER & KOLLER (P&K)
BRIGHT EYES
IL   1946   3 IN
LARGE $40

149-3221 PACHNER & KOLLER (P&K)
BRIGHT EYES
IL   1946   2 1/4 IN
SMALL $40

149-3193 PACHNER & KOLLER (P&K)
COON ATTRACTOR
IL   1946   3 IN
FOR COON TRAP $40

149-3200 PACHNER & KOLLER (P&K)
COON ATTRACTOR
IL   1946   2 IN
FOR COON TRAP $40

149-3215 PACHNER & KOLLER (P&K)
LIPPY
IL   1946   7 IN
SALTWATER $70

FISHING PLUGS

150-3210 PACHNER & KOLLER (P&K)
MIDGET WOBBLER
IL
  $50

150-3197 PACHNER & KOLLER (P&K)
MOUSE, P&K
IL   1946   1 1/4 IN
SMALL $30

150-3198 PACHNER & KOLLER (P&K)
MOUSE, P&K
IL   1946   2 1/4 IN
LARGE $30

150-3201 PACHNER & KOLLER (P&K)
MOUSE, WEEDLESS
IL
  $30

150-3194 PACHNER & KOLLER (P&K)
SOFTY THE WONDER CRAB
IL   1946   3 1/2 IN
  $30

150-3203 PACHNER & KOLLER (P&K)
SOFTY THE WONDER CRAB
IL
SMALL $30

150-3220 PACHNER & KOLLER (P&K)
SPINNING MINNIE
IL   1946   2 3/4 IN
  $70

150-3204 PACHNER & KOLLER (P&K)
SPOTTY THE WONDER FROG
IL   1946   3 IN
  $30

150-3214 PACHNER & KOLLER (P&K)
WALKIE TALKIE
IL   1946
  $40

150-3212 PACHNER & KOLLER (P&K)
WALKIE TALKIE,
IL   1946   5 1/2 IN   3 1/2 OZ
SALTWATER $100

150-3209 PACHNER & KOLLER (P&K)
WHIRL-A-WAY
IL   1946   3 IN   5/8 OZ
  $60

150-3211 PACHNER & KOLLER (P&K)
WOBBLER, P&K
IL   1946   4 1/2 IN
  $50

150-3224 PADRE ISLAND CO. (PICO)
DEEP DIVE PICO
TX   1946   2 1/4 IN
  $40

150-3206 PADRE ISLAND CO. (PICO)
DIGGER
TX   1960   2 1/2 IN
  $30

150-3207 NICHOLS LURE CO.
PIGGY PERCH
TX   1939   2 1/2 IN
  $400

FISHING PLUGS

151-3199 PADRE ISLAND CO. (PICO)
PEPPY
TX   1946   2 IN
  $40

151-3208 PADRE ISLAND CO. (PICO)
PICO DARTER
TX   1955   4 IN
  $40

151-3227 PADRE ISLAND CO. (PICO)
PICO DARTER
TX
  $40

151-3222 PADRE ISLAND CO. (PICO)
PICO MINNOW
TX   1946   3 IN
  $40

151-3223 PADRE ISLAND CO. (PICO)
PICO PAL
TX   1946   4 IN
  $40

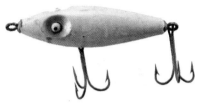

151-3225 PADRE ISLAND CO. (PICO)
PICO POP
TX   1946   3 IN
  $40

151-3226 PADRE ISLAND CO. (PICO)
PICO POP
TX   1960
SMALL $20

151-3229 PADRE ISLAND CO. (PICO)
PICO TOPPER
TX
  $20

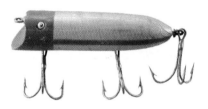

151-3216 PADRE ISLAND CO. (PICO)
PICO WOBBLER
TX   1946   4 IN
  $40

151-7002 PADRE ISLAND CO. (PICO)
SIDE SHAD
TX   1965
SMALLEST $60

151-3133 NICHOLS LURE CO.
SWIMMING MINNOW, PICO
TX   1939   2 1/4 IN
GLASS EYES $300

151-3134   NICHOLS LURE CO.
SWIMMING MINNOW, PICO
TX
GLASS EYES, SMALL $300

151-3231 PADRE ISLAND CO. (PICO)
SWIMMING MINNOW, PICO
TX
  $20

151-0638 PARADISE LURE CO.
OFFSIDE VANE
PA   1947
TROLLING $30

151-3309 PARKER, EWELL
EWELURE
TX   1958   2 IN
PLASTIC $40

FISHING PLUGS

152-24693 PAUL BUNYAN
WHIRL-A-BUG
MN
  $75

152-3239 PAUL BUNYAN BAIT CO.
DINA-MITE
MN   1946   2 IN
LARGE $20

152-3244 PAUL BUNYAN BAIT CO.
DINA-MITE
MN   1946   1 3/4 IN
SMALL $30

152-3246 PAUL BUNYAN BAIT CO.
DODGER
MN   1938   4 IN
  $90

152-3242 PAUL BUNYAN BAIT CO.
ELECTRO LURE
MN   1930
  $200

152-3261 PAUL BUNYAN BAIT CO.
LADYBUG DIVER
MN   1939   3 1/4 IN   5/8 OZ
LARGE $90

152-3262 PAUL BUNYAN BAIT CO.
LADYBUG DIVER
MN   1939   2 1/2 IN   1/2 OZ
SMALL $90

152-3263 PAUL BUNYAN BAIT CO.
LADYBUG, TOPWATER, WEEDLESS
MN   1939   3 1/4 IN   3/4 OZ
LARGE $90

152-3264 PAUL BUNYAN BAIT CO.
LADYBUG, TOPWATER, WEEDLESS
MN   1939   2 3/4 IN   1/2 OZ
SMALL $90

152-3235 PAUL BUNYAN BAIT CO.
MINNIE
MN   1939   2 1/4 IN   1/8 OZ
  $100

152-3243 PAUL BUNYAN BAIT CO.
MOBY DICK
MN   1949   3 IN
SMALL $20

152-3250 PAUL BUNYAN BAIT CO.
MOBY DICK
MN   1949   3 3/4 IN
LARGE $20

152-3251 PAUL BUNYAN BAIT CO.
MOBY DICK
MN   1949
MEDIUM $20

152-3233 PAUL BUNYAN BAIT CO.
PAUL BUNYAN MINNOW
MN   1939   3 5/8 IN
LARGE $100

152-3234 PAUL BUNYAN BAIT CO.
PAUL BUNYAN MINNOW
MN   1940   2 IN
SMALL $100

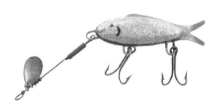

153-3232 PAUL BUNYAN BAIT CO.
SILVER SHINER
MN   1939   3 5/8 IN   9/16 OZ
   $100

153-3245 PAUL BUNYAN BAIT CO.
TWIRL BUG WIGGLER
MN   1940   2 1/2 IN
   $150

153-3236 PAUL BUNYAN BAIT CO.
WEAVER
MN   1946
   $60

153-3313 PAULSON, FRED
PAULSON WOBBLER
IL   1922   3 1/2 IN
   $400

153-3034 PAW PAW BAIT CO.
ARISTOCRAT MINNOW
MI   1946   3 1/2 IN
   $30

153-2997 PAW PAW BAIT CO.
PAW PAW, UNKNOWN
MI   1951   3 IN
   $90

153-2891 PAW PAW BAIT CO.
BASS SEEKER
MI
OLD STYLE $200

153-3074 PAW PAW BAIT CO.
BASS SEEKER
MI
OLD STYLE $90

153-3078 PAW PAW BAIT CO.
BASS SEEKER
MI   1955   3 IN   1/2 OZ
LATEST $30

153-3075 PAW PAW BAIT CO.
BASS SEEKER, BRILLIANT
MI   1940   4 IN
OLD STYLE $90

153-3079 PAW PAW BAIT CO.
BASS SEEKER, FIREFINISH
MI
LATEST $30

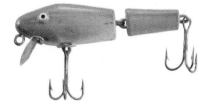

153-3081 PAW PAW BAIT CO.
BASS SEEKER, JOINTED
MI   1955   3 1/4 IN
LATEST $30

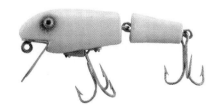

153-3080 PAW PAW BAIT CO.
BASS SEEKER, JOINTED, FIREFINISH
MI
LATEST $30

153-3003 PAW PAW BAIT CO.
BONEHEAD BRIGHT-EYED POPPER
MI   1958   2 IN
   $60

153-3004 PAW PAW BAIT CO.
BONEHEAD JTD SWAMP MINNOW
MI   1958   2 1/4 IN
   $60

FISHING PLUGS

154-3000 PAW PAW BAIT CO.
BONEHEAD MISS FLATSIDES
MI   1958   2 IN
  $60

154-2998 PAW PAW BAIT CO.
BONEHEAD SOUTHERN TORPEDO
MI   1958   4 IN
  $60

154-3001 PAW PAW BAIT CO.
BONEHEAD SPLASHER
MI   1958   1 7/8 IN
BABY $60

154-2999 PAW PAW BAIT CO.
BONEHEAD STRUTTIN' SAM
MI   1958   3 5/8 IN
  $60

154-3005 PAW PAW BAIT CO.
BONEHEAD SWAMP MINNOW
MI   1958   2 1/4 IN
  $60

154-3002 PAW PAW BAIT CO.
BONEHEAD WIGGLER
MI   1958   2 1/8 IN
  $60

154-3015 PAW PAW BAIT CO.
BUCKTAIL PAW PAW BAIT #9300
MI
  $100

154-3735 PAW PAW BAIT CO.
BULL FROG
MI
  $300

154-2962 PAW PAW BAIT CO.
CASTER
MI   1939   3 1/4 IN
NO EYES $300

154-2966 PAW PAW BAIT CO.
CASTER
MI   1941   2 1/2 IN
  $150

154-2968 PAW PAW BAIT CO.
CASTER
MI   1929
  $300

154-22745 PAW PAW BAIT CO.
CASTER
MI
  $15

154-2993 PAW PAW BAIT CO.
CASTER, BULLHEAD
MI   1928   4 1/2 IN
  $300

154-2961 PAW PAW BAIT CO.
CASTER, CHUB
MI   1936   4 IN
  $400

154-2957 PAW PAW BAIT CO.
CASTER, DACE NATURAL MINNOW
MI   1941   3 1/2 IN   1/2 OZ
  $200

FISHING PLUGS

155-2974 PAW PAW BAIT CO.
CASTER, GREAT INJURED MINNOW
MI   1926   4 IN
GLASS EYES $600

155-2985 PAW PAW BAIT CO.
CASTER, GREAT INJURED MINNOW
MI   1928   4 IN
TACK EYES $300

155-2959 PAW PAW BAIT CO.
CASTER, INJURED MINNOW
MI   1938
   $900

155-2954 PAW PAW BAIT CO.
CASTER, MUD MINNOW
MI   1936   3 1/2 IN
   $500

155-2956 PAW PAW BAIT CO.
CASTER, PERCH
MI   1941   2 1/2 IN
   $150

155-2969 PAW PAW BAIT CO.
CASTER, PERCH
MI   1936   5 IN
   $300

155-2963 PAW PAW BAIT CO.
CASTER, PIKE
MI   1939   5 1/2 IN
   $300

155-2986 PAW PAW BAIT CO.
CASTER, PIKE
MI   1939   3 1/2 IN
BABY $300

155-2965 PAW PAW BAIT CO.
CASTER, PIKE, BABY
MI   1941   2 3/4 IN
   $300

155-2964 PAW PAW BAIT CO.
CASTER, PIKE, JOINTED
MI   1941   5 1/2 IN
   $300

155-2958 PAW PAW BAIT CO.
CASTER, SPOON BELLY WOBBLER
MI   1940   5 1/2 IN
   $225

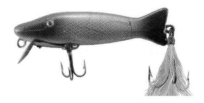

155-2955 PAW PAW BAIT CO.
CASTER, TROUT
MI   1941   3 3/4 IN   1/2 OZ
   $150

155-2960 PAW PAW BAIT CO.
CASTER, TROUT, JOINTED
MI   1941   4 1/2 IN
   $225

155-3084 PAW PAW BAIT CO.
CASTING MINNOW, PAW PAW
MI   1938   2 1/2 IN
   $150

155-3021 PAW PAW BAIT CO.
CHUB #900
MI   1940   2 5/8 IN   1/2 OZ
   $90

156-3076 PAW PAW BAIT CO.
CLOTHES PIN BAIT, PAW PAW
MI   1941   2 3/4 IN
  $60

156-3077 PAW PAW BAIT CO.
CLOTHES PIN BAIT, PAW PAW
MI   1941   2 1/2 IN
LATE $60

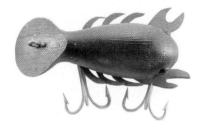

156-2971 PAW PAW BAIT CO.
CRAWDAD, PAW PAW
MI   1930
  $300

156-2994 PAW PAW BAIT CO.
CRAWDAD, PAW PAW
MI   1935   2 3/4 IN   3/4 OZ
  $100

156-2983 PAW PAW BAIT CO.
CRAYFISH
MI   1960   4 IN
RUBBER $70

156-2967 PAW PAW BAIT CO.
CROAKER, PAW PAW
MI   1935   3 IN
  $300

154-3068 PAW PAW BAIT CO.
DARTER, JOINTED, PAW PAW
MI   1941   3 3/4 IN
  $60

156-3069 PAW PAW BAIT CO.
DARTER, PAW PAW
MI   1940   3 3/4 IN   3/4 OZ
  $60

156-3009 PAW PAW BAIT CO.
DREADNOUGHT, JTD, PAW PAW
MI   1940   7 IN
  $200

156-3006 PAW PAW BAIT CO.
DREADNOUGHT, PAW PAW
MI   1940   6 1/2 IN
  $200

156-3102 PAW PAW BAIT CO.
FLAP JACK
MI   1946
MUSKY $100

156-3103 PAW PAW BAIT CO.
FLAP JACK
MI
2-HOOK $40

156-3107 PAW PAW BAIT CO.
FLAP JACK
MI
4-HOOK $40

156-3100 PAW PAW BAIT CO.
FLAP JACK JR
MI   1960   2 1/2 IN   1/4 OZ
  $40

156-3106 PAW PAW BAIT CO.
FLAP JACK PHANTOM
MI
  $60

FISHING PLUGS

157-3101 PAW PAW BAIT CO.
FLAP JACK, MUSKY
MI 1941 3 1/2 IN 3/4 OZ
$150

157-3052 PAW PAW BAIT CO.
INJURED MINNOW, FIRE FINISH
MI
$60

157-3039 PAW PAW BAIT CO.
LIPPY JOE
MI 1955 2 1/4 IN 3/8 OZ
$40

157-3038 PAW PAW BAIT CO.
LIPPY JOE DEEP DIVE
MI
$40

157-3035 PAW PAW BAIT CO.
LIPPY SUE
MI 1955 2 1/4 IN 3/8 OZ
$60

157-3085 PAW PAW BAIT CO.
LITTLE JIGGER
MI 1946 1 5/16 IN 5/8 OZ
$60

157-3047 PAW PAW BAIT CO.
LITTLE SHINER #8
MI 1940 4 IN 1/2 OZ
SMALL $60

157-3048 PAW PAW BAIT CO.
LITTLE SHINER #8
MI 1940 2 3/4 IN 3/8 OZ
SMALL $60

157-2991 PAW PAW BAIT CO.
MOUSE, FUZZY
MI 1958 2 1/4 IN 1/8 OZ
$60

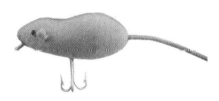

157-2992 PAW PAW BAIT CO.
MOUSE, FUZZY
MI 1958 2 IN
TOPWATER $60

157-2978 PAW PAW BAIT CO.
MOUSE, HAIR
MI 1930 2 1/2 IN 5/8 OZ
$150

157-2975 PAW PAW BAIT CO.
MOUSE, MINNIE
MI 1946 2 1/2 IN 5/8 OZ
OLD $200

157-2981 PAW PAW BAIT CO.
MOUSE, MINNIE
MI
NEW $100

157-2982 PAW PAW BAIT CO.
MOUSE, MINNIE
MI 1950 2 1/2 IN
NEW $100

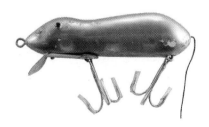

157-2980 PAW PAW BAIT CO.
MOUSE, MUSKY
MI 1956 1 IN
$1500

158-2976 PAW PAW BAIT CO.
MOUSE, MUSKY HAIR
MI   1930   4 1/2 IN
  $900

158-2977 PAW PAW BAIT CO.
MOUSE, SPINNERED HAIR
MI   1935   2 1/2 IN
  $150

158-2972 PAW PAW BAIT CO.
MOUSE, SWIMMING
MI   1946   2 IN   1/2 OZ
  $90

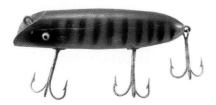

158-3022 PAW PAW BAIT CO.
OLD FAITHFUL
MI   1940   3 3/4 IN   5/8 OZ
  $60

158-3025 PAW PAW BAIT CO.
OLD FAITHFUL
MI   1941   3 IN   1/4 OZ
BABY $90

158-3040 PAW PAW BAIT CO.
PAW PAW BAIT #9100
MI
SMALL $40

158-3041 PAW PAW BAIT CO.
PAW PAW BAIT #9100
MI   1946   2 5/8 IN   3/8 OZ
  $60

158-3014 PAW PAW BAIT CO.
PAW PAW BAIT #9100, JOINTED
MI   1946   2 5/8 IN   3/8 OZ
  $40

158-3013 PAW PAW BAIT CO.
PAW PAW BAIT #9300
MI   1946   3 1/4 IN   1/2 OZ
  $40

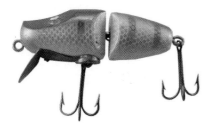

158-3011 PAW PAW BAIT CO.
PAW PAW BAIT #9300 , JOINTED
MI   1946   3 1/4 IN   1/2 OZ
  $40

158-3086 PAW PAW BAIT CO.
PAW PAW, UNKNOWN
MI   1946   3 IN
  $150

158-0614 PAW PAW BAIT CO.
PENCIL BAIT, PAW PAW
MI
SMALL $40

158-3010 PAW PAW BAIT CO.
PENCIL BAIT, PAW PAW
MI   1950   5 IN
  $90

158-3028 PAW PAW BAIT CO.
PENCIL BAIT, PAW PAW
MI   1950   4 IN
  $60

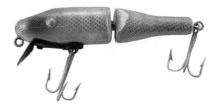

158-3043 PAW PAW BAIT CO.
PIKE, PAW PAW, JOINTED
MI
BABY $60

FISHING PLUGS

159-3024 PAW PAW BAIT CO.
PIKIE, FIRE FINISH
MI
BABY $60

159-3050 PAW PAW BAIT CO.
PIKIE, FIRE FINISH
MI
   $60

159-3049 PAW PAW BAIT CO.
PIKIE, FLUTED
MI   1935   4 1/2 IN
   $90

159-3020 PAW PAW BAIT CO.
PIKIE, MIDGET
MI
   $60

159-3018 PAW PAW BAIT CO.
PIKIE, MIDGET, JOINTED
MI   1946   3 1/4 IN
   $60

159-3019 PAW PAW BAIT CO.
PIKIE, MIDGET, JTD, FIREFINISH
MI
   $60

159-3007 PAW PAW BAIT CO.
PIKIE, MUSKY
MI   1946   6 1/2 IN
   $150

159-3008 PAW PAW BAIT CO.
PIKIE, MUSKY , JOINTED
MI   1946   7 IN
   $150

159-3023 PAW PAW BAIT CO.
PIKIE, PAW PAW
MI   1946   3 3/4 IN
BABY $60

159-3051 PAW PAW BAIT CO.
PIKIE, PAW PAW
MI   1940   4 1/2 IN   3/4 OZ
   $60

159-3045 PAW PAW BAIT CO.
PIKIE, JOINTED
MI   1940   4 1/2 IN
   $90

159-3027 PAW PAW BAIT CO.
PLATYPUS
MI   1946   4 IN
   $90

159-3031 PAW PAW BAIT CO.
PLENTY SPARKLE
MI   1958   4 IN
   $90

159-3032 PAW PAW BAIT CO.
PLENTY SPARKLE JR.
MI   1958   3 1/4 IN
   $90

159-2953 PAW PAW BAIT CO.
PLUNKER, PAW PAW
MI   1930
   $100

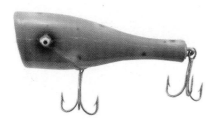

160-3088 PAW PAW BAIT CO.
PLUNKER, PAW PAW
MI   1940   2 3/4 IN
  $40

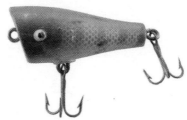

160-3089 PAW PAW BAIT CO.
PLUNKER, PAW PAW
MI
BABY, EARLY $60

160-3090 PAW PAW BAIT CO.
PLUNKER, PAW PAW
MI   1941   2 1/2 IN
  $150

160-3092 PAW PAW BAIT CO.
PLUNKER, PAW PAW
MI   1935   2 3/4 IN   3/4 OZ
EARLY $60

160-3087 PAW PAW BAIT CO.
PLUNKER, SPINNING, PAW PAW
MI   1941   2 IN
  $40

160-3063 PAW PAW BAIT CO.
POGO STICK, PAW PAW
MI   1950   3 3/4 IN
ALTERED SLIM LINDY $40

160-3042 PAW PAW BAIT CO.
RIVER GO GETTER
MI   1941   2 1/2 IN   1/2 OZ
EARLY $90

160-3044 PAW PAW BAIT CO.
RIVER GO GETTER
MI
LATER $60

160-3062 PAW PAW BAIT CO.
SHORE MINNOW
MI   1941   3 3/4 IN
  $40

160-3053 PAW PAW BAIT CO.
SLIM LINDY
MI   1955   4 IN   5/8 OZ
OLD $60

160-3054 PAW PAW BAIT CO.
SLIM LINDY
MI   4 IN   5/8 OZ
NEW, TACK EYES $60

160-3055 PAW PAW BAIT CO.
SLIM LINDY
MI   4 IN   5/8 OZ
OLD, PAINTED EYES $40

160-3056 PAW PAW BAIT CO.
SLIM LINDY
MI   4 IN   5/8 OZ
EMBOSSED EYES $40

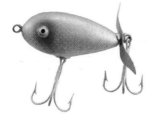

160-3033 PAW PAW BAIT CO.
SPINNING TOPPER
MI   1946   2 IN   1/4 OZ
  $60

160-3105 PAW PAW BAIT CO.
SPLIT-TAIL FLAP JACK
MI   1958
  $60

FISHING PLUGS

161-3036 PAW PAW BAIT CO.
STICK BAIT
MI   1941
NO EYES $300

161-3037 PAW PAW BAIT CO.
STICK BAIT
MI   1938
GLASS EYES $300

161-3083 PAW PAW BAIT CO.
SUCKER MINNOW, PAW PAW
MI
   $300

161-3082 PAW PAW BAIT CO.
SUCKER MINNOW, JOINTED
MI   1938   4 1/2 IN
   $300

161-3061 PAW PAW BAIT CO.
SURFACE MINNOW
MI
NO EYES $60

161-3057 PAW PAW BAIT CO.
SURFACE MINNOW PAW PAW
MI   1941   3 IN
   $60

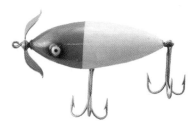

161-3058 PAW PAW BAIT CO.
SURFACE MINNOW, PAW PAW
MI   1941   3 IN
   $40

161-3070 PAW PAW BAIT CO.
TORPEDO, PAW PAW
MI   1946   4 IN   5/8 OZ
   $90

161-2866 PAW PAW BAIT CO.
UNDERWATER BAIT
MI   1912   2 IN
   $2000

161-3046 PAW PAW BAIT CO.
UNDERWATER MINNOW, PAW PAW
MI   1935   2 3/8 IN   1/2 OZ
   $150

161-2987 PAW PAW BAIT CO.
WEEDLESS WOW
MI   1940   2 1/12 IN
LARGE $120

161-2988 PAW PAW BAIT CO.
WEEDLESS WOW
MI   1941   2 IN
SMALL $120

161-3067 PAW PAW BAIT CO.
WIGGLER, PAW PAW
MI
   $60

161-3026 PAW PAW BAIT CO.
WOBBLE BUG
MI   1950   2 IN
   $90

161-3029 PAW PAW BAIT CO.
WOBBLER, PAW PAW
MI   1946   2 1/2 IN
   $90

162-3104 PAW PAW BAIT CO.
WOBBLER, PAW PAW
MI   1946   3 3/4 IN   3/8 OZ
#9101 $100

162-2970 PAW PAW BAIT CO.
WOOD CRAB
MI   1934   2 1/2 IN
BABY $300

162-2973 PAW PAW BAIT CO.
WOOD CRAB
MI   1934   3 IN
LARGE $300

162-2984 PAW PAW BAIT CO.
WOTTAFROG
MI   1940   2 1/4 IN   1/2 OZ
SMALL $150

162-2989 PAW PAW BAIT CO.
WOTTAFROG
MI   1950   2 IN   3/8 OZ
NEW $90

162-2995 PAW PAW BAIT CO.
WOTTAFROG
MI   1948   2 1/4 IN
LARGE $150

162-2996 PAW PAW BAIT CO.
WOTTAFROG, DELUXE
MI   1940   3 1/4 IN   5/8 OZ
LARGE $150

162-3059 PAW PAW BAIT CO.
WOUNDED MINNOW, PAW PAW
MI   1941   3 1/2 IN   3/4 OZ
FLATSIDE, OLD $60

162-3064 PAW PAW BAIT CO.
WOUNDED MINNOW, PAW PAW
MI   1941   3 1/4 IN
FLATSIDE, SMALL $60

162-3065 PAW PAW BAIT CO.
WOUNDED MINNOW, PAW PAW
MI   1941   3 3/4 IN
FLATSIDE 3 HOOK $60

162-2950 PAW PAW BAITS
DECOY, PAW PAW
MI   1929   5 1/4 IN
$600

162-2951 PAW PAW BAITS
DECOY, PAW PAW
MI   1930   6 IN
$600

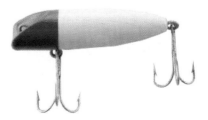

162-2941 PAW PAW BIT BAITS CO.
ZIPPER SERIES
MI   1930   3 IN
$60

162-2942 PAW PAW BIT BAITS CO.
ZIPPER SERIES
MI   1930   3 IN
$60

162-2943 PAW PAW BIT BAITS CO.
ZIPPER SERIES
MI   1930   3 IN
$60

FISHING PLUGS

163-2944 PAW PAW BIT BAITS CO.
ZIPPER SERIES
MI   1930   3 IN
  $60

163-3335 PAYNE BAIT CO.
PAYNE'S WOGGLE-BUG
IL   1915   3 1/2 IN
  $1500

163-3361 PEARL BAIT CO.
PEARL PLUG
    1922
  $800

163-3337 PEARL ROCKET BAIT CO.
PEARL ROCKET

  $30

163-3338 PELICAN BAIT CO.
PELICAN BAIT
FL   1941
  $60

163-3281 PEPPER, JOE E.
DELTA BUG SPINNER
NY
  $1000

163-3284 PEPPER, JOE E.
MANHATTAN MINNOW
NY   1900   3 1/2 IN
  $1500

163-3285 PEPPER, JOE E.
MANHATTAN MINNOW
NY
SMALL $1500

163-3286 PEPPER, JOE E.
NATIONAL MINNOW
NY   1905
  $1500

163-3287 PEPPER, JOE E.
NATIONAL MINNOW
NY   1905   3 1/4 IN
  $1200

163-3282 PEPPER, JOE E.
NEW CENTURY MINNOW
NY   1900   2 1/2 IN
1 HOOK $1500

163-3268 PEPPER, JOE E.
PEPPER, UNKNOWN
NY   1907
  $600

163-3291 PEPPER, JOE E.
PEPPER, UNKNOWN
NY
  $1500

163-4701 PEPPER, JOE E.
PEPPER, UNKNOWN
NY
  $500

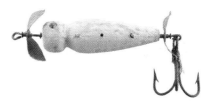

163-3272 PEPPER, JOE E.
ROAMER BAIT
NY   1908   3 IN
LARGE $1200

164-3273 PEPPER, JOE E.
ROAMER BAIT
NY   1908   1 3/4 IN
BABY, SMALL $1200

164-3277 PEPPER, JOE E.
ROAMER BAIT
NY   1912
HAND PAINTED, MUSKY $2100

164-3275 PEPPER, JOE E.
ROMAN DIVER
NY   1920
   $2000

164-3278 PEPPER, JOE E.
ROMAN DIVER
NY
   $1500

164-3271 PEPPER, JOE E.
ROMAN REDTAIL MINNOW
NY   1910   1 3/4 IN
BABY $1500

164-3283 PEPPER, JOE E.
ROMAN REDTAIL MINNOW
NY
SMALL $1500

164-3289 PEPPER, JOE E.
ROMAN REDTAIL MINNOW
NY   1912   3 1/4 IN
LARGE $1500

164-3290 PEPPER, JOE E.
ROMAN REDTAIL MINNOW
NY
MEDIUM $500

164-3292 PEPPER, JOE E.
ROMAN REDTAIL MINNOW
NY
SMALL $300

164-3276 PEPPER, JOE E.
ROMAN SPIDER
NY   1919   3 1/4 IN
NOTCHED HEAD $1500

164-3280 PEPPER, JOE E.
TOPWATER MINNOW, MUSKY
NY   1911
HAND PAINTED $2000

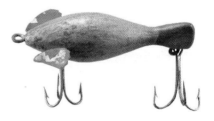

164-3279 PEPPER, JOE E.
YANKEE AERO BAIT
NY   1918   3 1/2 IN
   $1500

164-3274 PEPPER, JOE E.
YANKEE AERO BAIT, JOINTED
NY   1916   3 IN
   $1500

164-4866 PERMA BAIT CO.
PERMA BAIT
   1949
   $40

164-6986 PERRY'S FISH LURE CO.
ARKANSAS TRENCH-BACK POPPER
AR   1959
   $40

FISHING PLUGS

165-3739 PESCIA TACKLE
PESCIA MUSKY FISH LURE
  1956
  $100

165-3344 PETERS BAIT CO.
MINNOW, PETERS
IN   1919   4 1/4 IN
  $150

165-3343 PETERS BAIT CO.
WOBBLER, PETERS
IN
  $150

165-5353 PETERSON, OSCAR
FISH DECOY, PETERSON

  $1500

165-5433 PETERSON, OSCAR
FISH DECOY, PETERSON

  $1200

165-3314 PFEFFER, JIM
BANANA LURE
FL   1952   3 3/4 IN
  $120

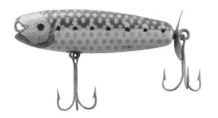

165-3319 PFEFFER, JIM
DARTER, PFEFFER
FL   1952   3 IN
SMALL $120

165-3320 PFEFFER, JIM
DARTER, PFEFFER
FL   1952   3 3/4 IN
LARGE $120

165-3317 PFEFFER, JIM
SHINER
FL   1952   3 1/2 IN
SMALL $120

165-3318 PFEFFER, JIM
SHINER
FL   1952   4 IN
LARGE $120

165-3321 PFEFFER, JIM
TOP SHINER
FL   1952   3 3/4 IN
SMALL $60

165-3322 PFEFFER, JIM
TOP SHINER
FL   1952   4 1/4 IN
LARGE $60

165-3323 PFEFFER, JIM
TOPPER, PFEFFER
FL   1952   4 IN
LARGE $60

165-3324 PFEFFER, JIM
TOPPER, PFEFFER
FL
SMALL $60

165-3315 PFEFFER, JIM
WOBBLER, JOINTED, PFEFFER
FL   1952   4 1/4 IN
  $120

166-3316 PFEFFER, JIM
WOBBLER, JOINTED, PFEFFER
FL   1952
  $120

166-3333 PFEIFFER LIVE BAIT HOLD CO.
PFEIFFER'S LIVE BAIT HOLDER
MI   1914   4 1/4 IN
ORIGINAL LIVE BAIT HOLDER $1500

166-3516 PFLUEGER
ADMIRAL BAIT
OH   1892   2 IN
  $400

166-3527 PFLUEGER
ADMIRAL BAIT
OH   1892
  $400

166-3528 PFLUEGER
ADMIRAL BAIT
OH   1892
  $400

166-3495 PFLUEGER
ALL-IN-ONE MINNOW
OH   1911
  $2000

166-3491 PFLUEGER
BALLERINA MINNOW
OH   1950   2 1/2 IN
JR SIZE $60

166-3488 PFLUEGER
BALLERINA MINNOW
OH   1950   4 1/4 IN
  $60

166-3450 PFLUEGER
BENDER
OH   1930   4 IN
  $1500

166-3426 PFLUEGER
CATALINA MINNOW
OH   1916   4 1/2 IN
  $1500

166-3431 PFLUEGER
CATALINA MINNOW
OH   1932   4 1/4 IN
LATEST $450

166-3521 PFLUEGER
COAST MINNOW, METALIZED
OH
  $3000

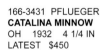

166-3505 PFLUEGER
CRAWDAD, PFLUEGER
OH   1900   3 IN
  $90

166-3507 PFLUEGER
CRAWFISH, PFLUEGER
OH   1900   3 IN
  $300

166-3500 PFLUEGER
DECOY, PFLUEGER
OH   1908   5 IN
  $10000

FISHING PLUGS

167-3509 PFLUEGER
DECOY, RUBBER, PFLUEGER
OH   1892   7 IN
 $4000

167-3506 PFLUEGER
EDGREN LUMINOUS GLASS MINNOW
OH
 $5000

167-3453 PFLUEGER
FAN-TAIL SQUID
OH   1941
CELLULOID CONE $75

167-3454 PFLUEGER
FAN-TAIL SQUID
OH   1928   3 1/2 IN
CELLULOID CONE $50

167-3389 PFLUEGER
FLYING HELGRAMITE
OH   1885   3 IN
 $12000

167-3451 PFLUEGER
FRISKY MINNOW
OH   1941   2 1/2 IN
JR SIZE $90

167-3452 PFLUEGER
FRISKY MINNOW
OH   1941   4 IN
 $90

167-3474 PFLUEGER
FRISKY
OH   1938   3 IN
 $150

167-3522 PFLUEGER
FROG, CONRAD
OH   1905   3 IN
FLOATING, RUBBER $400

167-3523 PFLUEGER
FROG, CONRAD
OH   1897   3 IN
RUBBER $500

167-3548 PFLUEGER
FROG, CONRAD
OH
LATE, RUBBER $200

167-3549 PFLUEGER
FROG, CONRAD
OH
LATE, RUBBER SINGLE HOOK $200

167-3554 PFLUEGER
FROG, CONRAD
OH   1900   3 IN
SINGLE HOOK, RUBBER $200

167-3532 PFLUEGER
FROG, FLOATING
OH   1885   2 3/4 IN
FLOATING $90

167-3553 PFLUEGER
FROG, FLOATING W/METAL LEGS
OH   1900   3 IN
 $1500

168-3496 PFLUEGER
FROG, KENT
OH   1920   2 IN   3/4 OZ
NEVERFAIL HARDWARE $1500

168-3497 PFLUEGER
FROG, KENT
OH   1931   2 IN   3/4 OZ
SURFACE HARDWARE $900

168-3498 PFLUEGER
FROG, KENT
OH   1912   2 IN   3/4 OZ
   $2000

168-3499 PFLUEGER
FROG, KENT, RESEARCH
OH
   $600

168-3543 PFLUEGER
FROG, KORMISH
OH
RUBBER $150

168-3546 PFLUEGER
FROG, KORMISH
OH   1900   1 IN
OLD, LARGE, RUBBER $150

168-3551 PFLUEGER
FROG, KORMISH
OH   1900   2 IN
OLD, SMALL $150

168-3552 PFLUEGER
FROG, LUMINOUS
OH   1900   3 IN
   $1500

168-3550 PFLUEGER
FROG, MEADOW
OH
(WESTWOOD) $500

168-3530 PFLUEGER
FROG, MEADOW, SURFACE
OH   1899   3 IN
   $300

168-3531 PFLUEGER
FROG, MEADOW, UNDERWATER
OH   1899   3 IN
   $400

168-3533 PFLUEGER
FROG, PFLUEGER
OH
   $30

168-3535 PFLUEGER
FROG, PFLUEGER
OH
   $30

168-3536 PFLUEGER
FROG, PFLUEGER
OH
   $30

168-3537 PFLUEGER
FROG, PFLUEGER
OH
OLD $150

FISHING PLUGS

169-3538 PFLUEGER
FROG, PFLUEGER
OH
 $60

169-3539 PFLUEGER
FROG, PFLUEGER
OH
 $30

169-3519 PFLUEGER
GAY BLADE
OH   1960   1 3/4 IN
 $30

169-3520 PFLUEGER
GAY BLADE
OH   1960   4 IN
MUSKY $40

169-3391 PFLUEGER
GLOBE BAIT
OH   1910   2 1/2 IN
SURFACE HARDWARE $50

169-3392 PFLUEGER
GLOBE BAIT
OH   1950   3 IN
2-PIECE HARDWARE,   SMALL $100

169-3393 PFLUEGER
GLOBE BAIT
OH   1912
NEVERFAIL HARDWARE, SMALL $150

169-3395 PFLUEGER
GLOBE BAIT
OH   1912   3 3/4 IN
WIRE-THROUGH $300

169-3396 PFLUEGER
GLOBE BAIT
OH   1912
WIRE-THROUGH, SMALL $300

169-3390 PFLUEGER
GLOBE BAIT, MUSKY
OH   1938   5 1/2 IN
 $100

169-3394 PFLUEGER
GLOBE NEVERFAIL MINNOW
OH   1912
 $150

169-5305 PFLUEGER
GLOBE, BABY
OH   1912
PAPERCLIP HARDWARE $200

169-3508 PFLUEGER
HOPTOIT BAIT
OH   1938   3 IN
 $400

169-3529 PFLUEGER
INVINCIBLE MINNOW
OH   1892
RUBBER $400

169-3489 PFLUEGER
JERK, PFLUEGER
OH
JR SIZE $60

Page 169

170-3490 PFLUEGER
JERK, PFLUEGER
OH   1955   5 IN
  $60

170-3417 PFLUEGER
LIVE-WIRE MINNOW
OH   1945   5 IN
PAINTED EYES, LARGE $300

170-3418 PFLUEGER
LIVE-WIRE MINNOW
OH   1932   3 1/2 IN   2/3 OZ
SMALL, OLD $400

170-3419 PFLUEGER
LIVE-WIRE MINNOW
OH   1932
LARGE, OLD, GLASS EYES $400

170-3424 PFLUEGER
LIVE-WIRE MINNOW
OH   1950   3 3/4 IN
LATEST $120

170-3440 PFLUEGER
MAGNET WOODEN BAIT
OH   1910   4 IN
WIRE-THROUGH $300

170-3441 PFLUEGER
MAGNET WOODEN BAIT
OH   1912   4 IN
NEVERFAIL $200

170-3442 PFLUEGER
MAGNET WOODEN BAIT
OH   1929   4 IN
SURFACE HARDWARE $150

170-3421 PFLUEGER
MIDGET SCOOP
OH   1946   2 1/4 IN
  $60

170-3405 PFLUEGER
MINNOW, CHROMED
OH   1927   3 3/4 IN
SURFACE $300

170-3384 PFLUEGER
MINNOW, COMPETITOR
OH   1908   2 1/2 IN
WOODEN, SMALL $300

170-3404 PFLUEGER
MINNOW, COMPETITOR
OH   1908   3 3/4 IN
SMALL $300

170-3380 PFLUEGER
MINNOW, COMPETITOR
OH   1908
WOODEN, 3-HOOK, TACK EYES $300

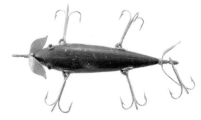

170-3406 PFLUEGER
MINNOW, COMPETITOR
OH   1908
TACK EYES, LARGE $400

170-3502 PFLUEGER
MINNOW, CUPPED PFLUEGER
OH
  $300

FISHING PLUGS

171-3414 PFLUEGER
MINNOW, ELECTRIC
OH   1912   2 3/4 IN
WOOD, NEVERFAIL $300

171-3415 PFLUEGER
MINNOW, ELECTRIC
OH   1910   2 3/4 IN
WIRE-THROUGH, WOOD $400

171-3427 PFLUEGER
MINNOW, FLOATING
OH
OLD $500

171-3428 PFLUEGER
MINNOW, FLOATING
OH
  $400

171-3382 PFLUEGER
MINNOW, GEM
OH   1908   2 1/2 IN
WOODEN $200

171-3383 PFLUEGER
MINNOW, GEM
OH   1908   2 1/2 IN
WOODEN $200

171-3402 PFLUEGER
MINNOW, METALIZED
OH   1912   3 IN
3-HOOK, SMALL $500

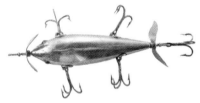

171-3403 PFLUEGER
MINNOW, METALIZED
OH   1912   3 5/8 IN
5-HOOK, LARGE $600

171-3398 PFLUEGER
MINNOW, MONARCH
OH   1912   3 IN
WOOD, NEVERFAIL HARDWARE $300

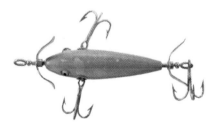

171-3399 PFLUEGER
MINNOW, MONARCH
OH   1908   2 3/4 IN
WOOD, WIRE-THROUGH $400

171-3400 PFLUEGER
MINNOW, MONARCH
OH   1908   3 3/4 IN
WOOD, WIRE-THROUGH $400

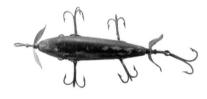

171-3401 PFLUEGER
MINNOW, MONARCH
OH   1908
WOOD, SCREW-THROUGH $600

171-3397 PFLUEGER
MINNOW, MONARCH, FANCY BACK
OH   1912   3 3/4 IN
WOOD, NEVERFAIL HARDWARE $400

171-3407 PFLUEGER
MINNOW, NEVERFAIL
OH   1927   3 3/4 IN
EMBOSSED EYES $100

171-3409 PFLUEGER
MINNOW, NEVERFAIL
OH   1927   3 IN
EMBOSSED EYES $100

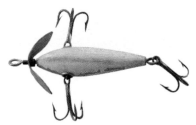

172-3434 PFLUEGER
MINNOW, NEVERFAIL TOPWATER
OH
  $100

172-2634 PFLUEGER
MINNOW, OLD PFLUEGER
MI   1900
  $1500

172-3381 PFLUEGER
MINNOW, PEERLESS
OH   1910   2 1/2 IN
  $150

172-3408 PFLUEGER
MINNOW, PEERLESS
OH   1928
  $100

172-3412 PFLUEGER
MINNOW, PEERLESS
OH
EYE-SCREW $90

172-3413 PFLUEGER
MINNOW, PEERLESS
OH   1910   2 1/2 IN
WIRE-THROUGH $200

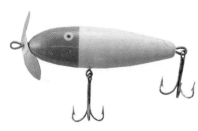

172-3410 PFLUEGER
MINNOW, PEERLESS, FLOATING
OH   1938   3 1/2 IN
LARGE $100

172-3411 PFLUEGER
MINNOW, PEERLESS, FLOATING
OH   1938   2 3/4 IN
SMALL $100

172-3433 PFLUEGER
MINNOW, SIMPLEX
OH   1905   1 3/4 IN
  $700

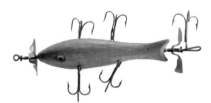

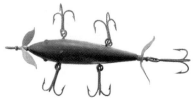

172-3501 PFLUEGER
MINNOW, TRORY
OH   1900
  $10000

172-3385 PFLUEGER
MINNOW, WIZARD
OH   1902   5 IN
WOOD, 5-HK, LG, GLASS EYES $900

172-3386 PFLUEGER
MINNOW, WIZARD
OH   1902   5 IN   OLD
WOOD, 5-HK, LG, GLASS EYES $900

172-3387 PFLUEGER
MINNOW, WIZARD
OH   1902   3 IN
WOOD, 3-HK, SM, GLASS EYES $900

172-3388 PFLUEGER
MINNOW, WIZARD, BABY
OH   1903   2 3/4 IN
WOOD, 3HK, GLASS EYES $900

172-3510 PFLUEGER
MUSKALLONGE MINNOW
OH   1892   7 IN
  $4500

FISHING PLUGS

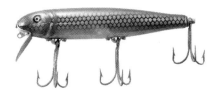

173-3468 PFLUEGER
MUSTANG MINNOW
OH   1938   4 IN
  $75

173-3470 PFLUEGER
MUSTANG MINNOW
OH   1927   4 IN
PYRALIN $1200

173-3471 PFLUEGER
MUSTANG MINNOW
OH   1938   5 IN   1 1/2 OZ
  $75

173-3469 PFLUEGER
MUSTANG MINNOW, FLOATING
OH   1940   2 1/2 IN
BABY $75

173-3472 PFLUEGER
MUSTANG MINNOW, JOINTED
OH   1940   2 1/2 IN
BABY SIZE $75

173-3473 PFLUEGER
MUSTANG MINNOW, JOINTED
OH   1929   6 1/2 IN
HUSKY SIZE $1200

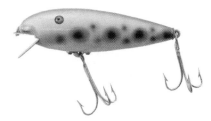

173-3492 PFLUEGER
O'BOY MINNOW
OH   1921   3 1/2 IN   3/4 OZ
  $600

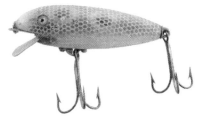

173-3493 PFLUEGER
O'BOY MINNOW
OH   1921   2 3/4 IN   1/2 OZ
  $450

173-3524 PFLUEGER
OLD RUBBER MINNOW
OH
LARGE $200

173-3525 PFLUEGER
OLD RUBBER MINNOW
OH   1892   2 IN
SMALL $200

173-3449 PFLUEGER
PAKRON MINNOW
OH   1930   2 3/4 IN   1 OZ
  $1200

173-3459 PFLUEGER
PAL-O-MINE MINNOW
OH   1928   4 1/4 IN   3/4 OZ
GLASS EYES $75

173-3462 PFLUEGER
PAL-O-MINE MINNOW
OH   1928   4 1/4 IN   3/4 OZ
  $60

173-3460 PFLUEGER
PAL-O-MINE MINNOW JR.
OH   1928   3 1/4 IN   1/2 OZ
  $75

173-3461 PFLUEGER
PAL-O-MINE MINNOW MIDGET
OH   1928   2 3/4 IN   1/3 OZ
  $80

FISHING PLUGS

174-3464 PFLUEGER
PAL-O-MINE MINNOW JR, JOINTED
OH   1932   3 1/4 IN   1/2 OZ
  $75

174-3467 PFLUEGER
PAL-O-MINE MINNOW, JOINTED
OH   1932   4 1/4 IN   3/4 OZ
GLASS EYES $100

174-3465 PFLUEGER
PAL-O-MINE MINNOW, JOINTED
OH   1932   4 1/4 IN   3/4 OZ
  $60

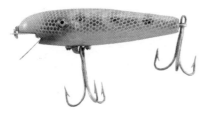

174-3463 PFLUEGER
PAL-O-MINE MINNOW, JR.
OH   1928   3 1/4 IN   1/2 OZ
GLASS EYES $100

174-3466 PFLUEGER
PAL-O-MINE MINNOW, MIDGET, JTD
OH   1932   3 1/4 IN   5/8 OZ
  $80

174-3416 PFLUEGER
PEERLESS MINNOW
OH   1912   2 1/2 IN
NEVERFAIL $150

174-22744 PFLUEGER
PFLUEGER BAIT
OH
  $100

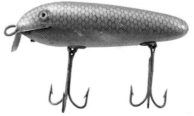

174-3457 PFLUEGER
PFLUEGER RESEARCH BAIT
OH   1926   3 1/2 IN
LARGE $300

174-3458 PFLUEGER
PFLUEGER RESEARCH BAIT
OH   1926   2 1/2 IN
SMALL $300

174-3494 PFLUEGER
PFLUEGER RESEARCH BAIT
OH
  $200

174-3477 PFLUEGER
PFLUEGER, UNKNOWN
OH   1948
  $100

174-3486 PFLUEGER
POPRITE MINNOW
OH   1953   4 IN   5/8 OZ
  $60

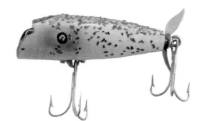

174-3485 PFLUEGER
POPRITE MINNOW JR.
OH   1953   3 IN   1/2 OZ
  $60

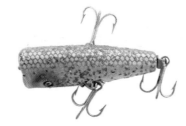

174-3484 PFLUEGER
POPRITE MINNOW, SIDE-HOOK
OH   1948   3 IN
FIRST STYLE $100

174-3547 PFLUEGER
PRACTICE CASTING FROG
OH   1905   3 IN
  $3000

FISHING PLUGS

175-3526 PFLUEGER
RAZEM MINNOW
OH   1938   2 1/2 IN
  $150

175-3476 PFLUEGER
RED DEVIL SPINNER
OH
  $75

175-3420 PFLUEGER
SCOOP JR.
OH   1937   3 IN
  $100

175-3423 PFLUEGER
SCOOP MINNOW
OH
  $70

175-3425 PFLUEGER
SCOOP MINNOW
OH
GLASS EYES $150

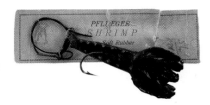

175-3511 PFLUEGER
SHRIMP, PFLUEGER
OH   1923
  $120

175-3435 PFLUEGER
SURPRISE MINNOW
OH   1929   3 IN
  $400

175-3437 PFLUEGER
SURPRISE MINNOW
OH   1916   3 3/4 IN
GLASS EYES $500

175-3438 PFLUEGER
SURPRISE MINNOW
OH   1914   3 3/4 IN
HOLE EYES $750

175-3439 PFLUEGER
SURPRISE MINNOW
OH   1938   4 IN
NO EYES $1000
BABY SIZE $400

175-3436 PFLUEGER
SURPRISE MINNOW, SPINNERED
OH   1917   3 3/4 IN
GLASS EYES,   BABY SIZE $600

175-3482 PFLUEGER
T. N. T. MINNOW
OH   1930   3 1/2 IN
METAL $200

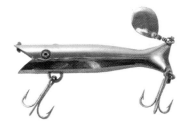

175-3483 PFLUEGER
T. N. T. MINNOW
OH   1930   4 1/4 IN
METALIZED,   GLASS EYES $400

175-3487 PFLUEGER
TANTRUM MNNOW
OH   1953   4 IN
  $90

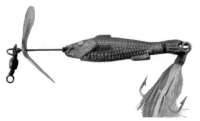

175-3512 PFLUEGER
TEELAN MINNOW
OH   1914   2 1/2 IN
RUBBER, SMALL $200

FISHING PLUGS

176-3513 PFLUEGER
TEELAN MINNOW
OH
RUBBER, LARGE $200

176-3455 PFLUEGER
UNKNOWN NAME
OH   1915   2 3/4 IN
  $200

176-3456 PFLUEGER
UNKNOWN NAME
OH   1915   3 3/4 IN
  $400

176-3518 PFLUEGER
VANITIE MINNOW
OH   1914   3 IN
RUBBER $250

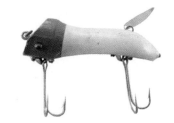

176-3443 PFLUEGER
WIZARD WIGGLER
OH
MEDIUM $150

176-3444 PFLUEGER
WIZARD WIGGLER
OH   1925   3 1/2 IN
LARGE $150

176-3446 PFLUEGER
WIZARD WIGGLER
OH   1925   2 1/4 IN
SMALL $150

176-3448 PFLUEGER
WIZARD WIGGLER
OH   1922   4 1/2 IN
MUSKY SIZE $1200

176-3326 PHILIP BAIT CO.
CRAB, PHILIP
WI   1934   2 1/4 IN
  $1200

176-3350 PHILLIPS FLY & TACKLE
CRIPPLED KILLER
PA
SMALL $20

176-3351 PHILLIPS FLY & TACKLE
CRIPPLED KILLER
PA   1948   2 IN
LARGE $20

176-3346 PHILLIPS FLY & TACKLE
CRIPPLED MINNOW
PA   1948   3 IN
  $20

176-3347 PHILLIPS FLY & TACKLE
CRIPPLED MINNOW
PA   1948   2 3/4 IN
LARGE $20

176-5479 PHILLIPS, FRED
PHILLIP'S PIKIE
MI   1940's
  $100

176-5156 PIRO REALISTIC BAIT CO.
WATER WACKER
LA   1942
  $50

FISHING PLUGS

177-3354 PITT-KAN BAIT CO
PITT-KAN LIVE ACTION MIINNOW
  1949
  $50

177-5108 PLANTICO & SON
YELLOW DUCKLING
WI   1940
  $60

177-5109 PLANTICO & SON
YELLOW DUCKLING
WI   1940
SMALL $60

177-7016 PLUMBER, BILL
FROG, PLUMBER
  1968
  $10

177-3362 POE
LOCO-MOTION
CA   1960
  $20

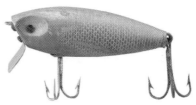

177-3364 POE
NERVOUS MINNIE
CA   1955   2 3/4 IN
  $20

177-3230 POE
NERVOUS MINNOW
CA   1955   2 3/4 IN
DEEP DIVE $15

177-5185 POINT JUDE
PUG NOSE
RI   1949
  $50

177-5189 POINT JUDE
SURF POPPER
RI   1949
  $50

177-3358 POLK MFG. CO.
MINNOW, POLK
MS   1952   4 IN
  $75

177-3359 POLK MFG. CO.
POPPER, POLK
MS
  $50

177-3360 PONTIAC MFG. CO.
PONTIAC MINNOW
MI   1908   2 7/8 IN
  $1500

177-4894 POPE, EDDIE & CO. INC.
FISHBACK
CA   1970's
  $15

177-3377 POPE, EDDIE & CO. INC.
HOT SHOT
CA   1954   3 3/4 IN
LARGE $15

177-3378 POPE, EDDIE & CO. INC.
HOT SHOT
CA   1954   2 3/4 IN
MED $15

178-3379 POPE, EDDIE & CO. INC.
HOT SHOT
CA   1954   1 3/4 IN
SMALL $15

178-5711 POPLIN, N.G.
POPLIN POPPER
OK   1946
    $30

178-3372 PORTER BAIT CO.
DARTER, PORTER
FL   1955   3 IN
    $60

178-3365 PORTER BAIT CO.
OL' CRIP
FL   1955
    $100

178-3375 PORTER BAIT CO.
PIRATE, PORTER
FL   1954   4 1/4 IN
    $90

178-3371 PORTER BAIT CO.
PLUNKER, PORTER
FL   1954   2 1/2 IN
BABY $60

178-3374 PORTER BAIT CO.
PLUNKER, PORTER
FL   1955   4 1/4 IN
    $90

178-3367 PORTER BAIT CO.
SCOOTER, PORTER
FL   1955   3 IN
    $60

178-3373 PORTER BAIT CO.
SPINDLE
FL   1954   4 3/4 IN
    $60

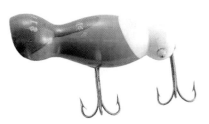

178-3366 PRESTO
MOTOR LURE
    1955   5 1/2 IN
    $120

178-3881 PROCTOR & GREY
PROCTOR'S DARTER
MI   1920   4 1/4 IN
    $600

178-3355 PROVEN BAIT CO.
WIGGLEFISH, SURFACE
OH   1946
    $120

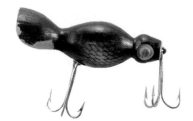

178-3357 PROVEN BAIT CO.
WIGGLEFISH, SURFACE
OH   1946
    $120

178-3356 PROVEN BAIT CO.
WIGGLEFISH, WOBBLER
OH   1946
    $120

178-3369 PULS & WENCKA
P & W LURE
WI   1953
    $300

FISHING PLUGS

179-3370 PULVER, LYNN E.
PUL-V-RISER
IA   1951
  $40

179-6097 RADFORD TACKLE
WOBBLER, RADFORD
MI   1947
  $20

179-3752 RAINEY BAIT CO.
RAINEY'S SECRET BAIT
1946   3 1/2 IN
$90

179-5429 RANDALL
DECOY, METAL, RANDALL
MN   1950
  $200

179-5373 RANDALL
FISH DECOY, RANDALL
MN
  $100

179-5426 RANDALL
FISH DECOY, RANDALL
MN
  $200

179-5410 RANDALL
PIKE DECOY
MN   1955
  $200

179-3754 RAPALA, LOURI
COUNT DOWN RAPALA
FIN
FINLAND $10

179-3753 RAPALA, LOURI
RAPALA BAIT
FIN
FINLAND, SMALL SIZE, ORIGINAL $30

179-3755 RAPALA, LOURI
RAPALA BAIT
FIN
FINLAND, SALTWATER SIZE $30

179-3756 RAPALA, LOURI
RAPALA BAIT
FIN   1960   4 1/4 IN
FINLAND, LARGE SIZE $30

179-3798 RAY-LURE TACKLE CO
RAY-LURE PLUG

  $20

179-3748 RED & GREEN TACKLE CO.
BASS KING
MI   1946
  $40

179-3744 RED'S BAIT CO.
RED'S BAIT
  1948   3 IN
  $50

179-3747 RED'S BAIT CO.
RED'S BAIT
  1948
  $50

180-3749 RED'S BAIT CO.
RED'S BAIT
  1948
  $50

180-5688 RED'S BAIT CO.
RED'S BAIT

  $20

180-4792 REEAL LURES, INC.
FRESHWATER NIKE
MA
  $40

180-5722 RENBARGER, BUD
WHAMMIE
OK   1943
  $30

180-3789 RESEARCH & MODEL CO.
WILL O' THE WISP
CT   1939   4 1/4 IN
ELECTRIC LIGHTED LURE $300

180-1486 REX BAIT CO
REX BAIT

  $600

180-3793 REYNOLD'S, J.W. DECOY CO.
SPIKE-TAIL MOTION BAIT
IL   1919   3 3/4 IN
  $1500

180-3794 REYNOLD'S, J.W. DECOY CO.
TEMPTER BAIT
IL   1920   4 IN
  $1500

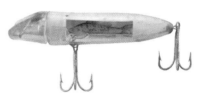

180-4759 RICE ENG. CO.
LIVE LURE
MI
  $30

180-2747 RIDGE RUNNER LURES INC
RIDGE RUNNER LURE
LA
  $40

180-3765 RINEHART TACKLE CO.
DEEP DIVE JINX
OH   1947
  $40

180-3764 RINEHART TACKLE CO.
JINX
OH   1947   2 1/4 IN
PLASTIC $30

180-3766 RINEHART TACKLE CO.
JINX
OH   1947   5 IN
MUSKY $40

180-7020 RIVER JACK
PENCIL BAIT, RIVER JACK
MI   1950
  $60

180-3779 ROBERTS, C.C.
MUD PUPPY, ROBERTS
WI   1940   7 IN   2 OZ
OLD $200

FISHING PLUGS

181-3780 ROBERTS, C.C.
MUD PUPPY, ROBERTS
WI   1941   5 1/2 IN   1 1/4 OZ
  $100

181-3781 ROBERTS, C.C.
MUD PUPPY, ROBERTS
WI   1941   7 IN   2 OZ
  $150

181-3782 ROBERTS, C.C.
RIVER PUP
WI   1949   4/12 IN   3/4 OZ
  $75

181-3746 ROBERTSON CO.
MOUSE, ROBERTSON
  1898
  $500

181-3745 ROBFIN
FINCHEROO
AZ   1970   2 3/4 IN
JR SIZE $60

181-3750 ROBFIN
FINCHEROO
AZ   1972   3 IN
  $60

181-3776 ROBINSON BAIT CO.
BASS KILLER
FL   1952   4 IN
  $70

181-3777 ROBINSON BAIT CO.
DARTER, ROBINSON
FL   1952   4 IN
  $70

181-3767 ROBINSON BAIT CO.
HANDMADE, ROBINSON
FL   1946   4 IN
  $200

181-3768 ROBINSON BAIT CO.
HANDMADE, ROBINSON
FL   1946   4 1/4 IN
  $200

181-3769 ROBINSON BAIT CO.
HANDMADE, ROBINSON
FL
  $200

181-3770 ROBINSON BAIT CO.
HANDMADE, ROBINSON
FL
  $200

181-3771 ROBINSON BAIT CO.
HANDMADE, ROBINSON
FL
  $200

181-3772 ROBINSON BAIT CO.
HANDMADE, ROBINSON
MI
  $200

181-3775 ROBINSON BAIT CO.
HANDMADE, ROBINSON
FL   1946   3 1/4 IN
SMALL $200

182-3774 ROBINSON BAIT CO.
INJURED MINNOW, ROBINSON
FL   1952   4 IN
$70

182-3805 ROGERS LURE CO.
CRAW PAP

$20

182-3732 ROLLER FLASHER CO
ROLLER FLASHER
MI
B & J TACKLE CO. $80

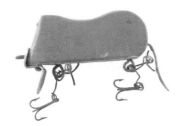

182-3773 ROOT, L.V.
MOUSE, ROOT
MI   1946   3 IN
$400

182-3743 ROSS MFG. CO
BASSNIK
TN   1960   3 3/4 IN
$30

182-3796 ROSS BAIT MFG. CO
SCUTTLE-BUT
OH   1952   3 IN
PLASTIC $60

182-5107 ROYAL OAK
CURV-A-LURE

$30

182-1302 RUBE, DICK
DARTER, RUBE
MO   1948
$20

182-2842 RUBE, DICK
RUBE, DICK LURE
MO   1946
$20

182-3815 RUSH, J.K.
FIELD SPECIAL
NY   1914   8 IN
$1500

182-3808 RUSH, J.K.
MIDGET TANGO
NY   1918
$300

182-3826 RUSH, J.K.
MIDGET TANGO
NY   1922
$300

182-5266 RUSH, J.K.
MIDGET TANGO BLANK
NY
$150

182-3807 RUSH, J.K.
MUSKY TANGO
NY   1918   5 1/2 IN
$1500

182-3814 RUSH, J.K.
RUSH TANGO
NY   1915   5 IN
FIRST MODEL $300

FISHING PLUGS

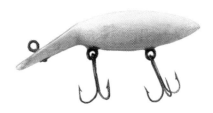

183-3813 RUSH, J.K.
RUSH TANGO JR.
NY   1914
FIRST MODEL $300

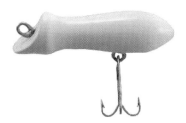

183-5264 RUSH, J.K.
RUSH TANGO LURE
NY
   $150

183-5265 RUSH, J.K.
RUSH TIGER BLANK
NY
   $150

183-5267 RUSH, J.K.
S.O.S BLANK
NY
   $150

183-3809 RUSH, J.K.
S.O.S. TANGO
NY   1920
"SWIMS ON SIDE" $300

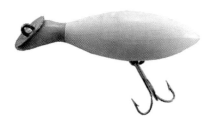

183-3811 RUSH, J.K.
TANGO, DELUXE
NY   1926   4 IN
   $600

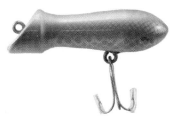

183-3825 RUSH, J.K.
TANGOLURE
NY   1922   3 1/4 IN
   $600

183-3816 RUSH, J.K.
TARPON TANGO
NY   1917   5 1/2 IN
   $1500

183-3812 RUSH, J.K.
TIGER TANGO
NY   1926   4 IN
   $600

183-3817 RUSH, J.K.
TIGER TANGO
NY   1925   3 3/4 IN
NEW $600

183-3810 RUSH, J.K.
TIGER TANGO, DELUXE
NY   1926   4 IN
   $1200

183-3822 RUSH, J.K. (L. YAKELEY)
YAKELEY BAIT
NY   1913   4 IN
   $600

183-3818 RUSH, J.K. (L. YAKELEY)
YAKELEY PATENT BAIT
NY   1914   2 3/4 IN
SMALL $600

183-3819 RUSH, J.K. (L. YAKELEY)
YAKELEY PATENT BAIT
NY   1914   3 3/4 IN
LARGE $600

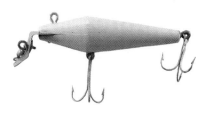

183-3821 RUSH, J.K. (L. YAKELEY)
YAKELEY PATENT BAIT
NY   1913   3 3/4 IN
   $500

FISHING PLUGS

184-1408 SAFE-T-LURE CO.
SAFE-T-LURE
OH
OLD $40

184-1409 SAFE-T-LURE CO.
SAFE-T-LURE
OH
NEW $40

184-4888 SALINE BAIT CO.
WAVEFISH
1958
$30

184-3850 SAN LUCO INC.
SAN LUCO LURE
CA   1952   4 IN
WOOD, GLASS EYE $40

184-3123 SCANDINAVIAN BAIT CO.
SCANDINAVIAN SOCKAROO
MN   1930   3 1/4 IN
$250

184-4729 SCHAEFER, O.C.
TURB-U-LURE SURFACE
1941   3 IN
$300

184-4728 SCHAEFER, O.C.
TURB-U-LURE WIGGLER
1941   3 IN
$300

184-3848 SCHALLER BAIT CO.
THREE-BAGGER
IL   1938   3 IN
$300

184-3911 SCHOONMAKER, JOHN
SCHOONIES SKOOTER
MI   1919   4 1/2 IN
LARGE $900

184-3912 SCHOONMAKER, JOHN
SCHOONIES SKOOTER JR.
MI   1919   4 IN
SMALL $900

184-2686 SCHROEDER
WONDER PLUG
WA   1934   5 1/2 IN
$300

184-3845 SCOOTERPOOPER SALES
SCOOTERPOOPER LURE
SC   1945   1 1/2 IN
$200

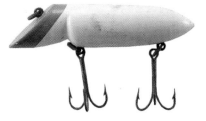

184-3827 SEALAND MFG. CO.
WEEDPLANE
FL   1940   2 1/2 IN
$90

184-3901 SEATTLE FISH LURE CO.
SEATTLE SALMON PLUG
WA   1936
$200

184-3851 SELBY, E.V. & CO.
FLATHEAD
IL   1948   3 IN   1/2 OZ
$40

FISHING PLUGS

185-5768 SEMINOLE BAIT CO.
SEMINOLE BAIT
MD   1930
   $200

185-3910 SEVDY ENTERPRISES
WEED KING
MN   1952   4 IN
   $200

185-3913 SHAFFER, CHARLES
WOOD MINNOW, SHAFFER
OH
   $1200

185-3914 SHAFFER, CHARLES
WOOD MINNOW, SHAFFER
OH
   $1200

185-4425 SHAKESPEARE, WILLIAM CO
RUBBER CASTING WEIGHT, SHAKE,
MI
   $20

185-4144 SHAKESPEARE, WILLIAM CO.
ARTIFICIAL TROLLING MINNOW
MI   1905   4 IN
   $1000

185-4286 SHAKESPEARE, WILLIAM CO.
BARNACLE BILL
MI   1930   3 IN   3/5 OZ
   $1500

185-4238 SHAKESPEARE, WILLIAM CO.
BASS-A-LURE
MI   1926   2 3/4 IN
MIDGET SIZE $200

185-4239 SHAKESPEARE, WILLIAM CO.
BASS-A-LURE
MI   1929   3 IN
BABY $200

185-4242 SHAKESPEARE, WILLIAM CO.
BASS-A-LURE
MI   1926   3 IN
JR. SIZE $200

185-4243 SHAKESPEARE, WILLIAM CO.
BASS-A-LURE
MI   1924   3 3/4 IN
   $200

185-4245 SHAKESPEARE, WILLIAM CO.
BASS-KAZOO MINNOW
MI   1923   4 IN
   $200

185-4246 SHAKESPEARE, WILLIAM CO.
BASS-KAZOO MINNOW
MI   1923   4 IN
   $200

185-4247 SHAKESPEARE, WILLIAM CO.
BASS-KAZOO MINNOW
MI   1923
WEEDLESS $200

185-4353 SHAKESPEARE, WILLIAM CO.
BLITZ
MI   1941   2 IN
   $100

FISHING PLUGS

186-4379 SHAKESPEARE, WILLIAM CO.
BUDDY
MI
 $30

186-4321 SHAKESPEARE, WILLIAM CO.
CASTING WEIGHT, SHAKESPEARE
MI   1939   5/8 OZ
 $100

186-4301 SHAKESPEARE, WILLIAM CO.
DARTING SHRIMP
MI   1927   4 1/4 IN
 $1200

186-4372 SHAKESPEARE, WILLIAM CO.
DOPEY
MI   1939   1 5/16 IN
 $30

186-4225 SHAKESPEARE, WILLIAM CO.
EGYPTIAN WOBBLER
MI   1940's
MIDGET $200

186-4229 SHAKESPEARE, WILLIAM CO.
EGYPTIAN WOBBLER
MI   1940's   3 5/8 IN   1/2 OZ
JR $200

186-4230 SHAKESPEARE, WILLIAM CO.
EGYPTIAN WOBBLER
MI   1940's   4 7/8 IN   1 OZ
 $200

186-4231 SHAKESPEARE, WILLIAM CO.
EGYPTIAN WOBBLER
MI   1940's   4 7/8 IN   1 OZ
GLASS EYES $300

186-4232 SHAKESPEARE, WILLIAM CO.
EGYPTIAN WOBBLER
MI   1940's   5 IN
SURFACE $300

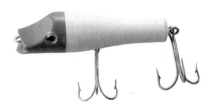

186-4251 SHAKESPEARE, WILLIAM CO.
EGYPTIAN WOBBLER
MI   1946
TOPWATER $200

186-4252 SHAKESPEARE, WILLIAM CO.
EGYPTIAN WOBBLER
MI   1946   3 5/8 UN   1/2 OZ
JR, TOPWATER $200

186-4253 SHAKESPEARE, WILLIAM CO.
EGYPTIAN WOBBLER
MI   1930   3 5/8 IN   1/2 OZ
JR $200

186-4226 SHAKESPEARE, WILLIAM CO.
EGYPTIAN WOBBLER, JOINTED
MI   1940's   3 5/8 IN   1/2 OZ
JR, SURFACE $300

186-4227 SHAKESPEARE, WILLIAM CO.
EGYPTIAN WOBBLER, JOINTED
MI   1940's   4 3/4 IN   1/2 OZ
GLASS EYES $300

186-4228 SHAKESPEARE, WILLIAM CO.
EGYPTIAN WOBBLER, JOINTED
MI   1940's   4 3/4 IN   1/2 OZ
 $200

187-4122 SHAKESPEARE, WILLIAM CO.
EVOLUTION BAIT
MI   1902   4 IN
SMALL $300

187-4138 SHAKESPEARE, WILLIAM CO.
EVOLUTION BAIT
MI   1910   2 1/8 IN
$400

187-4139 SHAKESPEARE, WILLIAM CO.
EVOLUTION BAIT
MI   1902   4 IN
$700

187-4300 SHAKESPEARE, WILLIAM CO.
FAVORITE FLOATING BAIT
MI   1908   3 5/8 IN
$3000

187-4256 SHAKESPEARE, WILLIAM CO.
FISHER BAIT
MI   1938   3 IN
JR SIZE $400

187-4257 SHAKESPEARE, WILLIAM CO.
FISHER BAIT
MI   1937   3 3/4 IN   3/5 OZ
$300

187-4145 SHAKESPEARE, WILLIAM CO.
FISHYLURE
MI   1936   4 3/4 IN
$300

187-4146 SHAKESPEARE, WILLIAM CO.
FISHYLURE EEL
MI   1936
$400

187-4277 SHAKESPEARE, WILLIAM CO.
FROG SKIN BAIT
MI   1930   3 IN
BABY $300

187-4278 SHAKESPEARE, WILLIAM CO.
FROG SKIN BAIT
MI   1930   3 3/4 IN
$300

187-4143 SHAKESPEARE, WILLIAM CO.
FROG, CASTING
MI   1902
$3000

187-4142 SHAKESPEARE, WILLIAM CO.
FROG, RHODES MECHANICAL
MI   1910   3 1/4 IN
$600

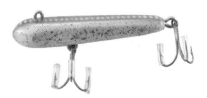

187-4141 SHAKESPEARE, WILLIAM CO.
FROG, WEEDLESS
MI   1903   3 1/4 IN
$1500

187-4374 SHAKESPEARE, WILLIAM CO.
GADABOUT
MI   1941   3 IN
$100

187-4377 SHAKESPEARE, WILLIAM CO.
GLO-LITE PUP
MI
$30

FISHING PLUGS

188-4376 SHAKESPEARE, WILLIAM CO.
GRUMPY
MI 1939 1 3/4 IN 4/10 OZ
$30

188-4322 SHAKESPEARE, WILLIAM CO.
HONG KONG PAW PAW
MI
$30

188-4323 SHAKESPEARE, WILLIAM CO.
HONG KONG PAW PAW
MI
$30

188-4324 SHAKESPEARE, WILLIAM CO.
HONG KONG PAW PAW
MI
$30

188-4328 SHAKESPEARE, WILLIAM CO.
HONG KONG PAW PAW
MI
$30

188-4263 SHAKESPEARE, WILLIAM CO.
HYDROPLANE
MI 1923 3 IN
JR SIZE $300

188-4264 SHAKESPEARE, WILLIAM CO.
HYDROPLANE
MI 1923 4 1/2 IN
$300

188-4237 SHAKESPEARE, WILLIAM CO.
INJUN JOE
MI
$200

188-4266 SHAKESPEARE, WILLIAM CO.
JACKSMITH LURE
MI 1937 2 3/4 IN
JR $150

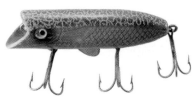

188-4269 SHAKESPEARE, WILLIAM CO.
JACKSMITH LURE
MI 1930 4 IN
2 TREBLES $200

188-4270 SHAKESPEARE, WILLIAM CO.
JACKSMITH LURE
MI 1936 4 IN
SALTWATER $150

188-4271 SHAKESPEARE, WILLIAM CO.
JACKSMITH LURE
MI 1936 4 IN
3 TREBLE $200

188-4352 SHAKESPEARE, WILLIAM CO.
JERKIN LURE
MI 1939 4 IN
$60

188-4276 SHAKESPEARE, WILLIAM CO.
JERKIN, FROG SKIN
MI 4 IN
$300

188-4216 SHAKESPEARE, WILLIAM CO.
JIM DANDY CRIPPLED MINNOW
MI 1932 3 3/4 IN
$200

FISHING PLUGS

189-4217 SHAKESPEARE, WILLIAM CO.
JIM DANDY CRIPPLED MINNOW
MI   1932   4 1/2 IN
   $200

189-4218 SHAKESPEARE, WILLIAM CO.
JIM DANDY CRIPPLED MINNOW
MI   1932   4 1/2 IN
   $200

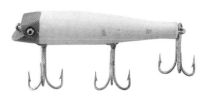

189-4236 SHAKESPEARE, WILLIAM CO.
JIM DANDY DARTER
MI   1932   4 IN
   $300

189-4240 SHAKESPEARE, WILLIAM CO.
JIM DANDY DARTER
MI   1930   3 IN
GLASS EYES $200

189-4241 SHAKESPEARE, WILLIAM CO.
JIM DANDY DARTER
MI   1930   3 IN
   $200

189-4265 SHAKESPEARE, WILLIAM CO.
JIM DANDY HYDROPLANE
MI   1930   5 IN
   $400

189-4304 SHAKESPEARE, WILLIAM CO.
JIM DANDY LURE
MI   1935   3 1/4 IN
SURFACE $200

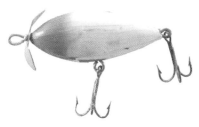

189-4221 SHAKESPEARE, WILLIAM CO.
JIM DANDY PUNKIN-SEED
MI   1918   2 3/4 IN
   $500

189-4219 SHAKESPEARE, WILLIAM CO.
JIM DANDY SIDE-HOOK FLOATER
MI   1932   4 1/2 IN
   $300

189-4220 SHAKESPEARE, WILLIAM CO.
JIM DANDY SIDE-HOOK FLOATER
MI   1932   4 1/2 IN
   $300

189-4290 SHAKESPEARE, WILLIAM CO.
JIM DANDY SPOON BILL WOBBLER
MI   1931   3 1/4 IN
JR $400

189-4291 SHAKESPEARE, WILLIAM CO.
JIM DANDY SPOON BILL WOBBLER
MI   1930   3 3/4 IN   3/4 OZ
   $400

189-4194 SHAKESPEARE, WILLIAM CO.
JIM DANDY SURFACE MINNOW
MI   1932   4 IN
   $200

189-4305 SHAKESPEARE, WILLIAM CO.
JIM DANDY SURFACE POPPER
MI   1938   4 1/2 IN
   $300

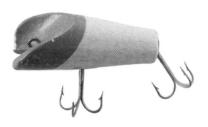

189-4292 SHAKESPEARE, WILLIAM CO.
JIM DANDY WOBBLER
MI   1925   2 1/2 IN
   $300

190-4308 SHAKESPEARE, WILLIAM CO.
KASMIROSKI SPECIAL
MI 1930 1 7/8 IN
$200

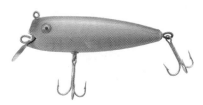

190-4244 SHAKESPEARE, WILLIAM CO.
KAZOO CHUB MINNOW
MI 1923 3 5/8 IN
$300

190-4288 SHAKESPEARE, WILLIAM CO.
KAZOO FLAPPER WING
MI 1925
$300

190-4287 SHAKESPEARE, WILLIAM CO.
KAZOO WOBBLE TAIL
MI 1924
$300

190-4248 SHAKESPEARE, WILLIAM CO.
KAZOO WOBBLER, JOINTED
MI 1927 5 1/4 IN
$200

190-4233 SHAKESPEARE, WILLIAM CO.
KINGFISH WOBBLER
MI 1939 4 7/8 IN 1 1/4 OZ
$400

190-4262 SHAKESPEARE, WILLIAM CO.
LITTLE JOE
MI 1940 2 1/8 IN 3/8 OZ
$200

190-4267 SHAKESPEARE, WILLIAM CO.
MERMAID
MI 1923 3 5/8 IN
$400

190-4268 SHAKESPEARE, WILLIAM CO.
MERMAID JR.
MI 1923 3 1/4 IN
$400

190-4201 SHAKESPEARE, WILLIAM CO.
MIDGET SPINNER
MI 1930 1 3/4 IN
$200

190-4203 SHAKESPEARE, WILLIAM CO.
MIDGET SPINNER
MI
$70

190-4157 SHAKESPEARE, WILLIAM CO.
MINNOW, BELLY HOOK, SHAKES.
MI 1906 3 3/4 IN
$500

190-4184 SHAKESPEARE, WILLIAM CO.
MINNOW, CASTING
MI 1908 3 3/4 IN
$400

190-4191 SHAKESPEARE, WILLIAM CO.
MINNOW, CASTING
MI
$400

190-4275 SHAKESPEARE, WILLIAM CO.
MINNOW, FLOATING
MI 1909 3 3/4 IN
$1000

191-4282 SHAKESPEARE, WILLIAM CO.
MINNOW, FLOATING
MI   1909   3 3/4 IN
MUSKY $1000

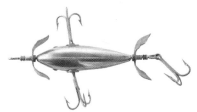

191-4179 SHAKESPEARE, WILLIAM CO.
MINNOW, METALIZED
MI   1910   2 3/4 IN
    $1000

191-4180 SHAKESPEARE, WILLIAM CO.
MINNOW, METALIZED
MI   1908   2 IN
    $1000

191-4181 SHAKESPEARE, WILLIAM CO.
MINNOW, METALIZED
MI   1910   3 IN
    $1000

191-4186 SHAKESPEARE, WILLIAM CO.
MINNOW, METALIZED
MI   1910   3 3/4 IN
    $1000

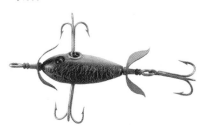

191-4210 SHAKESPEARE, WILLIAM CO.
MINNOW, MIDGET
MI   1914   2 IN
    $400

191-4212 SHAKESPEARE, WILLIAM CO.
MINNOW, MIDGET SURFACE
MI   1946   1 1/2 IN
    $60

191-4211 SHAKESPEARE, WILLIAM CO.
MINNOW, MIDGET UNDERWATER
MI   1925   2 IN
    $200

191-4188 SHAKESPEARE, WILLIAM CO.
MINNOW, MUSKY
MI   1908   4 1/2 IN
    $1200

191-4189 SHAKESPEARE, WILLIAM CO.
MINNOW, MUSKY
MI   1910   4 1/2 IN
    $1200

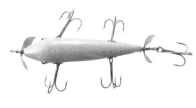

191-4190 SHAKESPEARE, WILLIAM CO.
MINNOW, MUSKY
MI   1908   5 1/2 IN
    $1500

191-4154 SHAKESPEARE, WILLIAM CO.
MINNOW, PIRATE
MI   1909   3 1/4 IN
MEDIUM $100

191-4155 SHAKESPEARE, WILLIAM CO.
MINNOW, PIRATE
MI   1909   2 1/2 IN
LARGE $100

191-4156 SHAKESPEARE, WILLIAM CO.
MINNOW, PIRATE
MI   1909   2 IN
SMALL $100

191-4115 SHAKESPEARE, WILLIAM CO.
MINNOW, RHODES
MI   1905   4 IN
RHODES, FRED $1500

FISHING PLUGS

192-4158 SHAKESPEARE, WILLIAM CO.
MINNOW, RHODES
MI   1908   3 3/4 IN
LARGE $300

192-4164 SHAKESPEARE, WILLIAM CO.
MINNOW, RHODES
MI   1906   3 IN
3 HOOK $400

192-4165 SHAKESPEARE, WILLIAM CO.
MINNOW, RHODES
MI
   $400

192-4166 SHAKESPEARE, WILLIAM CO.
MINNOW, RHODES
MI   1906   3 3/4 IN
5 HOOK $400

192-4167 SHAKESPEARE, WILLIAM CO.
MINNOW, RHODES
MI   1910   3 3/4 IN
5 HOOK $300

192-4182 SHAKESPEARE, WILLIAM CO.
MINNOW, RHODES
MI   1910   3 IN
   $200

192-4160 SHAKESPEARE, WILLIAM CO.
MINNOW, RHODES CASTING
MI   1904   4 IN
   $1500

192-7146 SHAKESPEARE, WILLIAM CO.
MINNOW, RHODES CASTING
MI   1904
KALAMAZOO TACKLE $2500

192-4116 SHAKESPEARE, WILLIAM CO.
MINNOW, RHODES COMBINATION
MI   1903   2 1/4 IN
RHODES, FRED $2500

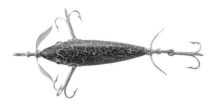

192-4174 SHAKESPEARE, WILLIAM CO.
MINNOW, RHODES FANCYBACK
MI   1914   2 3/4 IN
   $200

192-4147 SHAKESPEARE, WILLIAM CO.
MINNOW, RHODES KAZOO
MI   1910   3 IN
3 HOOK $300

192-4148 SHAKESPEARE, WILLIAM CO.
MINNOW, RHODES KAZOO
MI   1910   4 IN
5 HOOK $400

192-4118 SHAKESPEARE, WILLIAM CO.
MINNOW, RHODES MUSKY
MI   1900
RHODES, FRED $3000

192-4117 SHAKESPEARE, WILLIAM CO.
MINNOW, RHODES PERFECT CASTING
MI
RHODES, FRED, MEDIUM $2500

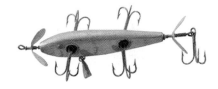

192-4120 SHAKESPEARE, WILLIAM CO.
MINNOW, RHODES PERFECT CASTING
MI   1904   4IN
RHODES, FRED, LARGE $3000

FISHING PLUGS

193-4176 SHAKESPEARE, WILLIAM CO.
MINNOW, RHODES SURFACE MUSKY
MI   1909   5 IN
  $600

193-4200 SHAKESPEARE, WILLIAM CO.
MINNOW, SHAKESPEARE
MI   1946   2 1/2 IN
BABY $100

193-4159 SHAKESPEARE, WILLIAM CO.
MINNOW, SHINER
MI   1909   2 3/4 IN
SMALL $700

193-4161 SHAKESPEARE, WILLIAM CO.
MINNOW, SHINER
MI   1909   3 7/8 IN
LARGE $700

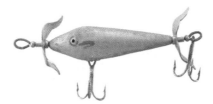

193-4185 SHAKESPEARE, WILLIAM CO.
MINNOW, SUBMARINE
MI   1910   3 IN
OLD $500

193-4187 SHAKESPEARE, WILLIAM CO.
MINNOW, SUBMARINE
MI   1923   3 5/8 IN
  $300

193-4193 SHAKESPEARE, WILLIAM CO.
MINNOW, SUBMARINE
MI   1923   3 3/4 IN
  $300

193-4192 SHAKESPEARE, WILLIAM CO.
MINNOW, SURFACE
MI
  $200

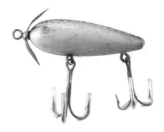

193-4199 SHAKESPEARE, WILLIAM CO.
MINNOW, SURFACE CASTING
MI   1940   2 3/4 IN
  $100

193-4149 SHAKESPEARE, WILLIAM CO.
MINNOW, TORPEDO
MI   1910
  $500

193-4150 SHAKESPEARE, WILLIAM CO.
MINNOW, TORPEDO
MI   1910   3 1/4 IN
  $500

193-4151 SHAKESPEARE, WILLIAM CO.
MINNOW, TORPEDO
MI   1905   3 IN
  $500

193-4183 SHAKESPEARE, WILLIAM CO.
MINNOW, UNDERWATER
MI   1910   2 3/4 IN
  $200

193-4197 SHAKESPEARE, WILLIAM CO.
MINNOW, UNDERWATER
MI   1908   3 3/4 IN
OLD $400

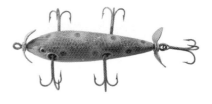

193-4198 SHAKESPEARE, WILLIAM CO.
MINNOW, UNDERWATER
MI   1925   3 3/4 IN
NEW $150

FISHING PLUGS

194-4363 SHAKESPEARE, WILLIAM CO.
MOUSE, GLO-LITE SWIMMING
MI   1930   2 3/4 IN   5/8 OZ
   $40

194-4272 SHAKESPEARE, WILLIAM CO.
NEW ALBANY BAIT
MI   1913   5 1/2 IN
   $10000

194-4284 SHAKESPEARE, WILLIAM CO.
NIGHT CASTER
MI   1908   3 1/2 IN
3 HOOK $300

194-4285 SHAKESPEARE, WILLIAM CO.
NIGHT CASTER
MI   1908   3 1/2 IN
2 HOOK $300

194-4214 SHAKESPEARE, WILLIAM CO.
NU-CRIP MINNOW
MI   1939   4 IN   5/8 OZ
   $150

194-4215 SHAKESPEARE, WILLIAM CO.
NU-CRIP MINNOW, JR.
MI   1939   3 IN
   $300

194-4259 SHAKESPEARE, WILLIAM CO.
PAD-LER
MI   1937   2 7/8 IN   7/10 OZ
SMALL $200

194-4260 SHAKESPEARE, WILLIAM CO.
PAD-LER
MI   1937   3 1/4 IN   1 OZ
   $200

194-4261 SHAKESPEARE, WILLIAM CO.
PAD-LER
MI   1937   3 3/4 IN   1 1/2 OZ
MUSKY $300

194-4249 SHAKESPEARE, WILLIAM CO.
PIKE-KAZOO
MI   1923
BABY $200

194-4250 SHAKESPEARE, WILLIAM CO.
PIKE-KAZOO
MI   1923
MIDGET $200

194-4254 SHAKESPEARE, WILLIAM CO.
PIKIE KAZOO
MI   1923
   $200

194-4255 SHAKESPEARE, WILLIAM CO.
PIKIE KAZOO
MI   1923
   $200

194-4371 SHAKESPEARE, WILLIAM CO.
PIN-HEAD
MI   1940   3 3/8 IN   1 OZ
   $75

194-4258 SHAKESPEARE, WILLIAM CO.
PLOPPER
MI   1930   3 3/4 IN   3/5 OZ
   $300

FISHING PLUGS

195-4311 SHAKESPEARE, WILLIAM CO.
POP-EYE FROG
MI   1946   3 IN
  $50

195-4312 SHAKESPEARE, WILLIAM CO.
POP-EYE FROG
MI   1936   3 1/2 IN
EARLY $200

195-4314 SHAKESPEARE, WILLIAM CO.
POP-EYE FROG JR.
MI   1936   3 IN
EARLY $200

195-4313 SHAKESPEARE, WILLIAM CO.
POP-EYE FROG, JR
MI   1946   1 1/2 IN
  $50

195-4208 SHAKESPEARE, WILLIAM CO.
PORKER
MI   1920   1 3/4 IN
  $600

195-4207 SHAKESPEARE, WILLIAM CO.
PORKER, WEEDLESS
MI   1930   1 3/4 IN
  $600

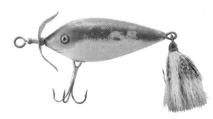

195-4195 SHAKESPEARE, WILLIAM CO.
PUNKIN-SEED FLOATER
MI   1912   3 IN
  $800

195-4196 SHAKESPEARE, WILLIAM CO.
PUNKIN-SEED SINKER
MI   1912
  $800

195-4378 SHAKESPEARE, WILLIAM CO.
PUP, SHAKESPEARE
MI   1939   2 5/8 IN   1/2 OZ
  $30

195-4273 SHAKESPEARE, WILLIAM CO.
RESEARCH ALL-IN-ONE BAIT
MI   1920   4 IN
  $2000

195-4283 SHAKESPEARE, WILLIAM CO.
RESEARCH BAIT, SHAKESPEARE
MI   1908   3 3/4 IN
  $2000

195-4202 SHAKESPEARE, WILLIAM CO.
RESEARCH BUCKTAIL BAIT
MI
  $500

195-4128 SHAKESPEARE, WILLIAM CO.
REVOLUTION BAIT
MI   1910
  $700

195-4129 SHAKESPEARE, WILLIAM CO.
REVOLUTION BAIT
MI   1905   3 IN
BABY $1000

195-4130 SHAKESPEARE, WILLIAM CO.
REVOLUTION BAIT
MI   1905
  $700

FISHING PLUGS

196-4131 SHAKESPEARE, WILLIAM CO.
REVOLUTION BAIT
MI   1915
  $700

196-4132 SHAKESPEARE, WILLIAM CO.
REVOLUTION BAIT
MI   1910   3 1/2 IN
  $700

196-4133 SHAKESPEARE, WILLIAM CO.
REVOLUTION BAIT
MI   1902   3 1/2 IN
POINTED NOSE $1500

196-4126 SHAKESPEARE, WILLIAM CO.
REVOLUTION BAIT, BABY
MI   1910   3 IN
  $1000

196-4123 SHAKESPEARE, WILLIAM CO.
REVOLUTION BAIT, MUSKY
MI   1905   4 1/4 IN
  $2000

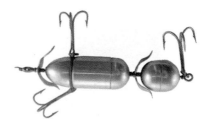

196-4125 SHAKESPEARE, WILLIAM CO.
REVOLUTION BAIT, MUSKY
MI   1910   4 1/4 IN
  $2000

196-4124 SHAKESPEARE, WILLIAM CO.
REVOLUTION WOOD BAIT
MI   1897   3 3/4 IN
FIRST WOODEN BAIT $15000

196-4127 SHAKESPEARE, WILLIAM CO.
REVOLUTION WOOD BAIT
MI   1898   4 IN
  $4000

196-4113 SHAKESPEARE, WILLIAM CO.
REVOLUTION, RHODES CORK
MI   1897   3 1/2 IN
RHODES, FRED $3000

196-4111 SHAKESPEARE, WILLIAM CO.
RHODES METAL MINNOW
MI   1907   3 IN
RHODES, FRED $1500

196-4114 SHAKESPEARE, WILLIAM CO.
RHODES METAL SURFACE BAIT
MI
RHODES, FRED $300

196-4112 SHAKESPEARE, WILLIAM CO.
RHODES SURFACE BAIT
MI   1906   2 3/4 IN
RHODES, FRED $1500

196-4175 SHAKESPEARE, WILLIAM CO.
RHODES,
MI
  $300

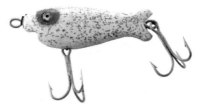

196-4309 SHAKESPEARE, WILLIAM CO.
SALTWATER SPECIAL, SHAKESPEARE
MI   1924   3 IN
  $2000

196-4310 SHAKESPEARE, WILLIAM CO.
SARDINIA SALTWATER SPECIAL
MI   1924   3 IN
  $2000

197-4274 SHAKESPEARE, WILLIAM CO.
SEA WITCH
MI   1928   4 IN   3/4 OZ
EARLY $200

197-4281 SHAKESPEARE, WILLIAM CO.
SEA WITCH
MI   1928   4 IN   3/4 OZ
    $100

197-4306 SHAKESPEARE, WILLIAM CO.
SEA WITCH
MI
    $100

197-4294 SHAKESPEARE, WILLIAM CO.
SEA WITCH BABY
MI   1928   3 3/4 IN   1/2 OZ
    $100

197-4295 SHAKESPEARE, WILLIAM CO.
SEA WITCH BABY
MI   1928   3 3/4 IN   1/2 OZ
EARLY $200

197-4296 SHAKESPEARE, WILLIAM CO.
SEA WITCH BABY
MI   1928   3 3/4 IN   1/2 OZ
GLASS EYES $200

197-4280 SHAKESPEARE, WILLIAM CO.
SEA WITCH BUCKTAIL, BABY
MI   1928
    $100

197-4297 SHAKESPEARE, WILLIAM CO.
SEA WITCH JR.
MI   1928   3 3/4 IN   1/2 OZ
EARLY $300

197-4279 SHAKESPEARE, WILLIAM CO.
SEA WITCH, MIDGET
MI   1928   2 3/4 IN   1/2 OZ
GLASS EYES $200

197-4307 SHAKESPEARE, WILLIAM CO.
SEA WITCH, MIDGET
MI   1928   2 3/4 IN   1/2 OZ
    $200

197-4302 SHAKESPEARE, WILLIAM CO.
SEA WITCH, SPINNERED
MI   1930   3 3/4 IN
    $300

197-5304 SHAKESPEARE, WILLIAM CO.
SHAKESPEARE BAIT
MI
    $1000

197-4354 SHAKESPEARE, WILLIAM CO.
SHAKESPEARE SPECIAL
MI   1939   4 IN   5/8 OZ
    $40

197-4355 SHAKESPEARE, WILLIAM CO.
SHAKESPEARE SPECIAL JR.
MI   1939   3 IN   1/2 OZ
    $40

197-4356 SHAKESPEARE, WILLIAM CO.
SHAKESPEARE SPECIAL, NOTCHED.
MI   1939   4 IN   5/8 OZ
    $100

198-4357 SHAKESPEARE, WILLIAM CO.
SHAKESPEARE SPECIAL, NOTCHED.
MI   1939   3 3/4 IN   1/2 OZ
JR. SIZE $100

198-4168 SHAKESPEARE, WILLIAM CO.
SLIM JIM, McKINNIE SPECIAL
MI   1930   4 IN
$200

198-4163 SHAKESPEARE, WILLIAM CO.
SLIM JIM, SHAKESPEARE
MI   1908   3 IN
$400

198-4169 SHAKESPEARE, WILLIAM CO.
SLIM JIM, SHAKESPEARE
MI   1930   4 IN
SALTWATER $150

198-4170 SHAKESPEARE, WILLIAM CO.
SLIM JIM, SHAKESPEARE
MI   1930
LATE $150

198-4171 SHAKESPEARE, WILLIAM CO.
SLIM JIM, SHAKESPEARE
MI   1955
$100

198-4171 SHAKESPEARE, WILLIAM CO.
SLIM JIM, SHAKESPEARE
MI   1955
$100

198-4173 SHAKESPEARE, WILLIAM CO.
SLIM JIM, SHAKESPEARE
MI   1930
$200

198-4177 SHAKESPEARE, WILLIAM CO.
SLIM JIM, SHAKESPEARE
MI   1915   4 1/2 IN
MUSKY $300

198-4178 SHAKESPEARE, WILLIAM CO.
SLIM JIM, SHAKESPEARE
MI   1915   4 5/8 IN
MUSKY $400

198-4162 SHAKESPEARE, WILLIAM CO.
SLIM JIM, SIDE- HOOK, SHAKESPEARE
MI   1908   3 3/4 IN
$400

198-4375 SHAKESPEARE, WILLIAM CO.
SPINTAIL
MI   1939   1 1/2 IN
$30

198-4224 SHAKESPEARE, WILLIAM CO.
STRIKE-IT
MI   1932   3 3/4 IN   4/5 OZ
$300

198-4235 SHAKESPEARE, WILLIAM CO.
STRIPED BASS WOBBLER
MI   1939   6 IN
$400

198-4234 SHAKESPEARE, WILLIAM CO.
STRIPED BASS WOBBLER, JOINTED
MI   1939   6 IN
$400

FISHING PLUGS

199-4121 SHAKESPEARE, WILLIAM CO.
SURE LURE
MI   1902   2 3/4 IN
OLD, RUBBER $3000

199-4140 SHAKESPEARE, WILLIAM CO.
SURE-LURE
MI   1930   2 5/8 IN   1/2 OZ
LATE $400

199-4373 SHAKESPEARE, WILLIAM CO.
SURFACE LURE, SHAKESPEARE
MI   1939   3 1/2 IN   5/8 OZ
   $30

199-4303 SHAKESPEARE, WILLIAM CO.
SURFACE POPPER
MI   1939   2 IN
   $150

199-4289 SHAKESPEARE, WILLIAM CO.
SURFACE WONDER
MI   1910   4 IN
   $500

199-4293 SHAKESPEARE, WILLIAM CO.
SURFACE WONDER
MI   1908   4 1/2 IN
OLD $1000

199-4299 SHAKESPEARE, WILLIAM CO.
SURFACE WONDER JR
MI   1915   4 IN
   $1000

199-4298 SHAKESPEARE, WILLIAM CO.
SURFACE WONDER, BABY
MI   1915   2 1/2 IN
   $700

199-4370 SHAKESPEARE, WILLIAM CO.
SWIMMING MOUSE POPPER
MI   1923   3 3/8 IN   4/5 OZ
   $200

199-4367 SHAKESPEARE, WILLIAM CO.
SWIMMING MOUSE TIGER
MI   1930   3 3/8 IN   4/5 OZ
   $75

199-4368 SHAKESPEARE, WILLIAM CO.
SWIMMING MOUSE, JIMMY SKUNK
MI   1930   3 3/8 IN   4/5 OZ
   $100

199-4359 SHAKESPEARE, WILLIAM CO.
SWIMMING MOUSE, SHAKESPEARE
MI   1939   2 3/4 IN   5/8 OZ
GLASS EYES, SMALL $60

199-4360 SHAKESPEARE, WILLIAM CO.
SWIMMING MOUSE, SHAKESPEARE
MI   1939   2 3/4 IN   5/8 OZ
SMALL $40

199-4361 SHAKESPEARE, WILLIAM CO.
SWIMMING MOUSE, SHAKESPEARE
MI   1930   2 3/4 IN   5/8 OZ
GLASS EYES $100

199-4362 SHAKESPEARE, WILLIAM CO.
SWIMMING MOUSE, SHAKESPEARE
MI   1930   2 3/4 IN   5/8 OZ
GLASS EYES, MEDIUM $60

FISHING PLUGS

200-4364 SHAKESPEARE, WILLIAM CO.
SWIMMING MOUSE, SHAKESPEARE
MI 1926 3 3/8 IN 4/5 OZ
SPECIAL COLOR $300

200-4365 SHAKESPEARE, WILLIAM CO.
SWIMMING MOUSE, SHAKESPEARE
MI 1919 3 3/8 IN 4/5 OZ
NO EYES, FIRST MODEL $300

200-4366 SHAKESPEARE, WILLIAM CO.
SWIMMING MOUSE, SHAKESPEARE
MI 1919 3 3/8 IN 4/5 OZ
NO NOTCH $300

200-4369 SHAKESPEARE, WILLIAM CO.
SWIMMING MOUSE, SHAKESPEARE
MI 1923 3 3/8 IN 4/5 OZ
OLD $150

200-4206 SHAKESPEARE, WILLIAM CO.
TANTALIZER
MI 1928 4 IN
$300

200-4222 SHAKESPEARE, WILLIAM CO.
TANTALIZER JR.
MI 1939 3 3/4 IN 3/4 OZ
$300

200-4205 SHAKESPEARE, WILLIAM CO.
TARPALUNGE
MI 2 3/4 OZ
$500

200-4223 SHAKESPEARE, WILLIAM CO.
TARPALUNGE
MI 1929 5 3/4 IN 1 2/4 OZ
OLD $2000

200-4213 SHAKESPEARE, WILLIAM CO.
WAUKAZOO SPINNER
MI 1932 2 1/2 IN
$300

200-4204 SHAKESPEARE, WILLIAM CO.
WHIRLWIND SPINNER
MI 1910 1 1/4 IN
$700

200-4380 SHAKESPEARE, WILLIAM CO.
WIGGLE DIVER
MI 1938 4 5/8 IN
LARGE $50

200-4381 SHAKESPEARE, WILLIAM CO.
WIGGLE DIVER
MI 1938 3 1/2 IN
MEDIUM $50

200-4382 SHAKESPEARE, WILLIAM CO.
WIGGLE DIVER
MI 1938 2 1/4 IN
SMALL $50

200-4134 SHAKESPEARE, WILLIAM CO.
WORDEN BUCKTAIL BAIT
MI 1915 2 1/4 IN
$500

200-4135 SHAKESPEARE, WILLIAM CO.
WORDEN BUCKTAIL BAIT
MI 1910
$500

201-4136 SHAKESPEARE, WILLIAM CO.
WORDEN BUCKTAIL BAIT
MI   1907   2 1/4 IN
  $500

201-4137 SHAKESPEARE, WILLIAM CO.
WORDEN BUCKTAIL BAIT
MI   1905
  $500

201-3915 SHIPLEY, MALCOLM A.
CEDAR PROPELLER BAIT
PA   1888   3 1/4 IN
OLD $1500

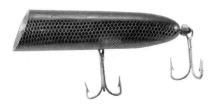

201-3205 SHIREY, S.O.
OUACHITA TRAVELER
AR   1958
  $60

201-5113 SHIVERDECKER, H.P.
YELLOW-HEADED BLACKBIRD
IL
  $30

201-3865 SHOFF TACKLE CO.
SHOFF SALMON PLUG
WA   1925   3 1/2 IN
SMALL $200

201-3866 SHOFF TACKLE CO.
SHOFF SALMON PLUG
WA   1925   5 IN
LARGE $200

201-3885 SHUREBITE ARTIFICAL BAIT CO.
SHUREBITE BAIT
OH   1938   4 IN
OLD $100

201-3883 SHUREBITE, INC.
SHEDEVIL LURE
MI   1946   4 IN
  $40

201-3884 SHUREBITE, INC.
SKATE
MI   1948   2 IN
  $40

201-3877 SHURLURE CO.
DOE'S SECRET WEAPON

  $100

201-3733 SIDEWINDER LURE CO.
PRETZ-L-LURE
  1960
  $50

201-3878 SIGNAL BAIT CO.
BILL FISH
FL
  $40

201-3856 SILVER CREEK NOVEL. WKS
PIKAROON MINNOW
MI   1923   4 IN
  $1500

201-3892 SILVER CREEK NOVEL. WKS
POLLYWOG
MI
SMALL $300

FISHING PLUGS

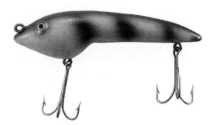

202-3893 SILVER CREEK NOVEL. WKS
SILVER CREEK POLLYWOG
MI   1921   4 IN   3/4 OZ
LARGE $300

202-3891 SILVER CREEK NOVEL. WKS
SILVER CREEK WIGGLER
MI   1921   3 1/2 IN
 $400

202-3896 SILVER CREEK NOVEL. WKS
TROUT- EAT-US
MI   1920   3 IN
 $200

202-3903 SILVER-TIP TACKLE CO.
SILVER-TIP HELLDIVER
OK   1945   5 IN
 $90

202-3902 SIREN LURE CO.
SIREN LURE
CA   1947   4 1/2 IN
 $50

202-2836 SIX, CHAS & CO.
SKIPPER, SIX, CHAS & CO

 $20

202-4084 SIX, CHAS & CO.
SWIMMY

LARGE $20

202-4085 SIX, CHAS & CO.
SWIMMY

MEDIUM $20

202-4087 SIX, CHAS & CO.
SWIMMY

SMALL $20

202-24231 SKEETER BOAT CO.
SKEETER HAWK LURE
IN   1973
 $30

202-4876 SKIPPER BAIT CO.
MOSS KING

 $20

202-5409 SLETTON
DECOY, PERCH, SLETTON
MN   1951
 $200

202-5423 SLETTON
DECOY, PIKE, SLETTON
MN   1951
 $200

202-5435 SLETTON
SUNFISH
MN   1951
 $200

202-3917 SMITH & YELTON
CRAWPAPPY
MO   1951   4 1/4 IN
1/2 OZ $200

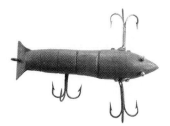

FISHING PLUGS

203-3906 SMITH, BOB SPORTING GOODS
BOB'S TEN CENT MINNOW
MA   1915   2 1/2 IN
  $100

203-3904 SMITH, CLARENCE
WIGGLING WORM
IL   1947   6 1/2 IN
  $300

203-3905 SMITH, CLARENCE
WIGGLING WORM , LIPPED
IL   1947   6 1/2 IN
  $300

203-5676 SMITHWICK, JACK K. & SON
BLINKER
LA   1966
  $20

203-4010 SMITHWICK, JACK K. & SON
BUCK- N- BRAWL
LA   1960
  $40

203-4017 SMITHWICK, JACK K. & SON
BUCK-N-BRAWL
LA   1960
  $40

203-4012 SMITHWICK, JACK K. & SON
CARROT TOP
LA   1960
  $40

203-4007 SMITHWICK, JACK K. & SON
DEVIL HORSE LURE
LA
SMALL $10

203-4008 SMITHWICK, JACK K. & SON
DEVIL HORSE LURE
LA   1958   4 1/4 IN
MEDIUM $10

203-4009 SMITHWICK, JACK K. & SON
DEVIL HORSE LURE
LA   1958   5 3/4 IN
LARGE $10

203-4001 SMITHWICK, JACK K. & SON
DEVIL HORSE TOPPER
LA
LARGE $10

203-4002 SMITHWICK, JACK K. & SON
DEVIL HORSE TOPPER
LA
MEDIUM $10

203-4014 SMITHWICK, JACK K. & SON
DEVIL HORSE TOPPER
LA   1958   4 IN
  $10

203-4015 SMITHWICK, JACK K. & SON
DEVIL HORSE TOPPER
LA   1958
  $10

203-4018 SMITHWICK, JACK K. & SON
DEVIL HORSE, DEEP DIVE
LA   1959
  $40

FISHING PLUGS

204-4013 SMITHWICK, JACK K. & SON
ROOTER
LA   1959
BABY $40

204-4016 SMITHWICK, JACK K. & SON
ROOTER
LA   1958
 $40

204-4011 SMITHWICK, JACK K. & SON
TOP-N-POP
LA
 $40

204-7044 SNAGPROOF BAIT CO.
BULL FROG
 1969
 $10

204-7042 SNAGPROOF BAIT CO.
EEL, SNAGPROOF
 1969
 $20

204-7045 SNAGPROOF BAIT CO.
FROG, SNAGPROOF
 1969
 $10

204-7041 SNAGPROOF BAIT CO.
LEECH, SNAGPROOF
 1969
 $10

204-7046 SNAGPROOF BAIT CO.
MINNOW, SNAGPROOF
 1969
 $10

204-7040 SNAGPROOF BAIT CO.
SNAGPROOF BAIT
 1969
 $10

204-5704 SNAGPROOF BAIT CO.
SOFTY WEEDLESS
WI
 $20

204-7043 SNAGPROOF BAIT CO.
TADPOLE
 1969
 $20

204-7047 SNAGPROOF BAIT CO.
WOBBLER, SNAGPROOF
 1969
SMALL $10

204-7048 SNAGPROOF BAIT CO.
WOBBLER, SNAGPROOF
 1969
 $10

204-7049 SNAGPROOF BAIT CO.
WORM, SNAGPROOF

 $10

204-3843 SNOOK BAIT CO
RUSSO BAIT

 $40

205-3844 SNOOK BAIT CO
SNOOK WIGGLER

$40

205-3932 SNYDER BAIT CO.
JERSEY SPINNER
NJ   1899   3 IN
JERSEY RIG $200

205-3927 SNYDER BAIT CO.
SNYDER SPINNER
NJ   1904

$200

205-3931 SNYDER BAIT CO.
SNYDER SPINNER
NJ   1899   3 IN
OLD $200

205-3928 SNYDER-MILLS
YELLOW BOY
NJ   1900's
  $200

205-3937 SOBECKI, ANTON
SOBECKI 1929 WIGGLER
IN   1929   4 IN
  $400

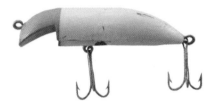

205-3936 SOBECKI, ANTON
TOPWATER WIGGLER
IN   1929   4 IN
  $400

205-6989 SOONER BAIT CO.
OKIE DOKIE
OK   1962
SMALL $20

205-6990 SOONER BAIT CO.
OKIE DOKIE
OK   1962
LARGE $20

205-4392 SOUTH BEND (WORDEN)
WORDEN 3 HOOK MINNOW
IN   1904   2 3/4 IN
  $1000

205-4393 SOUTH BEND (WORDEN)
WORDEN 5-HOOK MINNOW
IN   1906   3 3/4 IN
GLASS EYES $1000

205-4394 SOUTH BEND (WORDEN)
WORDEN 5-HOOK MINNOW
IN   1904   3 3/4 IN
  $1000

205-4390 SOUTH BEND (WORDEN)
WORDEN COMBINATION MINNOW
IN   1903   2 3/4 IN
  $1000

205-4391 SOUTH BEND (WORDEN)
WORDEN WHITE WONDER
IN   1903   2 3/4 IN
  $1000

205-4511 SOUTH BEND BAIT CO.
#999 MINNOW
IN   1931   4 IN   5/8 OZ
  $300

FISHING PLUGS

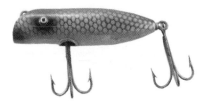

206-4577 SOUTH BEND BAIT CO.
BABE-OBITE
IN 1937 2 7/8 IN 1/2 OZ
$50

206-4579 SOUTH BEND BAIT CO.
BABE-ORENO
IN
EMBOSSED EYES $20

206-4580 SOUTH BEND BAIT CO.
BABE-ORENO
IN
TACK EYES $30

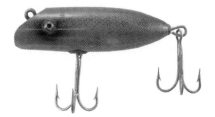

206-4581 SOUTH BEND BAIT CO.
BABE-ORENO
IN
GLASS EYES $40

206-4566 SOUTH BEND BAIT CO.
BABE-ORENO WITH PADGEN PATENT
IN 1927
$100

206-4564 SOUTH BEND BAIT CO.
BABE-ORENO, COMMEMORATIVE
IN 1926
$1000

206-4578 SOUTH BEND BAIT CO.
BABE-ORENO, JERSEY
IN 1916 2 3/4 IN 1/2 OZ
NO EYES $50

206-3757 SOUTH BEND BAIT CO.
BALSA MINNOW, SOUTH BEND
IN
$10

206-3758 SOUTH BEND BAIT CO.
BALSA MINNOW, SOUTH BEND
IN
$10

206-3759 SOUTH BEND BAIT CO.
BALSA MINNOW, SOUTH BEND
IN
$10

206-3760 SOUTH BEND BAIT CO.
BALSA MINNOW, SOUTH BEND
IN
$10

206-4576 SOUTH BEND BAIT CO.
BASS-OBITE
IN 1937 3 1/4 IN 5/8 OZ
$50

206-4570 SOUTH BEND BAIT CO.
BASS-ORENO
IN 1934 3 1/2 IN 5/8 OZ
BETTER $30

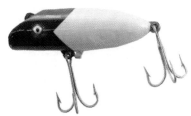

206-4571 SOUTH BEND BAIT CO.
BASS-ORENO
IN 1934
BABY, BETTER $30

206-4582 SOUTH BEND BAIT CO.
BASS-ORENO
IN 1929 3 1/2 IN
TACK EYES $30

FISHING PLUGS

207-4583 SOUTH BEND BAIT CO.
BASS-ORENO
IN   1950   3 1/2 IN
DECAL EYES $20

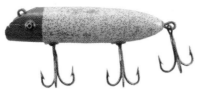

207-4584 SOUTH BEND BAIT CO.
BASS-ORENO
IN   1923   3 1/2 IN
GLASS EYES $40

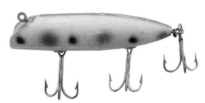

207-4585 SOUTH BEND BAIT CO.
BASS-ORENO
IN   1915   3 1/2 IN
NO EYES $50

207-4642 SOUTH BEND BAIT CO.
BASS-ORENO
IN
SALTWATER $100

207-4643 SOUTH BEND BAIT CO.
BASS-ORENO
IN
STEEL PLATE $500

207-4647 SOUTH BEND BAIT CO.
BASS-ORENO
IN   1918   3 1/2 IN
WEEDLESS $200

207-4648 SOUTH BEND BAIT CO.
BASS-ORENO
IN   1914   3 1/2 IN
EARLIEST, SOLID EYES $500

207-4565 SOUTH BEND BAIT CO.
BASS-ORENO, COMMEMORATIVE
IN
    $1000

207-4623 SOUTH BEND BAIT CO.
BE-BOP
IN   1950   4 1/2 IN   5/8 OZ
    $100

207-4624 SOUTH BEND BAIT CO.
BE-BOP
IN   1950   3 3/8 IN   1/2 OZ
BABY $100

207-4524 SOUTH BEND BAIT CO.
BEST-O-LUCK INJURED MINNOW
IN   1934   3 IN
SMALL $40

207-4525 SOUTH BEND BAIT CO.
BEST-O-LUCK INJURED MINNOW
IN   1934   3 5/8 IN
LARGE $40

207-4659 SOUTH BEND BAIT CO.
BEST-O-LUCK JOINTED PIKE-ORENO
IN   1934   3 1/2 IN   1/2 OZ
    $40

207-4529 SOUTH BEND BAIT CO.
BEST-O-LUCK LURE
IN   1934   4 1/4 IN
LARGE $40

207-4515 SOUTH BEND BAIT CO.
BEST-O-LUCK MINNOW
IN   1934   3 IN
SMALL $40

FISHING PLUGS

208-4654 SOUTH BEND BAIT CO.
BEST-O-LUCK PANATELLA WOBBLER
IN   1934   4 1/4 IN
  $40

208-4560 SOUTH BEND BAIT CO.
BEST-O-LUCK PIKE LURE
IN   4 3/8 IN
  $40

208-4599 SOUTH BEND BAIT CO.
BEST-O-LUCK PLUNK-ORENO
IN   1936   3 3/4 IN
  $100

208-4562 SOUTH BEND BAIT CO.
BEST-O-LUCK STANDARD WOBBLER
IN   1934   3 3/4 IN   5/8 OZ
  $40

208-4563 SOUTH BEND BAIT CO.
BEST-O-LUCK STANDARD WOBBLER
IN   1934   3 3/4 IN
BRILLIANT $50

208-4521 SOUTH BEND BAIT CO.
BEST-O-LUCK SURFACE LURE
IN
  $40

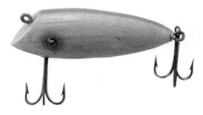

208-4522 SOUTH BEND BAIT CO.
BEST-O-LUCK UNDERWATER LURE
IN
  $40

208-4561 SOUTH BEND BAIT CO.
BEST-O-LUCK WOBBLER
IN   2 3/4 IN
  $40

208-4609 SOUTH BEND BAIT CO.
BEST-O-LUCK WOBBLER
IN   1932   3 1/4 IN
GLASS EYES $60

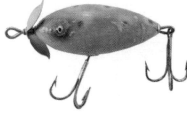

208-4517 SOUTH BEND BAIT CO.
BEST-O-LUCK WOUNDED MINNOW
IN   1934   3 IN   3/4 OZ
  $60

208-4523 SOUTH BEND BAIT CO.
BEST-O-LUCK WOUNDED MINNOW
IN   1934   3 IN
  $40

208-4479 SOUTH BEND BAIT CO.
CASTING WEIGHT, SOUTH BEND
IN
  $40

208-4640 SOUTH BEND BAIT CO.
COAST-ORENO
IN   1955   4 1/2 IN
  $100

208-4512 SOUTH BEND BAIT CO.
COMBINATION MINNOW, SOUTH BEND
IN   1916   2 3/4 IN
SURFACE $200

208-4513 SOUTH BEND BAIT CO.
COMBINATION MINNOW, SOUTH BEND
IN   1914   2 3/4 IN
  $150

FISHING PLUGS

211-4486 SOUTH BEND BAIT CO.
MINNOW, WEEDLESS, SOUTH BEND
IN   1916   3 1/4 IN
  $300

211-4625 SOUTH BEND BAIT CO.
MIN-ORENO
IN   1/4 OZ
BABY, PAINTED EYES $70

211-4626 SOUTH BEND BAIT CO.
MIN-ORENO
IN   1930   3 IN   1/4 OZ
BABY, TACK EYES $70

211-4627 SOUTH BEND BAIT CO.
MIN-ORENO
IN   1930   4 IN   5/8 OZ
  $70

211-4628 SOUTH BEND BAIT CO.
MIN-ORENO
IN   1930   5 5/8 IN   1/2 OZ
MUSKY $100

211-4631 SOUTH BEND BAIT CO.
MOUSE-ORENO
IN
  $100

211-4634 SOUTH BEND BAIT CO.
MOUSE-ORENO
IN   1931   2 3/4 IN   5/8 OZ
OLD $200

211-4644 SOUTH BEND BAIT CO.
MUSK-ORENO
IN
TACK EYES $70

211-4645 SOUTH BEND BAIT CO.
MUSK-ORENO
IN
GLASS EYES $100

211-4646 SOUTH BEND BAIT CO.
MUSK-ORENO
IN   1920   4 1/2 IN   1 1/8 OZ
NO EYES $200

211-4485 SOUTH BEND BAIT CO.
MUSKY MINNOW
IN   1914   5 1/2 IN   1 1/3 OZ
  $1000

211-4548 SOUTH BEND BAIT CO.
NIP-I-DIDDEE
IN   1947   3 IN   5/8 OZ
PAINTED EYES $40

211-4549 SOUTH BEND BAIT CO.
NIP-I-DIDDEE
IN   1947   3 IN   5/8 OZ
EMBOSSED EYES $30

211-4550 SOUTH BEND BAIT CO.
NIP-I-DIDDEE
IN   1947   3 IN   5/8 OZ
OLD $50

211-4498 SOUTH BEND BAIT CO.
O.V.B. PANETELLA
IN   1912   4 1/2 IN
'OUR VERY BEST' $200

FISHING PLUGS

212-4488 SOUTH BEND BAIT CO.
O.V.B. UNDERWATER MINNOW
IN
'OUR VERY BEST' $150

212-4672 SOUTH BEND BAIT CO.
OPTIC
IN 1955 2 1/2 IN
 $30

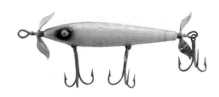

212-4490 SOUTH BEND BAIT CO.
PANATELLA MINNOW
IN 1923 4 1/4 IN 9/10 OZ
TACK EYES $100

212-4491 SOUTH BEND BAIT CO.
PANATELLA MINNOW
IN 1923 4 1/4 IN 9/10 OZ
 $150

212-4492 SOUTH BEND BAIT CO.
PANATELLA MINNOW
IN 1923 4 1/4 IN
SALTWATER $500

212-4493 SOUTH BEND BAIT CO.
PANATELLA MINNOW
IN 1923 4 1/4 IN 9/10 OZ
 $300

212-4497 SOUTH BEND BAIT CO.
PANATELLA MINNOW
IN 1923 4 1/4 IN 9/10 OZ
2- HOOK , SMALL $200

212-4500 SOUTH BEND BAIT CO.
PANATELLA MINNOW
IN 1912 4 1/4 IN 9/10 OZ
 $150

212-4450 SOUTH BEND BAIT CO.
PEACH-ORENO
IN 1941 3 IN
SMALL $70

212-4451 SOUTH BEND BAIT CO.
PEACH-ORENO
IN 1941 4 IN
 $70

212-4452 SOUTH BEND BAIT CO.
PEACH-ORENO
IN 1941 5 IN
MUSKY $100

212-4586 SOUTH BEND BAIT CO.
PIKE-ORENO
IN 1931 4 1/4 IN
 $20

212-4587 SOUTH BEND BAIT CO.
PIKE-ORENO
IN 1918 4 1/4 IN
OLD, NO EYES $150

212-4588 SOUTH BEND BAIT CO.
PIKE-ORENO
IN 4 1/4 IN
OLD, GLASS EYES $100

212-4589 SOUTH BEND BAIT CO.
PIKE-ORENO
IN 1931 4 1/4 IN
TACK EYES $30

213-4590 SOUTH BEND BAIT CO.
PIKE-ORENO
IN   1925   4 1/2 IN
GLASS EYES $40

213-4596 SOUTH BEND BAIT CO.
PIKE-ORENO
IN   1925
GLASS EYES $50

213-4597 SOUTH BEND BAIT CO.
PIKE-ORENO
IN   4 1/2 IN
TACK EYES $30

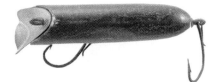

213-4664 SOUTH BEND BAIT CO.
PIKE-ORENO
IN   1918   3 1/4 IN
BABY, OLD, NO EYES $150

213-4665 SOUTH BEND BAIT CO.
PIKE-ORENO
IN   1925   3 1/4 IN
BABY, GLASS EYES $100

213-4594 SOUTH BEND BAIT CO.
PIKE-ORENO, JOINTED
IN   1931   4 IN   1/2 OZ
TACK EYES $30

213-4595 SOUTH BEND BAIT CO.
PIKE-ORENO, JOINTED
IN   1931   4 IN   1/2 OZ
    $30

213-4656 SOUTH BEND BAIT CO.
PIKE-ORENO, JOINTED
IN   1931   4 IN   1/2 OZ
BABY, EMBOSSED EYES $20

213-4657 SOUTH BEND BAIT CO.
PIKE-ORENO, JOINTED
IN   1931   4 IN   1/2 OZ
BABY, TACK EYES $30

213-4658 SOUTH BEND BAIT CO.
PIKE-ORENO, JOINTED
IN   1931   4 IN   1/2 OZ
TACK EYES $30

213-4655 SOUTH BEND BAIT CO.
PIKE-ORENO, JOINTED, SPINNING
IN   1931   4 IN   1/2 OZ
BABY $50

213-4632 SOUTH BEND BAIT CO.
PLUG-ORENO
IN   1929   3 3/4 IN   5/8 OZ
    $200

213-4591 SOUTH BEND BAIT CO.
PLUNK-ORENO
MI
TACK EYES $50

213-4592 SOUTH BEND BAIT CO.
PLUNK-ORENO
IN   1936   3 3/4 IN   5/8 OZ
GLASS EYES $150

213-4593 SOUTH BEND BAIT CO.
PLUNK-ORENO
IN   1929   3 3/4 IN   5/8 OZ
NO EYES $300

214-4598 SOUTH BEND BAIT CO.
PLUNK-ORENO
IN   1929   3 3/4 IN   5/8 OZ
OLD STYLE $200

214-4606 SOUTH BEND BAIT CO.
PLUNK-ORENO
IN   1929   3 3/4 IN   5/8 OZ
  $50

214-4673 SOUTH BEND BAIT CO.
RASCAL
IN   1960   5 1/2 IN
LARGE $20

214-4674 SOUTH BEND BAIT CO.
RASCAL
IN   1960   1 3/4 IN
SMALL $20

214-4676 SOUTH BEND BAIT CO.
ROCK HOPPER
IN   1952
SMALL $30

214-4671 SOUTH BEND BAIT CO.
RUBB-ORENO CRAWFISH
IN   1940   2 IN
  $50

214-4496 SOUTH BEND BAIT CO.
SLIM-ORENO
IN   1933   3 3/4 IN
  $150

214-4675 SOUTH BEND BAIT CO.
SLIM-ORENO
IN
  $100

214-4698 SOUTH BEND BAIT CO.
SOUTH BEND BAIT
IN
  $200

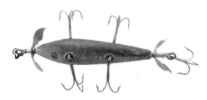

214-4506 SOUTH BEND BAIT CO.
SOUTH BEND MINNOW
IN   1912   3 3/4 IN
OLD, FIRST MODEL $1000

214-4507 SOUTH BEND BAIT CO.
SOUTH BEND MINNOW
IN   1916   3 3/4 IN
OLD, FIRST MODEL $1000

214-4544 SOUTH BEND BAIT CO.
SPIN-I-DIDDEE
IN   1955   2 3/4 IN   3/8 OZ
  $30

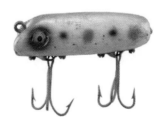

214-4547 SOUTH BEND BAIT CO.
SPIN-I-DIDDEE
IN   1955   2 3/4 IN   3/8 OZ
  $40

214-4573 SOUTH BEND BAIT CO.
SPIN-ORENO
IN
  $30

214-4680 SOUTH BEND BAIT CO.
STRIKE-ORENO
IN   1927   1 IN
  $60

FISHING PLUGS

215-4616 SOUTH BEND BAIT CO.
SUPER SNOOPER
IN 1955
LARGE $60

215-4617 SOUTH BEND BAIT CO.
SUPER SNOOPER
IN
SMALL $60

215-4531 SOUTH BEND BAIT CO.
SURFACE MINNOW, SOUTH BEND
IN
 $300

215-4519 SOUTH BEND BAIT CO.
SURFACE MINNOW, WEEDLESS. S.B.
IN
 $400

215-4520 SOUTH BEND BAIT CO.
SURFACE MINNOW, WEEDLESS. S.B.
IN
OLD $500

215-4532 SOUTH BEND BAIT CO.
SURF-ORENO
IN 1912 3 3/4 IN 1 OZ
OLD $300

215-4534 SOUTH BEND BAIT CO.
SURF-ORENO
IN 1916 3 3/4 IN 1 OZ
EMBOSSED EYE $60

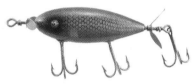

215-4535 SOUTH BEND BAIT CO.
SURF-ORENO
IN 1916
SALTWATER $300

215-4536 SOUTH BEND BAIT CO.
SURF-ORENO
IN 1913 3 3/4 IN 1 OZ
TACK EYES $100

215-4537 SOUTH BEND BAIT CO.
SURF-ORENO
IN 1913 2 3/4 IN
BABY, OLD $300

215-4538 SOUTH BEND BAIT CO.
SURF-ORENO
IN 1923 3 3/4 IN 1 OZ
GLASS EYES $150

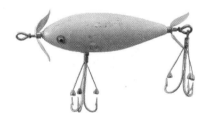

215-4539 SOUTH BEND BAIT CO.
SURF-ORENO
IN 1916 3 3/4 IN 1 OZ
WEEDLESS $300

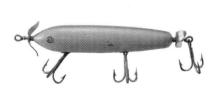

215-4554 SOUTH BEND BAIT CO.
SURF-ORENO
IN 1924 5 1/2 IN
MUSKY $1000

215-4556 SOUTH BEND BAIT CO.
SURF-ORENO
IN 1927 3 3/4 IN 1 OZ
BABY, EMBOSSED EYES $50

215-4557 SOUTH BEND BAIT CO.
SURF-ORENO
IN
BABY, TACK EYES $75

FISHING PLUGS

216-4558 SOUTH BEND BAIT CO.
SURF-ORENO
IN
BABY, LUMINOUS, OLD $150

216-4559 SOUTH BEND BAIT CO.
SURF-ORENO
IN   1923   2 3/4 IN
BABY, GLASS EYES $100

216-4635 SOUTH BEND BAIT CO.
TARP-ORENO
IN   1925   8 IN
LARGE $400

216-4637 SOUTH BEND BAIT CO.
TARP-ORENO
IN
TACK EYES $200

216-4638 SOUTH BEND BAIT CO.
TARP-ORENO
IN   1919
NO EYES $400

216-4639 SOUTH BEND BAIT CO.
TARP-ORENO
IN   1925
MEDIUM $300

216-4682 SOUTH BEND BAIT CO.
TEASER
IN   1927
  $300

216-4684 SOUTH BEND BAIT CO.
TEASER
IN   1925   8 IN
MEDIUM $300

216-4685 SOUTH BEND BAIT CO.
TEASER
IN   1925
SMALL $300

216-4681 SOUTH BEND BAIT CO.
TEASER CHEATER HOOKS
IN   1927
  $300

216-4683 SOUTH BEND BAIT CO.
TEASER, ZANE GRAY
IN   1950   11 IN
  $400

216-4615 SOUTH BEND BAIT CO.
TEAS-ORENO
IN   1929
BIGGER STYLE $100

216-4618 SOUTH BEND BAIT CO.
TEAS-ORENO
IN   1929
SMALL, TACK EYES $50

216-4619 SOUTH BEND BAIT CO.
TEAS-ORENO
IN   1929
MEDIUM, TACK EYES $50

216-4620 SOUTH BEND BAIT CO.
TEAS-ORENO
IN   1929
GLASS EYES $100

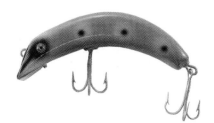

217-4621 SOUTH BEND BAIT CO.
TEAS-ORENO
IN   1929   4 1/8 IN   1/2 OZ
GLASS EYES $100

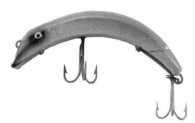

217-4622 SOUTH BEND BAIT CO.
TEAS-ORENO
IN   1929
LARGE, TACK EYES $50

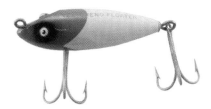

217-4612 SOUTH BEND BAIT CO.
TEX-ORENO FLOATER
IN   1938   2 3/4 IN
   $100

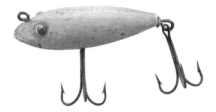

217-4611 SOUTH BEND BAIT CO.
TEX-ORENO SINKER
IN   1951   6 1/2 IN
   $200

217-4636 SOUTH BEND BAIT CO.
TROLL-ORENO
IN   1919
   $300

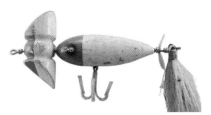

217-4551 SOUTH BEND BAIT CO.
TRUCK-ORENO
IN   1939   5 IN   5 OZ
   $4000

217-4601 SOUTH BEND BAIT CO.
TWO-O-BITE
IN
   $200

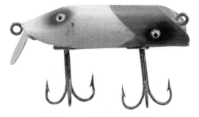

217-4602 SOUTH BEND BAIT CO.
TWO-O-BITE
IN
BABY $100

217-4603 SOUTH BEND BAIT CO.
TWO-ORENO
IN
   $200

217-4604 SOUTH BEND BAIT CO.
TWO-ORENO
IN   1925   3 1/2 IN
BABY $200

217-4516 SOUTH BEND BAIT CO.
UNDERWATER MINNOW, DELUXE, S.B.
IN   1916   3 IN   3/4 OZ
   $250

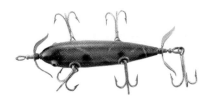

217-4518 SOUTH BEND BAIT CO.
UNDERWATER MINNOW, DELUXE, S.B.
IN
5 TREBLES $300

217-4487 SOUTH BEND BAIT CO.
UNDERWATER MINNOW, SOUTH BEND
IN   1929   3 IN   3/4 OZ
TACK EYES $100

217-4489 SOUTH BEND BAIT CO.
UNDERWATER MINNOW, SOUTH BEND
IN   1916   3 1/4 IN
   $200

217-4529 SOUTH BEND BAIT CO.
UNDERWATER MINNOW, SOUTH BEND
IN
BABY $200

218-4494 SOUTH BEND BAIT CO.
UNDERWATER MINNOW, SPINNING, S.B.
IN   2 IN
3 HOOK $200

218-4541 SOUTH BEND BAIT CO.
VACUUM BAIT
IN   1921   2 3/8 IN   3/4 OZ
GLASS EYES $300

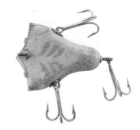

218-4542 SOUTH BEND BAIT CO.
VACUUM BAIT
IN   1921   2 3/8 IN   3/4 OZ
TACK EYES $300

218-4543 SOUTH BEND BAIT CO.
VACUUM BAIT
IN   1921   2 3/8 IN   3/4 OZ
NO EYES $300

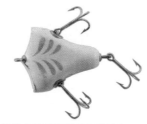

218-4540 SOUTH BEND BAIT CO.
VACUUM BAIT, SMALL
IN   1921   2 IN   1/2 OZ
NO EYES $400

218-4546 SOUTH BEND BAIT CO.
WEE-NIPPEE
IN   1951   2 1/2 IN
    $40

218-4633 SOUTH BEND BAIT CO.
WHIRL-ORENO
IN   1924   3 1/2 IN   5/8 OZ
    $300

218-4600 SOUTH BEND BAIT CO.
WIZ-ORENO
IN
    $250

218-4504 SOUTH BEND BAIT CO.
WOODPECKER
IN   1916   4 3/4 IN
    $150

218-4505 SOUTH BEND BAIT CO.
WOODPECKER
IN   1919   3 IN
BABY $100

218-5268 SOUTH BEND BAIT CO.
WOODPECKER BLANK
IN
BABY $50

218-4501 SOUTH BEND BAIT CO.
WOODPECKER, WEEDLESS
IN   1916   3 IN
    $150

218-4502 SOUTH BEND BAIT CO.
WOODPECKER, WEEDLESS
IN   1916   3 IN
    $200

218-4503 SOUTH BEND BAIT CO.
WOODPECKER, WEEDLESS
IN   1912   3 IN
FIRST MODEL $300

218-4530 SOUTH BEND BAIT CO.
ZIPPER TOPWATER
IN
    $60

219-4526 SOUTH BEND BAIT CO.
ZIPPER UNDERWATER
IN
SMALL $60

219-4528 SOUTH BEND BAIT CO.
ZIPPER, SPECIAL
IN   1924   3 1/2 IN
   $60

219-3989 SOUTH BEND LURE CO.
PELICAN
IN   1936   3 1/4 IN
   $100

219-3899 SOUTHERN ARTIFICAL BAIT CO.
SOUTHERN ARTIFICIAL BAIT
MO
   $100

219-0807 SOUTHWEST TACKLE CO.
BINGO MOUSE
IN   1930-1939   2 1/2 IN
   $150

219-0808 SOUTHWEST TACKLE CO.
BINGO MOUSE
IN   1930-1939   2 1/2 IN
   $150

219-3966 SPARK-DART CO.
SPARK-DART BAIT
OK   1948
LARGE $60

219-3969 SPARK-DART CO.
SPARK-DART BAIT
OK   1948
   $60

219-5706 SPARK-DART CO.
SPARK-DART BAIT
OK   1948
   $40

219-4081 SPLIT FISH LURE CO.
SPLIT FISH
OH   1951
   $40

219-3970 SPORTING INDUSTRIES
JUDAS FROG
IL   1947   3 3/4 IN   5/8 OZ
   $90

219-3963 SPORTSLAND MFG. CO.
SHIMMY DIVER
OK   1944   2 1/4 IN
SMALL $60

219-3965 SPORTSLAND MFG. CO.
SHIMMY DIVER
OK
LARGE $60

219-3962 SPORTSLAND MFG. CO.
SHIMMY SHINER
OK   1944   3 1/2 IN
OLD $60

219-3964 SPORTSLAND MFG. CO.
SHIMMY SHINER
OK   1956   3 1/2 IN
   $60

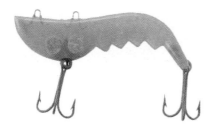

220-1221 SPORTSMAN LURE CO.
TEXAS SHORTY SHRIMP
TX
  $30

220-3974 SPORTSMAN RESEARCH
HI-SPORT
TX   1941   3 IN
  $20

220-4692 SPORTSMAN SPECIALTY
LUCID LURE
MI
  $30

220-3955 SPORTSMAN'S LURE CO.
LITTLE TOBE
TX
SMALL $20

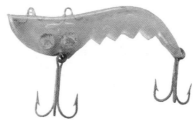

220-3956 SPORTSMAN'S LURE CO.
LITTLE TOBE
TX
  $20

220-3947 SPORTSMAN'S LURE CO.
NEON HUMPY
TX   1940's
  $20

220-3952 SPORTSMAN'S LURE CO.
SWIMMING MINNOW, SPORTSMAN'S
TX   1940   1 3/4 IN
  $20

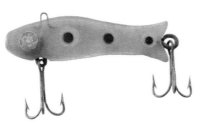

220-3949 SPORTSMAN'S LURE CO.
WIGGLER, SPORTSMAN'S
TX   1940's
LARGE $20

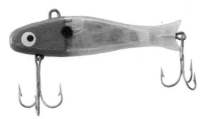

220-3953 SPORTSMAN'S LURE CO.
WIGGLING MINNOW
TX
LARGE $20

220-3976 SPORTSMAN'S PRODUCTS
SPARKLE TAIL
TX   1956
  $20

220-3975 SPORTSMAN'S PRODUCTS
SPARKLE TAIL JR.
TX   1956
  $20

220-0648 SPRINGFIELD NOVELTY
REEL LURE
MO   1934   2 1/4 IN
  $100

220-0650 SPRINGFIELD NOVELTY
REEL LURE
MO   1930   3 1/4 IN
MUSKY $1500

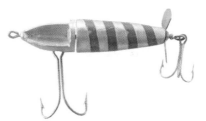

220-0657 SPRINGFIELD NOVELTY
REEL LURE, 1/2
MO   1934   3 IN
  $200

220-0649 SPRINGFIELD NOVELTY
REEL LURE, TOPWATER
MO   1934   2 IN
  $100

221-3852 ST. CROIX BAIT CO.
SNIPE
WI   1955   2 3/4 IN
   $20

221-3960 STAGE
STAGE FROG
OH   1919   2 3/4 IN
PEARL EYES $2000

221-3961 STAGE
STAGE FROG
OH   1923   3 1/2 IN
GLASS EYES $2000

221-3979 STALEY-JOHNSON MFG. CO.
FROG, STALEY-JOHNSON
IN   1940's
   $20

221-3984 STALEY-JOHNSON MFG. CO.
GILLOW
IN   1940's   2 1/2 IN
   $20

221-3983 STALEY-JOHNSON MFG. CO.
MINNOW, STALEY-JOHNSON
IN   1940's
   $20

221-3985 STALEY-JOHNSON MFG. CO.
PIKE TYPE, STALEY-JOHNSON
IN   1940's   2 1/2 IN
   $20

221-3981 STALEY-JOHNSON MFG. CO.
POPPER
IN   1940's   1 1/2 IN
   $20

221-3982 STALEY-JOHNSON MFG. CO.
RUNT
IN   1940's   1 1/2 IN
   $20

221-3977 STALEY-JOHNSON MFG. CO.
TWIN-MIN
IN   1947   3 IN
   $100

221-3980 STALEY-JOHNSON MFG. CO.
WIGGLER, STALEY-JOHNSON
IN   1940's   3 3/4 IN
   $20

221-2687 STAR
SALMON PLUG, STAR

   $75

221-7030 STEEL BAIT CO.
FROG, STEEL
   1958
   $60

221-3987 STEEL BAIT CO.
FROG, STEEL'S DIVING
   1958
   $60

221-3925 STEELSTAMP CO.
BASS THIEF
WI   1936   3 3/4 IN
   $200

FISHING PLUGS

222-3924 STEELSTAMP CO.
PIKE THIEF
WI   1898
  $200

222-3943 STETTNER, ANTONE
PLUGGIN' SHORTY
TX   1940   2 1/4 IN
SMALL $20

222-3944 STETTNER, ANTONE
PLUGGIN' SHORTY
TX   1940   3 IN
LARGE $20

222-4108 STEWART, BUD TACKLE
CRIPPLED FROG
MI   1930's
  $100

222-4101 STEWART, BUD TACKLE
CRIPPLED MOUSE
MI   1930's   2 1/4 IN
  $100

222-4100 STEWART, BUD TACKLE
CRIPPLED WIGGLER
MI   1930's
LARGE $100

222-4105 STEWART, BUD TACKLE
CRIPPLED WIGGLER
MI   1930's
BABY $100

222-4109 STEWART, BUD TACKLE
HAMMER HANDLE
MI   1930's
SMALL $100

222-4104 STEWART, BUD TACKLE
HAMMER HANDLE, JOINTED
MI   1930's
MEDIUM $100

222-4106 STEWART, BUD TACKLE
HAMMER HANDLE, MUSKY
MI   1930's
  $200

222-4107 STEWART, BUD TACKLE
LEECH, STEWART
MI   1930's
  $100

222-4102 STEWART, BUD TACKLE
PAD HOPPER
MI   1930's   3 IN
  $100

222-4103 STEWART, BUD TACKLE
PAD HOPPER DIVER
MI   1930's
  $100

222-4095 STORM MFG. CO.
GLOP
OK   1960   2 1/4 IN
  $50

222-3971 STREAM-EZE INC.
VIRGIN MERMAID BAIT
IN   1957   4 IN
LARGE $60

FISHING PLUGS

223-3972 STREAM-EZE INC.
VIRGIN MERMAID BAIT
IN   1957   1 1/2 IN
SMALL $60

223-3992 STREAMLINE PRODUCTS
CHUBBY MINNOW
IL
  $200

223-3993 STREAMLINE PRODUCTS
CHUBBY MINNOW, JOINTED
IL
  $200

223-5500 STREAMLINE PRODUCTS
MINNOW, KAUTH
IL   1939
BILL KAUTH $50

223-3990 STREICH MFG.
FLEX-O-MINO
IL   1915   3 1/2 IN
  $100

223-4029 STRIKE-MASTER LURES
BASS KING
OH   1925   3 3/4 IN
  $200

223-5470 STRIKE-MASTER LURES
UNDERWATER MINNOW
OH
  $200

223-4040 STRIKE-MASTER LURES
BUG, STRIKE-MASTER
OH   1920   3 1/4 IN
OLD $400

223-4028 STRIKE-MASTER LURES
CRAB, STRIKE-MASTER
OH   1922
OLD $300

223-4042 STRIKE-MASTER LURES
CRAB, STRIKE-MASTER
OH   1925   2 IN
SMALL $200

223-4055 STRIKE-MASTER LURES
CRAB, STRIKE-MASTER
OH   1925   3 IN
LARGE $200

223-4026 STRIKE-MASTER LURES
DEATH'S PRIDE
OH   1922   3 1/2 IN   3/4 OZ
OLD $300

223-4035 STRIKE-MASTER LURES
FROG, STRIKE-MASTER
OH   1932   2 1/2 IN   3/4 OZ
  $200

223-4037 STRIKE-MASTER LURES
FROG, STRIKE-MASTER
OH   1928   2 3/4 IN
OLD $300

223-4043 STRIKE-MASTER LURES
HELLGRAMITE, STRIKE-MASTER
OH   1927   4 IN
LARGE $200

FISHING PLUGS

224-4053 STRIKE-MASTER LURES
HELLGRAMITE,
OH   1925   2 IN
SMALL $200

224-4054 STRIKE-MASTER LURES
HELLGRAMITE,
OH   1925   3 IN
MEDIUM $200

224-4041 STRIKE-MASTER LURES
HOOT- ANNINNIE
OH   1922   2 IN
OLD $400

224-4050 STRIKE-MASTER LURES
MOUSE,
OH   1925
   $200

224-4033 STRIKE-MASTER LURES
MUSKY MINNOW,
OH   1925   3 3/4 IN   1 OZ
   $300

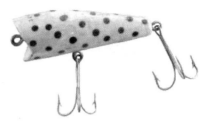

224-3790 STRIKE-MASTER LURES
NIGHT HAWK
OH
   $200

224-4024 STRIKE-MASTER LURES
NIGHT HAWK
OH   1925   3 1/2 IN   3/4 OZ
   $200

224-4023 STRIKE-MASTER LURES
NIGHT HAWK, SIDE HOOK
OH   1925   3 1/2 IN   3/4 OZ
OLD $300

224-4052 STRIKE-MASTER LURES
PIKE MINNOW,   STRIKE-MASTER
OH   1925   4 5/8 IN   1 OZ
   $200

224-4027 STRIKE-MASTER LURES
POPPER, STRIKE-MASTER
OH   1925
OLD $400

224-4034 STRIKE-MASTER LURES
POPPER, STRIKE-MASTER
OH   1922
OLD $300

224-4051 STRIKE-MASTER LURES
ROLLING DIVER
OH   1925   4 1/8 IN   3/4 OZ
   $300

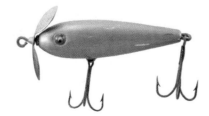

224-4039 STRIKE-MASTER LURES
SLIGHT UNDERWATER
OH   1923   3 IN
   $300

224-4031 STRIKE-MASTER LURES
SURFACE KILLER
OH   1928   3 3/4 IN   3/4 OZ
   $200

224-4038 STRIKE-MASTER LURES
SURFACE KILLER
OH   1922   3 3/4 IN
OLD $300

FISHING PLUGS

225-4044 STRIKE-MASTER LURES
SURFACE KILLER
OH   1925   2 3/4 IN   3/4 OZ
LARGE $200

225-4049 STRIKE-MASTER LURES
SURFACE KILLER
OH   1925
SMALL $200

225-4030 STRIKE-MASTER LURES
SURFACE SPRAYING GLIDER
OH   1928   3 1/2 IN   3/4 OZ
GLASS EYES $200

225-4032 STRIKE-MASTER LURES
SURFACE STRIKE-MASTER
OH   1921   3 3/4 IN
OLD $300

225-4036 STRIKE-MASTER LURES
SURFACE TEASER
OH   1925   3 IN
$200

225-4045 STRIKE-MASTER LURES
TOPWATER STRIKE-MASTER
OH   1925
OLD $300

225-4046 STRIKE-MASTER LURES
UNDERWATER STRIKE-MASTER
OH   1938   3 3/4 IN
OLD $300

225-4025 STRIKE-MASTER LURES
WATER WALTZER
OH   1925   3 IN   1 OZ
$200

225-4048 STRIKE-MASTER LURES
WIZARD
OH   1925   3 IN
BABY $200

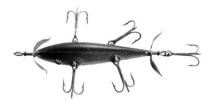

225-4019 STUART, WM. & CO.
ECLIPSE WOODEN MINNOW
OH   1907   3 1/2 IN
5-HOOK $3000

225-4020 STUART, WM. & CO.
ECLIPSE WOODEN MINNOW
OH   1907   3 1/2 IN
3-HOOK $3000

225-4005 SUGARWOOD LURE CO.
PIKE MINNOW

$20

225-5191 SUICK BAIT CO
SUICK MUSKIE THRILLER
WI
MUSKY $50

225-5013 SUMMER-WOODS
WEEDMASTER
MI
$20

225-3839 SUMMIT LURES
FISH,
OK   1948
$200

226-3840 SUMMIT LURES
HELEGRAMITE, SUMMIT
OK   1948
LARGE $100

226-3841 SUMMIT LURES
HELEGRAMITE, SUMMIT
OK   1948
SMALL $100

226-3837 SUMMIT LURES
SUMMIT LURE, TOPWATER
OK   1948
LARGE $200

226-3838 SUMMIT LURES
SUMMIT LURE, TOPWATER
OK   1948
SMALL $200

226-5145 SUR-CATCH
PENCIL PLUG
MI
   $30

226-3998 SWANBURG, JULIUS
PEACH-ORENO TYPE
IL   1941
SMALL $100

226-3919 SWEENEY, SLIM
TWINMINNOW BAIT
CA   1939   3 IN
TWINMINNOW BAIT CO. $300

226-3898 SWEET, A.J. CO.
SWEET MINNOW MOTION BAIT

$1500

226-0640 SWIMMING WHIZ BAIT CO.
SWIMMING WHIZ

$30

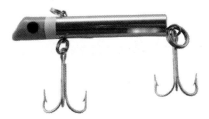

226-4086 SWIMMY BAIT CO.
SWIMMY LURE

$15

226-5187 SYLVESTER, JERRY
BASS-AQUA
MA   1947
   $50

226-5186 SYLVESTER, JERRY
BLUE STREAK WOBBLER
MA   1946
   $50

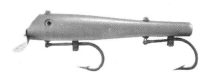

226-5190 SYLVESTER, JERRY
HEAVYWEIGHT
MA   1947
   $50

226-5193 SYLVESTER, JERRY
HEAVYWEIGHT, JOINTED
MA
   $50

226-1382 SYLVESTER, JERRY
JERRY'S MULLET
MA
   $40

227-5207 SYLVESTER, JERRY
MULLET
MA
  $50

227-3995 SZABO, BILL
CREE-DUK
OH   1950   3 3/4 IN
LARGE $100

227-3996 SZABO, BILL
CREE-DUK
OH   1950   2 1/2 IN
SMALL $100

227-3867 TACKLE INDUSTRIES
SKIP-JACK
LA   1958   2 1/2 IN
SMALL $15

227-3868 TACKLE INDUSTRIES
SKIP-JACK
LA   1958
LARGE $15

227-4688 TANTALURE CO.
TANTALURE
OH   1930
  $30

227-4695 TAR HEEL BAIT CO.
TAR HEEL FLAPPER
NC   1954
  $60

227-4697 TATE BAIT CO.
OLE LIZ
AR   1948   3 1/4 IN
  $30

227-4699 TATE BAIT CO.
OLE LIZ
AR   1948   2 1/4 IN
BABY $30

227-4710 TAYLOR MFG. CO.
BASS CHARMER
MN   1921   3 IN
  $200

227-4711 TAYLOR MFG. CO.
BASS CHARMER
MN   1921   3 IN
BUCKTAIL $200

227-4686 TEMPTER BAIT CO.
TEMPTER FROG
PA
NEEDS RUBBER LEGS $300

227-5725 THARP, EARL
THARP'S DEEP DIVE
OK   1950
  $30

227-2776 THOMPSON-MOORE
MITY ATOM BAIT
TX   1950   2 1/2 IN
  $50

227-5128 THREE-IN-ONE BAIT CO.
THREE-IN-ONE DIVER

  $40

FISHING PLUGS

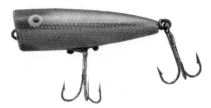

228-5129 THREE-IN-ONE BAIT CO.
THREE-IN-ONE TOPWATER

$40

228-1585 TIEDE ENTERPRISES
MIRACLE LURE, THE
CAN
T.D. DOODLER, ONTARIO $10

228-4725 TILL & WEAVER BAIT CO
TILL'S TOPPER
TX   3 IN
PAINTED EYES $40

228-4709 T-N-T TACKLE CO.
T-N-T TWISTER
  1946   2 1/2 IN
  $200

228-4694 TOLEDO BAIT CO.
TOLEDO WEEDLESS
OH   1925
  $300

228-4747 TOM BAIT CO.
GIZMO
IL   1947
PLASTIC $40

228-4748 TOM BAIT CO.
SHINEROO
IL   1947   3 3/4 IN
PLASTIC SPOON $40

228-4730 TOOLEY, L.J. CO.
BUNTY DARTER
MI   1916   2 1/4 IN
  $1500

228-4731 TOOLEY, L.J. CO.
BUNTY SPINNERED BAIT
MI   1917   2 1/2 IN
  $1500

228-4735 TRADEWINDS INC.
SPIN-IN-HERRY
WA   1950's
  $20

228-3240 TRANS-LURE BAIT CO.
TRANSPARENT LURE, THE
IL   1946   3 3/4 IN
JOHN INGALLS $100

228-4745 TRANSPARENT FISHING TACK.
LURETTE
CAN   1920's
CANADA $1200

228-5489 TRAVELURE CO.
TRAV-L-LURE
WI   1960
  $10

228-4737 TRENTON MFG. CO.
GURGLEHEAD
KY   1940's   3 1/4 IN   5/8 OZ
WOOD $100

228-4744 TRENTON MFG. CO.
MAD MOUSE
KY   1946   2 3/4 IN   1/2 OZ
  $100

229-4738 TRENTON MFG. CO.
SPIN DIVER, TRENTON
KY   1940's   4 IN   3/4 OZ
  $100

229-4736 TRENTON MFG. CO.
TAIL SPIN
KY   1940's   4 5/8 IN   5/8 OZ
WOOD $100

229-2690 TROLLER TACKLE CO.
PIRATE, TROLLER
OR
  $100

229-5553 TROPICAL BAIT CO.
DOUBLE MINNOW
IN   1940
  $100

229-4708 TROPICAL BAIT CO.
FUZZY DUCK
IN   1952
  $150

229-4097 TROPICAL BAIT CO.
STORMY FROG
IN   1947
  $50

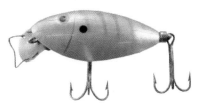

229-4712 TROPICAL BAIT CO.
STORMY FROG
IN   1947   1 1/2 IN
  $200

229-4098 TROPICAL BAIT CO.
STORMY PETREL BIRD
IN   1947   4 IN
  $300

229-1337 TRUE TEMPER
CRIPPLED SHAD, TRUE TEMPER
OH   1940's
  $40

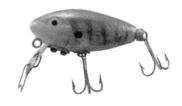

229-1338 TRUE TEMPER
SPEED SHAD JR, TRUE TEMPER
OH   1940's
  $75

229-1336 TRUE TEMPER
SPEED SHAD, TRUE TEMPER
OH   1940's
  $30

229-4753 TULSA FISHING TACKLE CO.
BEE
OK   1948   2 IN
  $30

229-4755 TULSA FISHING TACKLE CO.
BEE-BOP
OK   1948   2 IN
BABY $30

229-4756 TULSA FISHING TACKLE CO.
BEE-BOP
OK   1946   3 IN   2/5 OZ
  $30

229-4761 TULSA FISHING TACKLE CO.
BIZZY-BEE
OK   1948   1 1/2 IN
  $30

FISHING PLUGS

230-4763 TULSA FISHING TACKLE CO.
BIZZY-BEE
OK   1948   1 1/2 IN   1/3 OZ
NEW STYLE $30

230-4754 TULSA FISHING TACKLE CO.
DEEP-BEE
OK   1947   1 3/4 IN   1/3 OZ
    $30

230-4757 TULSA FISHING TACKLE CO.
DEEP-STUNTER
OK   1947   2 1/4 IN
    $30

230-4749 TULSA FISHING TACKLE CO.
DI-DIPPER BAIT
OK   1952   2 1/4 IN
SMALL, NEW STYLE $50

230-4750 TULSA FISHING TACKLE CO.
DI-DIPPER BAIT
OK   1952
SMALL $40

230-4751 TULSA FISHING TACKLE CO.
DI-DIPPER BAIT
OK   1952
LARGE $40

230-4752 TULSA FISHING TACKLE CO.
DI-DIPPER BAIT
OK   1946   2 1/2 IN   2/5 OZ
LARGE, NEW STYLE $40

230-4758 TULSA FISHING TACKLE CO.
STUNTER
OK   1946   1 3/4 IN   1/4 OZ
    $30

230-4762 TULSA FISHING TACKLE CO.
WATER WIGGLER
OK   1948   2 1/2 IN   2/5 OZ
    $30

230-4724 TURNER, ZACHARY
TURNER CASTING MINNOW
MI   1903   4 1/2 IN
    $1500

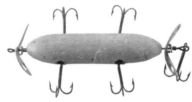

230-4727 TURNER, O.A.
TURNER CASTING MINNOW
MI   1905   4 1/2 IN
    $1500

230-4726 TURNER, O.A.
TURNER TOPWATER BAIT
MI   1907   3 1/4 IN
    $1500

230-4721 TWIN MINNOW BAIT & TACKLE
TWIN MINNOW
NY   1933   3 IN
    $40

230-4722 TWIN MINNOW BAIT & TACKLE
TWIN MINNOW
NY   1933   3 IN
SMALL $40

230-4742 TYNE-LYNE BAIT CO.
TYNE-MYTE BAIT
OK   1952
SMALL $10

231-4743 TYNE-LYNE BAIT CO.
TYNE-MYTE BAIT
OK   1952   2 IN
LARGE $10

231-1648 UNCA HUB'S ENTERPRISES
DOOFER
FL   1946   2 IN
SMALL $30

231-4691 UNCLE ASHER'S BAIT & TACKLE
UNCLE ASHER'S BAIT
AR   1969
   $75

231-2692 UNCLE ASHER'S BAIT & TACKLE
UNCLE ASHER'S BAIT
AR   1969
   $40

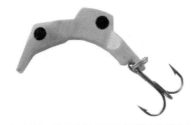

231-2693 UNCLE ASHER'S BAIT & TACKLE
UNCLE ASHER'S BAIT
AR   1969
   $40

231-4764 UNILINE MFG. CO.
SPINNO MINNO
TX   1947   2 3/4 IN
   $40

231-4768 UNION SPRINGS SPECIALTY
MILLER'S REVERSIBLE MINNOW
NY   1916   4 1/4 IN
WOOD $5000

231-4787 VAL PRODUCTS
VAL-CHIPPEWA-LUR
IL   1936
   $100

231-4785 VAL PRODUCTS
VAL-ELEREE-LUR
IL   1936   2 1/4 IN
   $100

231-4788 VAL PRODUCTS
VAL-PIKY-LUR
IL   1936   3 1/4 IN
   $100

231-4790 VAL PRODUCTS
VAL-PIKY-LUR, BABY
IL   1936   2 3/4 IN
   $100

231-4791 VAL PRODUCTS
VAL-PIKY-LUR, BABY
IL   1936   2 3/4 IN
WEEDLESS $100

231-4786 VAL PRODUCTS
VAL-PIKY-LUR, JOINTED
IL   1936   4 IN
   $100

231-4789 VAL PRODUCTS
VAL-PIKY-LUR, WEEDLESS
IL   1936   2 3/4 IN
   $100

231-4783 VANN-CLAY CO., THE
VANN-CLAY MINNOW
GA   1928   4 IN
   $500

232-4784 VANN-CLAY CO., THE
VANN-CLAY WOBBLER
GA   1928   4 1/4 IN
$500

232-4782 VAUGHN TACKLE CO.
VAUGHN'S LURE
MI   1932   3 3/4 IN
$300

232-5443 VEIHL, RAY/ERVIN
GOLDFISH DECOY

$300

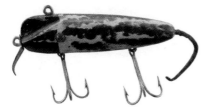

232-4795 VERMILION BAIT CO.
VERMILION MOUSE
OH   1922   3 3/4 IN
OLD $300

232-4796 VERMILION BAIT CO.
VERMILION MOUSE
OH   1924   3 3/4 IN
NEW $300

232-4780 VESCO BAIT CO.
VESCO BAIT
NY   1922
LARGE $300

232-4781 VESCO BAIT CO.
VESCO BAIT
NY   1922   3 1/4 IN
SMALL $300

232-4777 VIVI BAIT CO.
VIVI BASS LURE
FRA
MEDIUM $10

232-4778 VIVI BAIT CO.
VIVI BASS LURE
FRA   1960   2 3/4 IN
SMALL $10

232-4779 VIVI BAIT CO.
VIVI BASS LURE
FRA   1960   5 3/4 IN
LARGE $10

232-1299 VOGEL'S OF CALIFORNIA
FENNEY FERRET
CA   1965
$10

232-4893 WAIT TACKLE CO.
WHIRLING DERVISH
MI   1952   2 1/4 IN
$40

232-2688 WALLACE
WALLACE HIGHLINER
WA   1942   7 IN
$75

232-4839 WALLSTEN CO.
CISCO KID
IL   1950
LARGE, JOINTED $20

232-4840 WALLSTEN CO.
CISCO KID
IL   1960   1 3/4 IN
SMALL, JOINTED $20

FISHING PLUGS

233-4823 WALLSTEN CO.
CISCO KID DEEP DIVER
IL   1955   3 1/2 IN
MEDIUM $20

233-4825 WALLSTEN CO.
CISCO KID DEEP DIVER
IL   1955   2 1/4 IN
SMALL $20

233-4824 WALLSTEN CO.
CISCO KID DIVER
IL   1958   2 IN
MEDIUM $20

233-4842 WALLSTEN CO.
CISCO KID FLASHER
IL   1960   3 IN
   $20

233-4841 WALLSTEN CO.
CISCO KID INJURED MINNOW
IL   1950   3 1/4 IN
   $20

233-4821 WALLSTEN CO.
CISCO KID INJURED SPINNER
IL   1950's
OLD $10

233-4826 WALLSTEN CO.
CISCO KID LURE
IL   1955
   $20

233-4815 WALLSTEN CO.
SKIP-N-CISCO
IL   1950
PLASTIC $15

233-4820 WALLSTEN CO.
TOPPER, WALLSTEN
IL   1950's
MUSKY SIZE $20

233-4830 WALTON, EVANS CO.
WEED QUEEN
MI   1936   2 3/4 IN
   $100

233-5153 WARNER TACKLE CO.
MINNOW, BILL WARNER

   $100

233-5434 WASHALL, TY
DECOY, PIKE, WASHALL
MN   1934
   $200

233-4806 WASWYLER, DR. C.S.
MARVELOUS ELECTRIC GLOW MINN.
WI   1915
CASTING MINNOW $3000

233-4845 WATT TACKLE CO.
TWIRLING TWIRP
MI   1950's
   $200

233-4831 WEBER TACKLE CO.
BIG SHOT
WI   1954   2 1/4 IN
   $30

FISHING PLUGS

234-4850 WEBER TACKLE CO.
FLIP-FROG
WI   1955   2 IN
  $20

234-4844 WEBER TACKLE CO.
MOUSE, WEBER
WI   1960   2 IN
  $20

234-4837 WEBER TACKLE CO.
SHADRAC
WI   1960
SMALL $10

234-4838 WEBER TACKLE CO.
SHADRAC
WI   1960
LARGE $10

234-4843 WEBER TACKLE CO.
SN2 SPINNING LURE
WI   1957   2 1/2 IN
  $20

234-6997 WEBER TACKLE CO.
WEBER BAIT
WI
  $100

234-4891 WEBFOOT, JOHN
WEBFOOT LURE
IL   1958
  $20

234-4862 WEEZEL BAIT CO.
WEEZEL BOPPER
OH   1946   3 IN   1/2 OZ
  $100

234-4861 WEEZEL BAIT CO.
WEEZEL SPARROW
OH   1948   3 IN   1/2 OZ
  $75

234-4807 WELLER, ERWIN CO.
CLASSIC MINNOW, WELLER
IA   1927   4 1/2 IN
LARGE $150

234-4811 WELLER, ERWIN CO.
CLASSIC MINNOW, WELLER
IA   1927   3 1/4 IN
SMALL $150

234-4812 WELLER, ERWIN CO.
CLASSIC MINNOW, WELLER
IA   1927   3 1/2 IN
NEWER, JOINTED $150

234-4813 WELLER, ERWIN CO.
CLASSIC MINNOW, WELLER
IA   1925   3 1/2 IN
JOINTED $150

234-4814 WELLER, ERWIN CO.
CLASSIC MINNOW, WELLER
IA   1924   3 1/2 IN
JOINTED $150

234-4809 WELLER, ERWIN CO.
MOUSE, WELLER
IA   1925   2 IN
  $200

Page 234

235-4810 WELLER, ERWIN CO.
OZARK WIGGLER
IA   1927   2 1/2 IN   1/2 OZ
$200

235-4816 WELLER, ERWIN CO.
SIMPLEX MINNOW
IA   1924   5 IN
$150

235-4819 WELLER, ERWIN CO.
WELLER MINNOW, MUSKIE
IA   1925   6 1/2 IN
$1500

235-4865 WELSH, STEWART
WELSHERANA BAIT
CA   1920
$150

235-5973 WENGER MFG. CO.
BASS ENTICER
IN   1933
$60

235-4846 WETHALL, HANS G.
BOBBIN BASS BAIT

LARGE $300

235-4847 WETHALL, HANS G.
BOBBIN BASS BAIT

SMALL $300

235-3336 WHEELER-LUNBECK MFG CO.
PELICAN
IN
$40

235-4890 WHING DING BAIT CO
WHING DING BAIT

$30

235-4858 WHISTLER, BERT
BASS KILLER
    4 IN
$200

235-4859 WHISTLER, BERT
BASS KILLER

SMALL $200

235-4860 WHISTLER, BERT
BASS KILLER

LARGE $200

235-0498 WHITE'S WONDER BAIT CO.
WHITE'S WONDER
OH   1908   3 IN
$600

235-5083 WHOPPER-STOPPER BAIT CO.
BAYOU BOOGIE
TX   1952   3 IN
$10

235-5084 WHOPPER-STOPPER BAIT CO.
BAYOU BOOGIE
TX   1952   4 1/4 IN
SALTWATER $20

FISHING PLUGS

236-5085 WHOPPER-STOPPER BAIT CO.
BAYOU BOOGIE
TX   1953   2 IN
SMALL $10

236-5063 WHOPPER-STOPPER BAIT CO.
LIZARD BAIT
TX   1952   4 IN
LARGE $60

236-5064 WHOPPER-STOPPER BAIT CO.
LIZARD BAIT
TX   1952
SMALL $60

236-5089 WHOPPER-STOPPER BAIT CO.
WHOPPER-STOPPER BAIT
TX   1947   2 IN
SMALL $40

236-5090 WHOPPER-STOPPER BAIT CO.
WHOPPER-STOPPER BAIT
TX   1947
MEDIUM $40

236-5091 WHOPPER-STOPPER BAIT CO.
WHOPPER-STOPPER BAIT
TX   1947   3 IN
LARGE $40

236-5074 WHOPPER-STOPPER BAIT CO.
WHOPPER-STOPPER BAIT, POPPER
TX   1948
 $1200

236-5077 WHOPPER-STOPPER BAIT CO.
WHOPPER-STOPPER BAIT,   POPPER
TX   1948   2 IN
LARGE $20

236-5092 WHOPPER-STOPPER BAIT CO.
WHOPPER-STOPPER BAIT, JOINTED
TX   1960   3 3/4 IN
 $40

236-5072 WHOPPER-STOPPER BAIT CO.
WHOPPER-STOPPER BAIT, TOPPER
TX   1958
 $30

236-5086 WHOPPER-STOPPER BAIT CO.
WOBBLER, WHOPPER STOPPER
TX   1958
SMALL $40

236-5088 WHOPPER-STOPPER BAIT CO.
WOBBLER, WHOPPER STOPPER
TX   1948   3 IN
 $40

236-4905 WIESE BAIT CO.
WIESE IKE TYPE
IA   1939
 $90

236-4903 WIESE BAIT CO.
WIESE RUNT TYPE
IA   1939
 $90

236-5075 WIFORD, L.A. & CO.
CROAKER WOBBLER
MI   1911
 $700

FISHING PLUGS

237-5066 WIFORD, L.A. & CO.
CROAKER, WIFORD
MI   1911   4 IN
OLD $700

237-5076 WIFORD, L.A. & CO.
CROAKER, WIFORD
MI   1911
$700

237-5067 WIFORD, L.A. & CO.
WIFORD, UNKNOWN
MI
$300

237-5068 WIFORD, L.A. & CO.
WIFORD, UNKNOWN
MI
$300

237-5069 WIFORD, L.A. & CO.
WIFORD, UNKNOWN
MI
$300

237-5070 WIFORD, L.A. & CO.
WIFORD, UNKNOWN
MI   1917   4 1/2 IN
$300

237-5071 WIFORD, L.A. & CO.
WIFORD, UNKNOWN
MI
$300

237-5073 WIFORD, L.A. & CO.
WIFORD, UNKNOWN
MI   1917   6 IN
$300

237-4979 WILSON (HASTINGS)
ALGER'S GETSEM
MI   1916   2 1/4 IN
$300

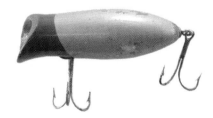

237-4923 WILSON (HASTINGS)
BASS SEEKER
MI   1919   3 1/4 IN
BABY $200

237-4926 WILSON (HASTINGS)
BASS SEEKER
MI   1919   3 1/2 IN
NEW $200

237-4927 WILSON (HASTINGS)
BASS SEEKER
MI   1915   4 IN
OLD $200

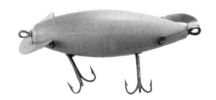

237-4982 WILSON (HASTINGS)
BASSMERIZER
MI   1917   3 5/8 IN
$500

237-4922 WILSON (HASTINGS)
CUPPED WOBBLER
MI   1915   4 IN
OLD $300

237-4920 WILSON (HASTINGS)
FLANGED WOBBLER
MI   1919   4 IN
$200

238-4921 WILSON (HASTINGS)
FLANGED WOBBLER
MI 1915 4 IN
OLD $300

238-4980 WILSON (HASTINGS)
GRASS WIDOW
MI 1917 2 1/4 IN
  $400

238-4913 WILSON (HASTINGS)
SIX-IN-ONE WOBBLER
MI 1915 4 IN
ADJUSTABLE LIP $700

238-4981 WILSON (HASTINGS)
STAGGERBUG
MI 1918 3 3/4 IN
  $2000

238-4911 WILSON (HASTINGS)
SUPER-WOBBLER
MI 1919 3 1/2 IN
SMALL $100

238-4912 WILSON (HASTINGS)
SUPER-WOBBLER
MI 1919 4 IN
  $100

238-4925 WILSON (HASTINGS)
WILSON CUPPED WOBBLER
MI 1919 4 IN
  $200

238-4914 WILSON (HASTINGS)
WILSON LUMINOUS WOBBLER
MI 1915
  $100

238-4906 WILSON (HASTINGS)
WILSON WOBBLER
MI 1920 4 IN
  $70

238-4907 WILSON (HASTINGS)
WILSON WOBBLER
MI 1920
GLASS EYES $300

238-4908 WILSON (HASTINGS)
WILSON WOBBLER
MI 1920
  $70

238-4909 WILSON (HASTINGS)
WILSON WOBBLER
MI 1920 5 IN
MUSKY SIZE $300

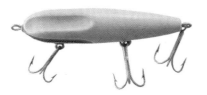

238-4918 WILSON (HASTINGS)
WILSON WOBBLER
MI 1920
NEW STYLE $70

238-4919 WILSON (HASTINGS)
WILSON WOBBLER
MI 1920
BABY $100

238-4915 WILSON (HASTINGS)
WILSON WOBBLER, WEEDLESS
MI 1914 4 IN
  $100

239-4910 WILSON (HASTINGS)
WILSON, UNKNOWN
MI   1920
  $300

239-4967 WILSON BAIT CO.
WILSON FROG
OH   1915
  $200

239-4977 WINCHESTER BAIT & MFG.
NEVERMIS
IN   1927
LUCKY HIT BAIT $600

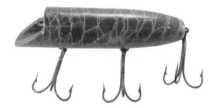

239-4978 WINCHESTER BAIT & MFG.
WINCHESTER BAIT, UNKNOWN
IN
LUCKY HIT BAIT $600

239-4983 WINCHESTER BAIT & MFG.
WINCHESTER, UNKNOWN
IN
  $600

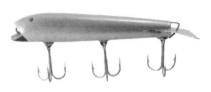

239-5057 WINCHESTER REPEAT. ARMS
BOBBIE BAIT
CT   1946   6 IN
WINCHESTER WAS JOBBER $100

239-5040 WINCHESTER REPEAT. ARMS
MULTI-WOBBLER
CT   1925   3 1/4 IN
DECAL EYES $500

239-5041 WINCHESTER REPEAT. ARMS
MULTI-WOBBLER
CT   1920   3 1/4 IN
GLASS EYES $500

239-5049 WINCHESTER REPEAT. ARMS
WINCHESTER CHEAPLINE MINNOW
CT   1924
  $500

239-5058 WINCHESTER REPEAT. ARMS
WINCHESTER MARKED
CT   1946
WINCHESTER WAS JOBBER $100

239-5059 WINCHESTER REPEAT. ARMS
WINCHESTER MARKED
CT   1946
WINCHESTER WAS JOBBER $100

239-5043 WINCHESTER REPEAT. ARMS
WINCHESTER MINNOW
CT   1919   3 1/4 IN
GLASS EYES $1000

239-5044 WINCHESTER REPEAT. ARMS
WINCHESTER MINNOW
CT   1925   3 1/4 IN
LATER $1000

239-5050 WINCHESTER REPEAT. ARMS
WINCHESTER MINNOW
CT   1919   4 IN
  $1500

239-4889 WINKIN' WOBBLER BAIT CO
WINKIN' WOBBLER BAIT

  $50

240-4973 WINNIE , BERT BAIT CO.
DECOY , WINNIE
MI   1919   6 IN
LARGE $1000

240-4818 WINNIE , BERT BAIT CO.
DECOY, STUMP DODGER
MI   1919   7 IN
  $1500

240-4968 WINNIE , BERT BAIT CO.
MUSKY STUMP DODGER
MI   1915   5 IN
  $500

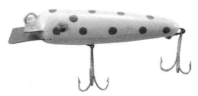

240-4965 WINNIE , BERT BAIT CO.
STUMP DODGER
MI   1916   3 1/2 IN
SMALL, OLD $300

240-4969 WINNIE , BERT BAIT CO.
STUMP DODGER
MI   1914   3 3/4 IN
OLD, MEDIUM $200

240-4970 WINNIE , BERT BAIT CO.
STUMP DODGER
MI   1914   3 1/4 IN
SURFACE $200

240-4971 WINNIE , BERT BAIT CO.
STUMP DODGER
MI   1914   2 3/4 IN
SURFACE $200

240-4972 WINNIE , BERT BAIT CO.
STUMP DODGER
MI   1914
  $200

240-24686 WISCONSIN FROG CO
WISCONSIN FROG
WI
  $30

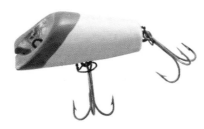

240-4898 WISE SPORTSMAN'S SUPPLY
JIM-DANDY BASS WOBBLER
IL   1915   2 1/4 IN
  $200

240-4897 WISE SPORTSMAN'S SUPPLY
JIM-DANDY PIKE WOBBLER
IL   1915   2 1/2 IN
  $200

240-4899 WISE SPORTSMAN'S SUPPLY
JIM-DANDY POPPER
IL   1915   2 1/2 IN
  $500

240-4900 WISE SPORTSMAN'S SUPPLY
JIM-DANDY WOBBLER
IL   1915
MUSKY SIZE $500

240-4896 WISE SPORTSMAN'S SUPPLY
WISE WOBBLER
IL   1915
  $200

240-4901 WISE, LEO B.
MOUSE, WISE
MI   1940   1 5/8 IN
  $400

241-5640 WISE, LEO B.
WOBBLE, WISE
MI   1937   4 5/8 IN
   $200

241-5595 WITCH FIRE LURES
WITCH FIRE
WI   1962
   $20

241-5630 WITCH FIRE LURES
WITCH FIRE
WI   1962
   $20

241-4895 WIZARD LIVE MFG. CO.
FANTAIL WIZARD, THE
OH   1948   2 IN
   $60

241-5029 WONDER STATE PRODUCTS
BUG-R-BIRD
AR   1946
   $200

241-5056 WONDER STATE PRODUCTS
BUG-R-BIRD
AR   1948
   $200

241-5033 WONDER STATE PRODUCTS
STEELHEAD
AR   1948
   $90

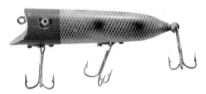

241-5034 WONDER STATE PRODUCTS
STEELHEAD
AR   1948
   $90

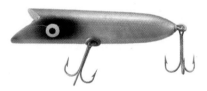

241-5002 WOOD MANUFACTURING CO.
BIG POPPA
AR   1950   4 IN   1/2 OZ
   $20

241-4996 WOOD MANUFACTURING CO.
DEEP-R-DOODLE
AR   1950   1 3/8 IN
   $20

241-4997 WOOD MANUFACTURING CO.
DEEP-R-DOODLE
AR   1950   2 1/4 IN
LARGE $20

241-4994 WOOD MANUFACTURING CO.
DIPSY DOODLE
AR   1947   1 3/4 IN
OLD $20

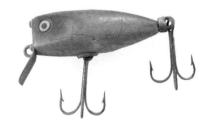

241-4995 WOOD MANUFACTURING CO.
DIPSY DOODLE
AR   1950   1 3/4 IN   1/2 oz
LARGE $20

241-5008 WOOD MANUFACTURING CO.
DIPSY DOODLE
AR   1950   2 1/2 IN
SINKER $20

241-5009 WOOD MANUFACTURING CO.
DIPSY DOODLE
AR   1950   2 IN
   $20

242-4998 WOOD MANUFACTURING CO.
DOODLER
AR   1950   4 IN
LARGE $20

242-4999 WOOD MANUFACTURING CO.
DOODLER
AR   1950   3 1/4 in
     $20

242-5004 WOOD MANUFACTURING CO.
LITTLE POPPA
AR   1950   1/4 OZ
     $20

242--5005 WOOD MANUFACTURING CO.
POPPA DOODLE
AR   1950   1.4 OZ
SMALL $20

242-5006 WOOD MANUFACTURING CO.
POPPA DOODLE
AR   1950   3 3/4 IN   1/2 OZ
LARGE $20

242-4989 WOOD MANUFACTURING CO.
POPPER, WOODS
AR   1950   3 IN
     $20

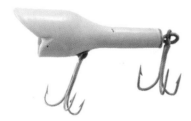

242-4987 WOOD MANUFACTURING CO.
RESEARCH BAIT, WOODS
AR   1944
     $50

242-4992 WOOD MANUFACTURING CO.
SPOT TAIL MINNOW
AR   1950   3 IN
     $20

242-4993 WOOD MANUFACTURING CO.
SPOT TAIL MINNOW
AR   1950
     $20

242-5001 WOOD MANUFACTURING CO.
SPOT TAIL MINNOW
AR   1950
SMALL $20

242-5007 WOOD MANUFACTURING CO.
SPOT TAIL MINNOW
AR   1950   2 1/4 IN
     $20

242-5010 WOOD MANUFACTURING CO.
SPOT TAIL MINNOW
AR   1950   3 IN   1/2 OZ
LARGE $20

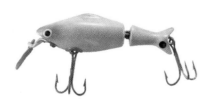

242-4984 WOOD MANUFACTURING CO.
SPOT TAIL MINNOW, JOINTED
AR   1950   3 1/4 IN   1/2 OZ
     $20

242-5000 WOOD MANUFACTURING CO.
TOP DIPSY DOODLE
AR   1950   2 IN
     $20

242-4990 WOOD MANUFACTURING CO.
TOP DOODLER
AR   1950
     $20

FISHING PLUGS

243-4991 WOOD MANUFACTURING CO.
TOP DOODLER
AR   1950
LARGE $20

243-4988 WOOD MANUFACTURING CO.
TOP POPPER
AR
OLD $30

243-5003 WOOD MANUFACTURING CO.
WOOD'S, UNKNOWN
AR   1950   2 3/4 IN
$20

243-5765 WOOD TURNING, INC.
PIKER, THE

$80

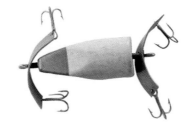

243-5018 WOODS & WATERS BAIT CO.
WHIR-LI-GIG LURE
MI   1949   2 1/2 IN
WOOD $100

243-5027 WOODS, F.C.
EXPERT FLAT WOOD MINNOW
OH   1903
$700

243-5028 WOODS, F.C.
EXPERT FLAT WOOD MINNOW
OH   1903
$700

243-5023 WOODS, F.C.
EXPERT WOOD MINNOW,   WOODS
OH   1903   2 1/2 IN
MEDIUM, BABY $700

243-5024 WOODS, F.C.
EXPERT WOOD MINNOW,   WOODS
OH   1903
SMALL, BABY $700

243-5025 WOODS, F.C.
EXPERT WOOD MINNOW,   WOODS
OH   1903
ROUND $700

243-5026 WOODS, F.C.
EXPERT WOOD MINNOW,   WOODS
OH   1905   3 3/4 IN
ROUND PROP $700

243-5020 WOODS, F.C.
ROUND EXPERT WOOD MINNOW
OH   1903   3 3/4 IN
LARGE $700

243-5021 WOODS, F.C.
ROUND EXPERT WOOD MINNOW
OH   1903
LARGE $700

243-5022 WOODS, F.C.
ROUND EXPERT WOOD MINNOW
OH   1903
SMALL $700

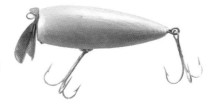

243-5030 WORTH BAIT CO.
FLUTTER FIN
WI   1940   3 1/4 IN
MUSKY SIZE $300

244-5031 WORTH BAIT CO.
FLUTTER FIN
WI   1955   1 IN
  $40

244-4954 WRIGHT & McGILL CO.
BASS NABBER
CO   1941   2 1/4 IN
OLD $150

244-4955 WRIGHT & McGILL CO.
BASS NABBER
CO   1941   2 1/2 IN
MEDIUM $150

244-4956 WRIGHT & McGILL CO.
BASS NABBER
CO   1940   2 1/4 IN
SMALL $150

244-4957 WRIGHT & McGILL CO.
BASS NABBER
CO   1939   3 1/4 IN
LARGE $150

244-4932 WRIGHT & McGILL CO.
BASS-O-GRAM
CO   1929   4 IN
LARGE $300

244-4961 WRIGHT & McGILL CO.
BIG HAWK
CO   1949   2 1/2 IN
PLASTIC $40

244-4951 WRIGHT & McGILL CO.
BUG-A-BOO
CO   1953   2 3/8 IN   1/2 OZ
LARGE $20

244-4959 WRIGHT & McGILL CO.
BUG-A-BOO
CO   1953   2 3/4 IN   1/2 OZ
LARGE, OLD $20

244-4960 WRIGHT & McGILL CO.
BUG-A-BOO
CO   1953   2 1/2 IN   3/8 OZ
SMALL, OLD $20

244-4962 WRIGHT & McGILL CO.
BUG-A-BOO

SMALL $20

244-4928 WRIGHT & McGILL CO.
CRAWFISH
CO   1930   2 3/4 IN
LARGE $150

244-4930 WRIGHT & McGILL CO.
CRAWFISH
CO   1929   1/2 OZ
SMALL $150

244-4924 WRIGHT & McGILL CO.
FLAPPER CRAB
CO   1932   2 IN
SMALL $100

244-4929 WRIGHT & McGILL CO.
FLAPPER CRAB
CO   1930   2 1/2 IN
LARGE $100

FISHING PLUGS

245-4945 WRIGHT & McGILL CO.
HIJACKER
CO   1952   3 1/2 IN   5/8 OZ
OLD $20

245-4948 WRIGHT & McGILL CO.
HIJACKER
CO   1952   3 1/2 IN
  $20

245-4949 WRIGHT & McGILL CO.
HIJACKER,
CO   1952   3 1/2 IN
TOPWATER $20

245-4946 WRIGHT & McGILL CO.
MIRACLE MINNOW
CO   1951   3 1/2 IN
FLOATER, LARGE $30

245-4947 WRIGHT & McGILL CO.
MIRACLE MINNOW
CO   1951   3 IN
FLOATER, SMALL $30

245-4958 WRIGHT & McGILL CO.
MIRACLE MINNOW
CO   1950   2 IN
TOPWATER $30

245-4939 WRIGHT & McGILL CO.
MIRACLE MINNOW, CHROMED
CO   1949   2 IN
  $20

245-4938 WRIGHT & McGILL CO.
MIRACLE MINNOW, DELUXE
CO   1949   2 IN
  $20

245-4935 WRIGHT & McGILL CO.
MIRACLE MINNOW, JOINTED
CO   1949   2 1/2 IN
  $20

245-4937 WRIGHT & McGILL CO.
MIRACLE MINNOW, JOINTED
CO   1950   2 1/2 IN
  $20

245-4936 WRIGHT & McGILL CO.
NICKY MOUSE
CO   1931   2 IN
  $200

245-4940 WRIGHT & McGILL CO.
SHRIMP, WRIGHT & McGILL
CO   1917   2 IN
OLDEST $300

245-4934 WRIGHT & McGILL CO.
SWIMMING MOUSE, WRIGHT & McGILL
CO   1929
  $300

245-4931 WRIGHT & McGILL CO.
WIGGLING SHRIMP
CO   1929   2 IN
  $300

245-4963 WRIGHT & McGILL CO.
WOBBLER, WRIGHT & McGILL
CO   1949   2 IN
SMALL $40

FISHING PLUGS

246-4964 WRIGHT & McGILL CO.
WOBBLER, WRIGHT & McGILL
CO   1949   2 1/2 IN
LARGE $40

246-5053 WYNNE PRECISION CO.
GRAN' POPPA
GA   1946   2 1/2 IN
   $50

246-5052 WYNNE PRECISION CO.
LUCKY TAIL WOBBLER
GA   1946   3 1/2 IN
LARGE $50

246-5054 WYNNE PRECISION CO.
LUCKY TAIL WOBBLER
GA   1946
   $50

246-5055 WYNNE PRECISION CO.
LUCKY TAIL WOBBLER, JOINTED
GA   1946   3 3/4 IN
   $50

246-7007 YELLNICK
CHAIN BEAD BAIT
MN
   $40

246-5179 YINDA
WINCHESTER SHELL BAIT
WI
   $40

246-5096 YORK BAIT CO.
KER-PLUNK
PA   1960
OLD $20

246-5097 YORK BAIT CO.
KER-PLUNK
PA   1960
   $20

246-5078 YPSILANTI BAIT CO.
YPSILANTI MINNOW
MI   1920   3 3/4 IN
   $300

246-5079 YPSILANTI BAIT CO.
YPSILANTI MINNOW
MI   1920
   $300

246-5080 YPSILANTI BAIT CO.
YPSILANTI MINNOW
MI   1920   3 3/4 IN
ULTRA CAST. MINNOW $300

246-5081 YPSILANTI BAIT CO.
YPSILANTI MINNOW
MI   1920
   $300

246-5082 YPSILANTI BAIT CO.
YPSILANTI MINNOW
MI   1920
   $300

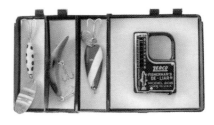

246-5100 ZEBCO
ZEBCO LURE SET
OK
   $30

UNKNOWN FISHING PLUGS

249-5131 UNKNOWN FOREIGN MAKER
UNKNOWN NAME

$40

249-5398 UNKNOWN COMMERICAL
FISH DECOY, COMMERCIAL

$200

249-5437 UNKNOWN DECOY MAKER
CRAWFISH DECOY
1930's
$200

249-5357 UNKNOWN DECOY MAKER
DECOY, TURTLE
1920'S
$300

249-5451 UNKNOWN DECOY MAKER
DECOY, TURTLE

$300

249-5344 UNKNOWN DECOY MAKER
DECOY, UNKNOWN

UNKNOWN COMMERICAL $100

249-5345 UNKNOWN DECOY MAKER
DECOY, UNKNOWN

UNKNOWN COMMERICAL $300

249-5346 UNKNOWN DECOY MAKER
DECOY, UNKNOWN

UNKNOWN COMMERICAL $300

249-5347 UNKNOWN DECOY MAKER
DECOY, UNKNOWN

HOMEMADE FOLKART $100

249-5348 UNKNOWN DECOY MAKER
DECOY, UNKNOWN

HOMEMADE FOLKART $100

249-5349 UNKNOWN DECOY MAKER
DECOY, UNKNOWN

HOMEMADE FOLKART $100

249-5350 UNKNOWN DECOY MAKER
DECOY, UNKNOWN

HOMEMADE FOLKART $300

249-5351 UNKNOWN DECOY MAKER
DECOY, UNKNOWN

COMMERICAL $100

249-5354 UNKNOWN DECOY MAKER
DECOY, UNKNOWN

HOMEMADE FOLKART $100

249-5355 UNKNOWN DECOY MAKER
DECOY, UNKNOWN

HOMEMADE FOLKART $200

UNKNOWN FISHING PLUGS

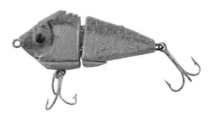

250-5356 UNKNOWN DECOY MAKER
DECOY, UNKNOWN

$1200

250-5358 UNKNOWN DECOY MAKER
DECOY, UNKNOWN

HOMEMADE FROM SOUTH BEND $100

250-1360 UNKNOWN FLORIDA BAIT
FLORIDA BAIT
FL
$300

250-5166 UNKNOWN FOREIGN MAKER
UNKNOWN NAME

$20

250-5360 UNKNOWN HOMEMADE
DECOY, HOMEMADE

$100

250-5361 UNKNOWN HOMEMADE
FISH DECOY, HOMEMADE

$100

250-5362 UNKNOWN HOMEMADE
FISH DECOY, HOMEMADE

$100

250-5368 UNKNOWN HOMEMADE
FISH DECOY, HOMEMADE

HOMEMADE FOLKART $100

250-5370 UNKNOWN HOMEMADE
FISH DECOY, HOMEMADE

HOMEMADE FOLKART $100

250-5372 UNKNOWN HOMEMADE
FISH DECOY, HOMEMADE

HOMEMADE FOLKART $100

250-5374 UNKNOWN HOMEMADE
FISH DECOY, HOMEMADE

HOMEMADE FOLKART $100

250-5375 UNKNOWN HOMEMADE
FISH DECOY, HOMEMADE

HOMEMADE FOLKART $100

250-5376 UNKNOWN HOMEMADE
FISH DECOY, HOMEMADE

HOMEMADE FOLKART $100

250-5377 UNKNOWN HOMEMADE
FISH DECOY, HOMEMADE

HOMEMADE FOLKART $100

250-5378 UNKNOWN HOMEMADE
FISH DECOY, HOMEMADE

HOMEMADE FOLKART $100

251-5379 UNKNOWN HOMEMADE
FISH DECOY, HOMEMADE

HOMEMADE FOLKART $100

251-5385 UNKNOWN HOMEMADE
FISH DECOY, HOMEMADE

HOMEMADE FOLKART $100

251-5386 UNKNOWN HOMEMADE
FISH DECOY, HOMEMADE

HOMEMADE FOLKART $100

251-5388 UNKNOWN HOMEMADE
FISH DECOY, HOMEMADE

HOMEMADE FOLKART $100

251-5389 UNKNOWN HOMEMADE
FISH DECOY, HOMEMADE

HOMEMADE FOLKART $100

251-5391 UNKNOWN HOMEMADE
FISH DECOY, HOMEMADE

HOMEMADE FOLKART $100

251-5396 UNKNOWN HOMEMADE
FISH DECOY, HOMEMADE

HOMEMADE FOLKART $100

251-5400 UNKNOWN HOMEMADE
FISH DECOY, HOMEMADE

HOMEMADE FOLKART $100

251-5403 UNKNOWN HOMEMADE
FISH DECOY, HOMEMADE

HOMEMADE FOLKART $100

251-5404 UNKNOWN HOMEMADE
FISH DECOY, HOMEMADE

HOMEMADE FOLKART $100

251-5405 UNKNOWN HOMEMADE
FISH DECOY, HOMEMADE

HOMEMADE FOLKART $100

251-5406 UNKNOWN HOMEMADE
FISH DECOY, HOMEMADE

HOMEMADE FOLKART $100

251-5407 UNKNOWN HOMEMADE
FISH DECOY, HOMEMADE

HOMEMADE FOLKART $100

251-5408 UNKNOWN HOMEMADE
FISH DECOY, HOMEMADE

HOMEMADE FOLKART $100

251-5411 UNKNOWN HOMEMADE
FISH DECOY, HOMEMADE

HOMEMADE FOLKART $100

UNKNOWN FISHING PLUGS

252-5412 UNKNOWN HOMEMADE
FISH DECOY, HOMEMADE

HOMEMADE FOLKART $100

252-5413 UNKNOWN HOMEMADE
FISH DECOY, HOMEMADE

HOMEMADE FOLKART $100

252-7033 UNKNOWN
UNKNOWN NAME

$30

252-5415 UNKNOWN HOMEMADE
FISH DECOY, HOMEMADE

HOMEMADE FOLKART $100

252-5416 UNKNOWN HOMEMADE
FISH DECOY, HOMEMADE

HOMEMADE FOLKART $100

252-5419 UNKNOWN HOMEMADE
FISH DECOY, HOMEMADE

HOMEMADE FOLKART $100

252-5421 UNKNOWN HOMEMADE
FISH DECOY, HOMEMADE

HOMEMADE FOLKART $100

252-5430 UNKNOWN HOMEMADE
FISH DECOY, HOMEMADE

HOMEMADE FOLKART $100

252-5431 UNKNOWN HOMEMADE
FISH DECOY, HOMEMADE

HOMEMADE FOLKART $100

252-5432 UNKNOWN HOMEMADE
FISH DECOY, HOMEMADE

HOMEMADE FOLKART $100

252-5438 UNKNOWN HOMEMADE
FISH DECOY, HOMEMADE

HOMEMADE FOLKART $100

252-5440 UNKNOWN HOMEMADE
FISH DECOY, HOMEMADE

HOMEMADE FOLKART $100

252-5444 UNKNOWN HOMEMADE
FISH DECOY, HOMEMADE

HOMEMADE FOLKART $100

252-5445 UNKNOWN HOMEMADE
FISH DECOY, HOMEMADE

HOMEMADE FOLKART $100

252-5450 UNKNOWN HOMEMADE
FISH DECOY, HOMEMADE

$100

253-5164 UNKNOWN MAKER
AIRPLANE LURE

$40

253-3761 UNKNOWN MAKER
BALSA BAIT, UNKNOWN
   1960   7 IN
$60

253-5204 UNKNOWN MAKER
CEDAR POPPER

$100

253-24631 UNKNOWN MAKER
CLOTHES PIN TYPE

$201

253-7145 UNKNOWN MAKER
COD JIG

$10

253-5369 UNKNOWN MAKER
DECOY, PIKE, UNKNOWN
   1930's
$300

253-5365 UNKNOWN MAKER
DECOY, TURTLE

CONTEMPORARY $100

253-4110 UNKNOWN MAKER
DECOY, UNKNOWN
   1885   6 IN
RHODES, FRED $1000

253-5447 UNKNOWN MAKER
DUCK DECOY, UNKNOWN

$1500

253-5448 UNKNOWN MAKER
DUCK DECOY, UNKNOWN

$1500

253-5449 UNKNOWN MAKER
DUCK DECOY, UNKNOWN

$1500

253-5269 UNKNOWN MAKER
ENGLISH EXPERIMENTAL LURE
ENG
$100

253-5270 UNKNOWN MAKER
ENGLISH EXPERIMENTAL LURE
ENG
$100

253-5271 UNKNOWN MAKER
ENGLISH EXPERIMENTAL LURE
ENG
$100

253-5272 UNKNOWN MAKER
ENGLISH EXPERIMENTAL LURE
ENG
$100

UNKNOWN FISHING PLUGS

254-5363 UNKNOWN MAKER
FISH DECOY, COMMERCIAL

$500

254-5364 UNKNOWN MAKER
FISH DECOY, COMMERCIAL

$200

254-5390 UNKNOWN MAKER
FISH DECOY, COMMERCIAL

$150

254-5371 UNKNOWN MAKER
FISH DECOY, HOMEMADE

HOMEMADE FOLKART $100

254-5401 UNKNOWN MAKER
FISH DECOY, HOMEMADE

$200

254-2830 UNKNOWN MAKER
FLATHEAD

$100

254-1298 UNKNOWN MAKER
FLATHEAD SALMON PLUG

$400

254-5366 UNKNOWN MAKER
FROG DECOY

CONTEMPORARY $100

254-24696 UNKNOWN MAKER
HOMEMADE

$10

254-5436 UNKNOWN MAKER
HOMEMADE FOLKART

$150

254-7060 UNKNOWN MAKER
JUMPING WORM

254--7032 UNKNOW MAKER
UNKNOWN NAME

$30

254-5367 UNKNOWN MAKER
LIZARD DECOY

CONTEMPORARY $100

254-7031 UNKNOWN MAKER
UNKNOWN NAME

$100

254-5259 UNKNOWN MAKER
NYLON JIG

$10

UNKNOWN FISHING PLUGS

255-5127 UNKNOWN MAKER
OLD RAT TAIL

$30

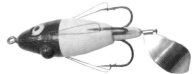

255-24733 UNKNOWN MAKER
PAPPY JOE
1960
$50

255-1180 UNKNOWN MAKER
PENCIL BAIT, UNKNOWN

$10

255-3352 UNKNOWN MAKER
PT 109

$20

255-5418 UNKNOWN MAKER
SUCKER
MN   1930'S
$150

255-3806 UNKNOWN MAKER
UNKNOWN NAME

$60

255-5118 UNKNOWN MAKER
UNKNOWN BIRD

$60

255-1473 UNKNOWN MAKER
UNKNOWN MAKER

$30

255-5656 UNKNOWN MAKER
UNKNOWN MAKER

$150

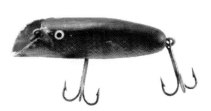

255-6993 UNKNOWN MAKER
UNKNOWN MAKER

$20

255-0516 UNKNOWN MAKER
UNKNOWN NAME

$10

255-0642 UNKNOWN MAKER
UNKNOWN NAME

$10

255-1071 UNKNOWN MAKER
UNKNOWN NAME

$1000

255-1411 UNKNOWN MAKER
UNKNOWN NAME

$10

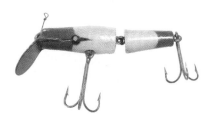

255-24691 UNKNOWN MAKER
UNKNOWN NAME

$30

UNKNOWN FISHING PLUGS

256-0517 UNKNOWN MAKER
UNKNOWN SHRIMP

$10

256-2344 UNKNOWN MAKER
UNKNOWN NAME

$10

256-2347 UNKNOWN MAKER
UNKNOWN NAME
3 IN
$150

256-24690 UNKNOWN MAKER
UNKNOWN NAME

$30

256-2683 UNKNOWN MAKER
UNKNOWN NAME

$75

256-2684 UNKNOWN MAKER
UNKNOWN NAME

$75

256-2685 UNKNOWN MAKER
UNKNOWN NAME

$200

256-24233 UNKNOWN MAKER
UNKNOWN NAME

$40

256-2835 UNKNOWN MAKER
UNKNOWN NAME

$20

256-2843 UNKNOWN MAKER
UNKNOWN NAME

$40

256-3978 UNKNOWN MAKER
UNKNOWN NAME

$300

256-4082 UNKNOWN MAKER
UNKNOWN NAME

$500

256-6127 UNKNOWN MOUSE
UNKNOWN NAME

$30

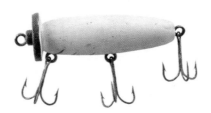

256-5035 UNKNOWN MAKER
UNKNOWN NAME

$300

256-5094 UNKNOWN MAKER
UNKNOWN NAME

$100

UNKNOWN FISHING PLUGS

257-5121   UNKNOWN MAKER
UNKNOWN NAME

$20

257-5144   UNKNOWN MAKER
UNKNOWN NAME

$40

257-5146   UNKNOWN MAKER
UNKNOWN NAME

$150

257-5147   UNKNOWN MAKER
UNKNOWN NAME

$150

257-5148   UNKNOWN MAKER
UNKNOWN NAME

$150

257-5149   UNKNOWN MAKER
UNKNOWN NAME

$150

257-5150   UNKNOWN MAKER
UNKNOWN NAME

$150

257-5151   UNKNOWN MAKER
UNKNOWN NAME

$150

257-5152   UNKNOWN MAKER
UNKNOWN NAME

$50

257-5158   UNKNOWN MAKER
UNKNOWN NAME

$150

257-5159   UNKNOWN MAKER
UNKNOWN NAME

$200

257-5160   UNKNOWN MAKER
UNKNOWN NAME

$300

257-5161   UNKNOWN MAKER
UNKNOWN NAME

$30

257-5162   UNKNOWN MAKER
UNKNOWN NAME

$75

257-5163   UNKNOWN MAKER
UNKNOWN NAME

$75

UNKNOWN FISHING PLUGS

258-5165   UNKNOWN MAKER
UNKNOWN NAME

$50

258-5167   UNKNOWN MAKER
UNKNOWN NAME

$300

25822747   UNKNOWN MAKER
UNKNOWN NAME

$30-

258-5169   UNKNOWN MAKER
UNKNOWN NAME

$40

258-5170   UNKNOWN MAKER
UNKNOWN NAME

$30

258-5171   UNKNOWN MAKER
UNKNOWN NAME
MONTANA
$150

258-5172   UNKNOWN MAKER
UNKNOWN NAME
MONTANA
 $150

258-5173   UNKNOWN MAKER
UNKNOWN NAME
MONTANA
 $150

258-24232   UNKNOWN MAKER
UNKNOWN NAME

$30

258-5175   UNKNOWN MAKER
UNKNOWN NAME

$30

258-24684   UNKNOWN MAKER
UNKNOWN NAME

$30

258-5177   UNKNOWN MAKER
UNKNOWN NAME

$100

258-5178   UNKNOWN MAKER
UNKNOWN NAME

$50

258-24683   UNKNOWN MAKER
UNKNOWN NAME

$30

258-5181   UNKNOWN MAKER
UNKNOWN NAME

$300

UNKNOWN FISHING PLUGS

259-5182 UNKNOWN MAKER
UNKNOWN NAME

$20

259-5188 UNKNOWN MAKER
UNKNOWN NAME

$30

259-5192 UNKNOWN MAKER
UNKNOWN NAME

$50

259-5194 UNKNOWN MAKER
UNKNOWN NAME

$50

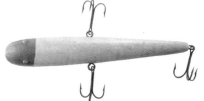

259-5196 UNKNOWN MAKER
UNKNOWN NAME

$50

259-5200 UNKNOWN MAKER
UNKNOWN NAME

$50

259-5203 UNKNOWN MAKER
UNKNOWN NAME

$50

259-5205 UNKNOWN MAKER
UNKNOWN NAME

$50

259-5206 UNKNOWN MAKER
UNKNOWN NAME

$200

259-5218 UNKNOWN MAKER
UNKNOWN NAME

$150

259-5220 UNKNOWN MAKER
UNKNOWN NAME

$30

259-5223 UNKNOWN MAKER
UNKNOWN NAME

$50

259-5253 UNKNOWN MAKER
UNKNOWN NAME

$50

259-5263 UNKNOWN MAKER
UNKNOWN NAME

$80

259-5454 UNKNOWN MAKER
UNKNOWN NAME

$50

UNKNOWN FISHING PLUGS

260-5455 UNKNOWN MAKER
UNKNOWN NAME

$50

260-5457 UNKNOWN MAKER
UNKNOWN NAME

$100

260-5458 UNKNOWN MAKER
UNKNOWN NAME

$200

260-5459 UNKNOWN MAKER
UNKNOWN NAME

$50

260-5460 UNKNOWN MAKER
UNKNOWN NAME

$100

260-5461 UNKNOWN MAKER
UNKNOWN NAME

$50

260-5462 UNKNOWN MAKER
UNKNOWN NAME

$50

260-5463 UNKNOWN MAKER
UNKNOWN NAME

$50

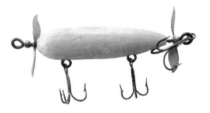

260-5464 UNKNOWN MAKER
UNKNOWN NAME

$100

260-5465 UNKNOWN MAKER
UNKNOWN NAME

$50

260-5466 UNKNOWN MAKER
UNKNOWN NAME

$50

260-5467 UNKNOWN MAKER
UNKNOWN NAME

$50

260-5468 UNKNOWN MAKER
UNKNOWN NAME

$200

260-7025 UNKNOWN MAKER
UNKNOWN NAME

$30

260-5474 UNKNOWN MAKER
UNKNOWN NAME

$300

UNKNOWN FISHING PLUGS

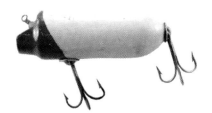

261-5475 UNKNOWN MAKER
UNKNOWN NAME

$100

261-5478 UNKNOWN MAKER
UNKNOWN NAME

$30

261-5481 UNKNOWN MAKER
UNKNOWN NAME

$300

261-5482 UNKNOWN MAKER
UNKNOWN NAME

$50

261-5483 UNKNOWN MAKER
UNKNOWN NAME

$30

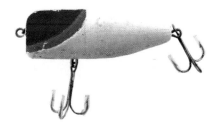

261-5484 UNKNOWN MAKER
UNKNOWN NAME

$200

261-5486 UNKNOWN MAKER
UNKNOWN NAME

$200

261-5487 UNKNOWN MAKER
UNKNOWN NAME

$20

261-5488 UNKNOWN MAKER
UNKNOWN NAME

$30

261-5490 UNKNOWN MAKER
UNKNOWN NAME

$30

261-5491 UNKNOWN MAKER
UNKNOWN NAME

$50

261-5492 UNKNOWN MAKER
UNKNOWN NAME

$100

261-5493 UNKNOWN MAKER
UNKNOWN NAME

$50

261-5494 UNKNOWN MAKER
UNKNOWN NAME

$50

261-5496 UNKNOWN MAKER
UNKNOWN NAME

$40

UNKNOWN FISHING PLUGS

262-5497 UNKNOWN MAKER
UNKNOWN NAME

$100

262-5498 UNKNOWN MAKER
UNKNOWN NAME

$20

262-5499 UNKNOWN MAKER
UNKNOWN NAME

$100

262-5501 UNKNOWN MAKER
UNKNOWN NAME

$30

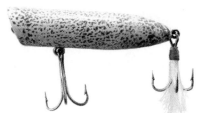

262-5502 UNKNOWN MAKER
UNKNOWN NAME

$10

262-5504 UNKNOWN MAKER
UNKNOWN NAME

$20

262-5506 UNKNOWN MAKER
UNKNOWN NAME

$100

262-5507 UNKNOWN MAKER
UNKNOWN NAME

$400

262-5509 UNKNOWN MAKER
UNKNOWN NAME

$400

262-5510 UNKNOWN MAKER
UNKNOWN NAME

$100

262-5512 UNKNOWN MAKER
UNKNOWN NAME

$200

262-5514 UNKNOWN MAKER
UNKNOWN NAME

$300

262-5515 UNKNOWN MAKER
UNKNOWN NAME

$10

262-5518 UNKNOWN MAKER
UNKNOWN NAME

$100

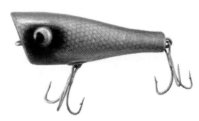

262-5519 UNKNOWN MAKER
UNKNOWN NAME

$10

UNKNOWN FISHING PLUGS

263-5520 UNKNOWN MAKER
UNKNOWN NAME

$20

263-5521 UNKNOWN MAKER
UNKNOWN NAME

$200

263-5522 UNKNOWN MAKER
UNKNOWN NAME

$30

263-5523 UNKNOWN MAKER
UNKNOWN NAME

$30

263-5525 UNKNOWN MAKER
UNKNOWN NAME

$100

263-5526 UNKNOWN MAKER
UNKNOWN NAME

$400

263-5527 UNKNOWN MAKER
UNKNOWN NAME

$20

263-5528 UNKNOWN MAKER
UNKNOWN NAME

$100

263-5529 UNKNOWN MAKER
UNKNOWN NAME

$20

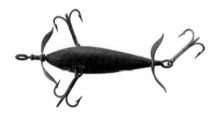

263-5531 UNKNOWN MAKER
UNKNOWN NAME

$100

263-5532 UNKNOWN MAKER
UNKNOWN NAME

$100

263-5533 UNKNOWN MAKER
UNKNOWN NAME

$50

263-5534 UNKNOWN MAKER
UNKNOWN NAME

$100

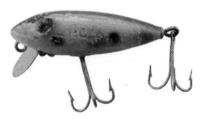

263-5535 UNKNOWN MAKER
UNKNOWN NAME

$50

263-5537 UNKNOWN MAKER
UNKNOWN NAME

$200

UNKNOWN FISHING PLUGS

264-5538   UNKNOWN MAKER
UNKNOWN NAME

$100

264-5539   UNKNOWN MAKER
UNKNOWN NAME

$50

264-5540   UNKNOWN MAKER
UNKNOWN NAME

$50

264-5541   UNKNOWN MAKER
UNKNOWN NAME

$50

264-5543   UNKNOWN MAKER
UNKNOWN NAME

$30

264-5544   UNKNOWN MAKER
UNKNOWN NAME

$30

264-5546   UNKNOWN MAKER
UNKNOWN NAME

$150

264-5547   UNKNOWN MAKER
UNKNOWN NAME

$300

264-5548   UNKNOWN MAKER
UNKNOWN NAME

$30

264-5549   UNKNOWN MAKER
UNKNOWN NAME

$100

264-5552   UNKNOWN MAKER
UNKNOWN NAME

$100

264-5555   UNKNOWN MAKER
UNKNOWN NAME

$100

264-5556   UNKNOWN MAKER
UNKNOWN NAME

$40

264-5557   UNKNOWN MAKER
UNKNOWN NAME

$200

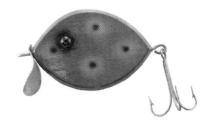

264-5559   UNKNOWN MAKER
UNKNOWN NAME

$100

UNKNOWN FISHING PLUGS

265-5560 UNKNOWN MAKER
UNKNOWN NAME

$40

265-5561 UNKNOWN MAKER
UNKNOWN NAME

$50

265-5562 UNKNOWN MAKER
UNKNOWN NAME

$200

265-5563 UNKNOWN MAKER
UNKNOWN NAME

$40

265-5564 UNKNOWN MAKER
UNKNOWN NAME

$300

265-5565 UNKNOWN MAKER
UNKNOWN NAME

$40

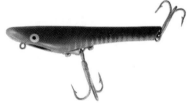

265-5566 UNKNOWN MAKER
UNKNOWN NAME

$300

265-5568 UNKNOWN MAKER
UNKNOWN NAME

$40

265-5569 UNKNOWN MAKER
UNKNOWN NAME

$30

265-5571 UNKNOWN MAKER
UNKNOWN NAME

$40

265-5572 UNKNOWN MAKER
UNKNOWN NAME

$100

265-5573 UNKNOWN MAKER
UNKNOWN NAME

$20

265-5574 UNKNOWN MAKER
UNKNOWN NAME

$100

265-5575 UNKNOWN MAKER
UNKNOWN NAME

$100

265-5576 UNKNOWN MAKER
UNKNOWN NAME

$20

UNKNOWN FISHING PLUGS

266-5577 UNKNOWN MAKER
UNKNOWN NAME

$40

266-5578 UNKNOWN MAKER
UNKNOWN NAME

$30

266-5580 UNKNOWN MAKER
UNKNOWN NAME

$50

266-5581 UNKNOWN MAKER
UNKNOWN NAME

$50

266-5582 UNKNOWN MAKER
UNKNOWN NAME

$200

266-5583 UNKNOWN MAKER
UNKNOWN NAME

$20

266-5584 UNKNOWN MAKER
UNKNOWN NAME

$30

266-5585 UNKNOWN MAKER
UNKNOWN NAME

$50

266-5586 UNKNOWN MAKER
UNKNOWN NAME

$40

266-5587 UNKNOWN MAKER
UNKNOWN NAME

$100

266-5588 UNKNOWN MAKER
UNKNOWN NAME

$40

266-5589 UNKNOWN MAKER
UNKNOWN NAME

$50

266-5590 UNKNOWN MAKER
UNKNOWN NAME

$200

266-5591 UNKNOWN MAKER
UNKNOWN NAME

$40

266-5592 UNKNOWN MAKER
UNKNOWN NAME

$30

UNKNOWN FISHING PLUGS

267-5593   UNKNOWN MAKER
UNKNOWN NAME

$20

267-5594   UNKNOWN MAKER
UNKNOWN NAME

$30

267-5596   UNKNOWN MAKER
UNKNOWN NAME

$20

267-5597   UNKNOWN MAKER
UNKNOWN NAME

$20

267-5598   UNKNOWN MAKER
UNKNOWN NAME

$20

267-5599   UNKNOWN MAKER
UNKNOWN NAME

$30

267-5600   UNKNOWN MAKER
UNKNOWN NAME

$50

267-5601   UNKNOWN MAKER
UNKNOWN NAME

$40

267-5602   UNKNOWN MAKER
UNKNOWN NAME

$300

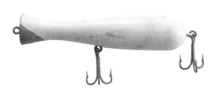

267-5603   UNKNOWN MAKER
UNKNOWN NAME

$300

267-5604   UNKNOWN MAKER
UNKNOWN NAME

$20

267-5605   UNKNOWN MAKER
UNKNOWN NAME

$100

267-5606   UNKNOWN MAKER
UNKNOWN NAME

$20

267-5607   UNKNOWN MAKER
UNKNOWN NAME

$20

267-5608   UNKNOWN MAKER
UNKNOWN NAME

$20

UNKNOWN FISHING PLUGS

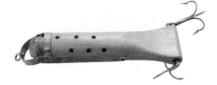

268-5609 UNKNOWN MAKER
UNKNOWN NAME

$200

268-5610 UNKNOWN MAKER
UNKNOWN NAME

$70

268-5612 UNKNOWN MAKER
UNKNOWN NAME

$100

268-5613 UNKNOWN MAKER
UNKNOWN NAME

$40

268-5614 UNKNOWN MAKER
UNKNOWN NAME

$30

268-5615 UNKNOWN MAKER
UNKNOWN NAME

$30

268-5616 UNKNOWN MAKER
UNKNOWN NAME

$30

268-5617 UNKNOWN MAKER
UNKNOWN NAME

$100

268-5618 UNKNOWN MAKER
UNKNOWN NAME

$100

268-5619 UNKNOWN MAKER
UNKNOWN NAME

$30

268-5620 UNKNOWN MAKER
UNKNOWN NAME

$20

268-5622 UNKNOWN MAKER
UNKNOWN NAME

$40

268-5623 UNKNOWN MAKER
UNKNOWN NAME

$100

268-5624 UNKNOWN MAKER
UNKNOWN NAME

$100

268-5625 UNKNOWN MAKER
UNKNOWN NAME

$100

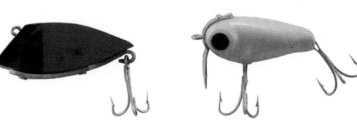

UNKNOWN FISHING PLUGS

269-5626 UNKNOWN MAKER
UNKNOWN NAME

$100

269-5627 UNKNOWN MAKER
UNKNOWN NAME

$50

269-5628 UNKNOWN MAKER
UNKNOWN NAME

$100

269-5631 UNKNOWN MAKER
UNKNOWN NAME

$10

269-5632 UNKNOWN MAKER
UNKNOWN NAME

$10

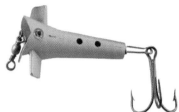

269-5633 UNKNOWN MAKER
UNKNOWN NAME

$10

269-5634 UNKNOWN MAKER
UNKNOWN NAME

$30

269-5635 UNKNOWN MAKER
UNKNOWN NAME

$20

269-5636 UNKNOWN MAKER
UNKNOWN NAME

$30

269-5637 UNKNOWN MAKER
UNKNOWN NAME

$100

269-5638 UNKNOWN MAKER
UNKNOWN NAME

$30

269-5641 UNKNOWN MAKER
UNKNOWN NAME

$30

269-5642 UNKNOWN MAKER
UNKNOWN NAME

$30

269-5643 UNKNOWN MAKER
UNKNOWN NAME

$30

269-5644 UNKNOWN MAKER
UNKNOWN NAME

$30

UNKNOWN FISHING PLUGS

270-5645 UNKNOWN MAKER
UNKNOWN NAME

$50

270-5646 UNKNOWN MAKER
UNKNOWN NAME

$100

270-5647 UNKNOWN MAKER
UNKNOWN NAME

$20

270-5648 UNKNOWN MAKER
UNKNOWN NAME

$20

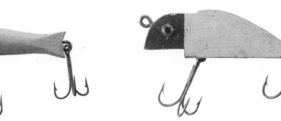

270-5651 UNKNOWN MAKER
UNKNOWN NAME

$20

270-5652 UNKNOWN MAKER
UNKNOWN NAME

$40

270-5653 UNKNOWN MAKER
UNKNOWN NAME

$20

270-5654 UNKNOWN MAKER
UNKNOWN NAME

$20

270-5655 UNKNOWN MAKER
UNKNOWN NAME

$30

270-5658 UNKNOWN MAKER
UNKNOWN NAME

$50

270-5659 UNKNOWN MAKER
UNKNOWN NAME

$40

270-5660 UNKNOWN MAKER
UNKNOWN NAME

$30

270-5661 UNKNOWN MAKER
UNKNOWN NAME

$200

270-5662 UNKNOWN MAKER
UNKNOWN NAME

$40

270-5663 UNKNOWN MAKER
UNKNOWN NAME

$200

271-5664 UNKNOWN MAKER
UNKNOWN NAME

$40

271-5665 UNKNOWN MAKER
UNKNOWN NAME

$10

271-5666 UNKNOWN MAKER
UNKNOWN NAME

$40

271-5667 UNKNOWN MAKER
UNKNOWN NAME

$100

271-5668 UNKNOWN MAKER
UNKNOWN NAME

$100

271-5669 UNKNOWN MAKER
UNKNOWN NAME

$300

271-5670 UNKNOWN MAKER
UNKNOWN NAME

$300

271-5671 UNKNOWN MAKER
UNKNOWN NAME

$100

271-5672 UNKNOWN MAKER
UNKNOWN NAME

$100

271-5673 UNKNOWN MAKER
UNKNOWN NAME

$100

271-5674 UNKNOWN MAKER
UNKNOWN NAME

$100

271-5675 UNKNOWN MAKER
UNKNOWN NAME

$30

271-5678 UNKNOWN MAKER
UNKNOWN NAME

$100

271-5679 UNKNOWN MAKER
UNKNOWN NAME

$100

271-5680 UNKNOWN MAKER
UNKNOWN NAME

$20

UNKNOWN FISHING PLUGS

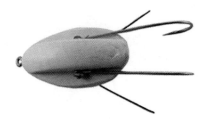

272-5682 UNKNOWN MAKER
UNKNOWN NAME

$40

272-5683 UNKNOWN MAKER
UNKNOWN NAME

$20

272-5685 UNKNOWN MAKER
UNKNOWN NAME

$200

272-5687 UNKNOWN MAKER
UNKNOWN NAME

$60

272-5690 UNKNOWN MAKER
UNKNOWN NAME

$20

272-5691 UNKNOWN MAKER
UNKNOWN NAME

$20

272-5692 UNKNOWN MAKER
UNKNOWN NAME

$30

272-5693 UNKNOWN MAKER
UNKNOWN NAME

$40

272-5694 UNKNOWN MAKER
UNKNOWN NAME

$20

272-5695 UNKNOWN MAKER
UNKNOWN NAME

$30

272-5696 UNKNOWN MAKER
UNKNOWN NAME

$30

272-5697 UNKNOWN MAKER
UNKNOWN NAME

$40

272-5698 UNKNOWN MAKER
UNKNOWN NAME

$300

272-5699 UNKNOWN MAKER
UNKNOWN NAME

$20

272-5701 UNKNOWN MAKER
UNKNOWN NAME

$80

UNKNOWN FISHING PLUGS

273-5702 UNKNOWN MAKER
UNKNOWN NAME

$30

273-5703 UNKNOWN MAKER
UNKNOWN NAME

$30

273-5708 UNKNOWN MAKER
UNKNOWN NAME

$20

273-5710 UNKNOWN MAKER
UNKNOWN NAME

$100

273-5712 UNKNOWN MAKER
UNKNOWN NAME

$30

273-5713 UNKNOWN MAKER
UNKNOWN NAME

$200

273-5714 UNKNOWN MAKER
UNKNOWN NAME

$300

273-5716 UNKNOWN MAKER
UNKNOWN NAME

$40

273-5717 UNKNOWN MAKER
UNKNOWN NAME

$100

273-5718 UNKNOWN MAKER
UNKNOWN NAME

$100

273-5719 UNKNOWN MAKER
UNKNOWN NAME

$40

272-5720 UNKNOWN MAKER
UNKNOWN NAME

$200

273-5723 UNKNOWN MAKER
UNKNOWN NAME

$100

273-5724 UNKNOWN MAKER
UNKNOWN NAME

$100

273-5726 UNKNOWN MAKER
UNKNOWN NAME

$40

UNKNOWN FISHING PLUGS

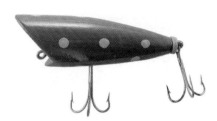

274-5727 UNKNOWN MAKER
UNKNOWN NAME

$40

274-5728 UNKNOWN MAKER
UNKNOWN NAME

$40

274-5729 UNKNOWN MAKER
UNKNOWN NAME

$100

274-5730 UNKNOWN MAKER
UNKNOWN NAME

$100

274-5732 UNKNOWN MAKER
UNKNOWN NAME

$200

274-5733 UNKNOWN MAKER
UNKNOWN NAME

$40

274-5734 UNKNOWN MAKER
UNKNOWN NAME

$100

274-5735 UNKNOWN MAKER
UNKNOWN NAME

$50

274-5736 UNKNOWN MAKER
UNKNOWN NAME

$50

274-5738 UNKNOWN MAKER
UNKNOWN NAME

$30

274-5739 UNKNOWN MAKER
UNKNOWN NAME

$40

274-5740 UNKNOWN MAKER
UNKNOWN NAME

$50

274-5741 UNKNOWN MAKER
UNKNOWN NAME

$50

274-5742 UNKNOWN MAKER
UNKNOWN NAME

$50

274-5743 UNKNOWN MAKER
UNKNOWN NAME

$50

UNKNOWN FISHING PLUGS

275-5746 UNKNOWN MAKER
UNKNOWN NAME

$40

275-22575 UNKNOWN MAKER
UNKNOWN NAME

$20

275-5748 UNKNOWN MAKER
UNKNOWN NAME

$20

275-5749 UNKNOWN MAKER
UNKNOWN NAME

$30

275-5751 UNKNOWN MAKER
UNKNOWN NAME

$200

275-5755 UNKNOWN MAKER
UNKNOWN NAME

$30

275-5756 UNKNOWN MAKER
UNKNOWN NAME

$30

275-5757 UNKNOWN MAKER
UNKNOWN NAME

$30

275-5758 UNKNOWN MAKER
UNKNOWN NAME

$30

275-5759 UNKNOWN MAKER
UNKNOWN NAME

$20

275-5760 UNKNOWN MAKER
UNKNOWN NAME

$20

275-5761 UNKNOWN MAKER
UNKNOWN NAME

$30

275-7012 UNKNOWN MAKER
UNKNOWN NAME

$20

275-5764 UNKNOWN MAKER
UNKNOWN NAME

$200

275-5766 UNKNOWN MAKER
UNKNOWN NAME

$200

UNKNOWN FISHING PLUGS

276-5772 UNKNOWN MAKER
UNKNOWN NAME

$80

276-5773 UNKNOWN MAKER
UNKNOWN NAME

$100

276-5774 UNKNOWN MAKER
UNKNOWN NAME

$50

276-5775 UNKNOWN MAKER
UNKNOWN NAME

$30

276-5776 UNKNOWN MAKER
UNKNOWN NAME

$30

276-5777 UNKNOWN MAKER
UNKNOWN NAME

$50

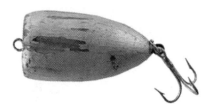

276-5778 UNKNOWN MAKER
UNKNOWN NAME

$50

276-5779 UNKNOWN MAKER
UNKNOWN NAME

$50

276-5780 UNKNOWN MAKER
UNKNOWN NAME

$50

276-5781 UNKNOWN MAKER
UNKNOWN NAME

$50

276-5783 UNKNOWN MAKER
UNKNOWN NAME

$50

276-5785 UNKNOWN MAKER
UNKNOWN NAME

$30

276-5786 UNKNOWN MAKER
UNKNOWN NAME

$20

276-5787 UNKNOWN MAKER
UNKNOWN NAME

$20

276-5788 UNKNOWN MAKER
UNKNOWN NAME

$80

UNKNOWN FISHING PLUGS

277-5789 UNKNOWN MAKER
UNKNOWN NAME

$80

277-5397 UNKNOWN MAKER
WHITEFISH DECOY
MN   1930's
$200

277-5791 UNKNOWN MAKER
UNKNOWN NAME

$80

277-5792 UNKNOWN MAKER
UNKNOWN NAME

$30

277-5793 UNKNOWN MAKER
UNKNOWN NAME

$300

277-5796 UNKNOWN MAKER
UNKNOWN NAME

$20

277-5797 UNKNOWN MAKER
UNKNOWN NAME

$50

277-5798 UNKNOWN MAKER
UNKNOWN NAME

$50

277-5799 UNKNOWN MAKER
UNKNOWN NAME

$50

277-5800 UNKNOWN MAKER
UNKNOWN NAME

$40

277-5801 UNKNOWN MAKER
UNKNOWN NAME

$40

277-5803 UNKNOWN MAKER
UNKNOWN NAME

$40

277-5804 UNKNOWN MAKER
UNKNOWN NAME

$40

277-5805 UNKNOWN MAKER
UNKNOWN NAME

$40

277-5807 UNKNOWN MAKER
UNKNOWN NAME

$80

UNKNOWN FISHING PLUGS

278-5809 UNKNOWN MAKER
UNKNOWN NAME

$200

278-5810 UNKNOWN MAKER
UNKNOWN NAME

$200

278-5811 UNKNOWN MAKER
UNKNOWN NAME

$200

278-5812 UNKNOWN MAKER
UNKNOWN NAME

$200

278-5813 UNKNOWN MAKER
UNKNOWN NAME

$200

278-5814 UNKNOWN MAKER
UNKNOWN NAME

$50

278-5815 UNKNOWN MAKER
UNKNOWN NAME

$20

278-5816 UNKNOWN MAKER
UNKNOWN NAME

$100

278-5817 UNKNOWN MAKER
UNKNOWN NAME

$200

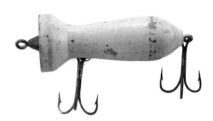

278-5818 UNKNOWN MAKER
UNKNOWN NAME

$50

278-5820 UNKNOWN MAKER
UNKNOWN NAME

$200

278-5823 UNKNOWN MAKER
UNKNOWN NAME

$200

278-5850 UNKNOWN MAKER
UNKNOWN NAME

$20

278-5912 UNKNOWN MAKER
UNKNOWN NAME

$20

278-5915 UNKNOWN MAKER
UNKNOWN NAME

$100

UNKNOWN FISHING PLUGS

279-7133 UNKNOWN MAKER
UNKNOWN NAME

$20

279-6094 UNKNOWN MAKER
UNKNOWN NAME

$200

279-6095 UNKNOWN MAKER
UNKNOWN NAME

$100

279-6096 UNKNOWN MAKER
UNKNOWN NAME

$100

279-7037 UNKNOWN MAKER
UNKNOWN NAME

$500

279-6100 UNKNOWN MAKER
UNKNOWN NAME

$20

279-6101 UNKNOWN MAKER
UNKNOWN NAME

$20

279-6102 UNKNOWN MAKER
UNKNOWN NAME

$20

279-6103 UNKNOWN MAKER
UNKNOWN NAME

$20

279-6104 UNKNOWN MAKER
UNKNOWN NAME

$100

279-6105 UNKNOWN MAKER
UNKNOWN NAME

$20

279-6106 UNKNOWN MAKER
UNKNOWN NAME

$20

279-6107 UNKNOWN MAKER
UNKNOWN NAME

$20

279-7025 UNKNOWN MAKER
UNKNOWN NAME

$100

279-7024 UNKNOWN MAKER
UNKNOWN NAME

$40

UNKNOWN FISHING PLUGS

280-6110 UNKNOWN MAKER
UNKNOWN NAME

$20

280-6111 UNKNOWN MAKER
UNKNOWN NAME

$100

280-6112 UNKNOWN MAKER
UNKNOWN NAME

$20

280-6113 UNKNOWN MAKER
UNKNOWN NAME

$40

280-6114 UNKNOWN MAKER
UNKNOWN NAME

$20

280-6115 UNKNOWN MAKER
UNKNOWN NAME

$100

280-6116 UNKNOWN MAKER
UNKNOWN NAME

$30

280-6117 UNKNOWN MAKER
UNKNOWN NAME

$30

280-6118 UNKNOWN MAKER
UNKNOWN NAME

$30

280-6119 UNKNOWN MAKER
UNKNOWN NAME

$10

280-6120 UNKNOWN MAKER
UNKNOWN NAME

$30

280-6121 UNKNOWN MAKER
UNKNOWN NAME

$50

280-6122 UNKNOWN MAKER
UNKNOWN NAME

$30

280-6123 UNKNOWN MAKER
UNKNOWN NAME

$30

280-6124 UNKNOWN MAKER
UNKNOWN NAME

$30

UNKNOWN FISHING PLUGS

281-6125 UNKNOWN MAKER
UNKNOWN NAME

$30

281-7023 UNKNOWN MAKER
UNKNOWN NAME

$100

281-7034 UNKNOWN MAKER
UNKNOWN NAME

$30

281-6128 UNKNOWN MAKER
UNKNOWN NAME

$20

281-6129 UNKNOWN MAKER
UNKNOWN NAME

$30

281-6130 UNKNOWN MAKER
UNKNOWN NAME

$20

281-7022 UNKNOWN MAKER
UNKNOWN NAME

$100

281-6132 UNKNOWN MAKER
UNKNOWN NAME

$100

281-7013 UNKNOWN MAKER
UNKNOWN NAME

$100

281-6134 UNKNOWN MAKER
UNKNOWN NAME

$50

281-6135 UNKNOWN MAKER
UNKNOWN NAME

$30

281-6136 UNKNOWN MAKER
UNKNOWN NAME

$20

281-6137 UNKNOWN MAKER
UNKNOWN NAME

$50

281-7036 UNKNOWN MAKER
UNKNOWN NAME

$100

281-6140 UNKNOWN MAKER
UNKNOWN NAME

$30

UNKNOWN FISHING PLUGS

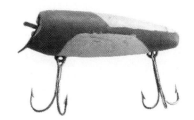

282-6141 UNKNOWN MAKER
UNKNOWN NAME

$30

281-6142 UNKNOWN MAKER
UNKNOWN NAME

$30

282-6143 UNKNOWN MAKER
UNKNOWN NAME

$30

282-6144 UNKNOWN MAKER
UNKNOWN NAME

$30

282-6145 UNKNOWN MAKER
UNKNOWN NAME

$30

282-6146 UNKNOWN MAKER
UNKNOWN NAME

$30

282-6148 UNKNOWN MAKER
UNKNOWN NAME

$30

282-6149 UNKNOWN MAKER
UNKNOWN NAME

$30

282-6150 UNKNOWN MAKER
UNKNOWN NAME

$30

282-6151 UNKNOWN MAKER
UNKNOWN NAME

$30

282-6152 UNKNOWN MAKER
UNKNOWN NAME

$20

282-6153 UNKNOWN MAKER
UNKNOWN NAME

$30

282-6154 UNKNOWN MAKER
UNKNOWN NAME

$30

282-6155 UNKNOWN MAKER
UNKNOWN NAME

$30

282-6156 UNKNOWN MAKER
UNKNOWN NAME

$20

UNKNOWN FISHING PLUGS

283-6157 UNKNOWN MAKER
UNKNOWN NAME

$20

283-6159 UNKNOWN MAKER
UNKNOWN NAME

$50

283-6160 UNKNOWN MAKER
UNKNOWN NAME

$20

283-6161 UNKNOWN MAKER
UNKNOWN NAME

$20

283-6162 UNKNOWN MAKER
UNKNOWN NAME

$20

283-6163 UNKNOWN MAKER
UNKNOWN NAME

$30

283-6164 UNKNOWN MAKER
UNKNOWN NAME

$20

283-6165 UNKNOWN MAKER
UNKNOWN NAME

$20

283-6166 UNKNOWN MAKER
UNKNOWN NAME

$20

283-7035 UNKNOWN MAKER
UNKNOWN NAME

$20

283-6168 UNKNOWN MAKER
UNKNOWN NAME

$30

283-6169 UNKNOWN MAKER
UNKNOWN NAME

$20

283-6170 UNKNOWN MAKER
UNKNOWN NAME

$50

283-6171 UNKNOWN MAKER
UNKNOWN NAME

$50

283-6172 UNKNOWN MAKER
UNKNOWN NAME

$50

UNKNOWN FISHING PLUGS

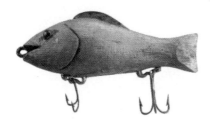

284-6173 UNKNOWN MAKER
UNKNOWN NAME

$50

284-6174 UNKNOWN MAKER
UNKNOWN NAME

$50

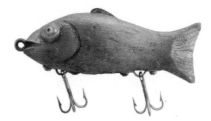

284-6175 UNKNOWN MAKER
UNKNOWN NAME

$50

284-6176 UNKNOWN MAKER
UNKNOWN NAME

$50

284-6177 UNKNOWN MAKER
UNKNOWN NAME

$50

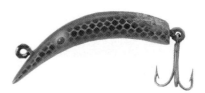

284-2528 UNKNOWN MAKER
UNKNOWN NAME
WI

$50

284-7021 UNKNOWN MAKER
UNKNOWN NAME

$60

284-6995 UNKNOWN MAKER
UNKNOWN NAME

$20

284-6996 UNKNOWN MAKER
UNKNOWN NAME

$40

284-24692 UNKNOWN MAKER
UNKNOWN NAME

$30

284-6999 UNKNOWN MAKER
UNKNOWN NAME

$20

284-7001 UNKNOWN MAKER
UNKNOWN NAME

$40

284-7004 UNKNOWN MAKER
UNKNOWN NAME

$60

284-7008 UNKNOWN MAKER
UNKNOWN NAME

$40

284-7009 UNKNOWN MAKER
UNKNOWN NAME

$40

VARIOUS RIVER RUNTS

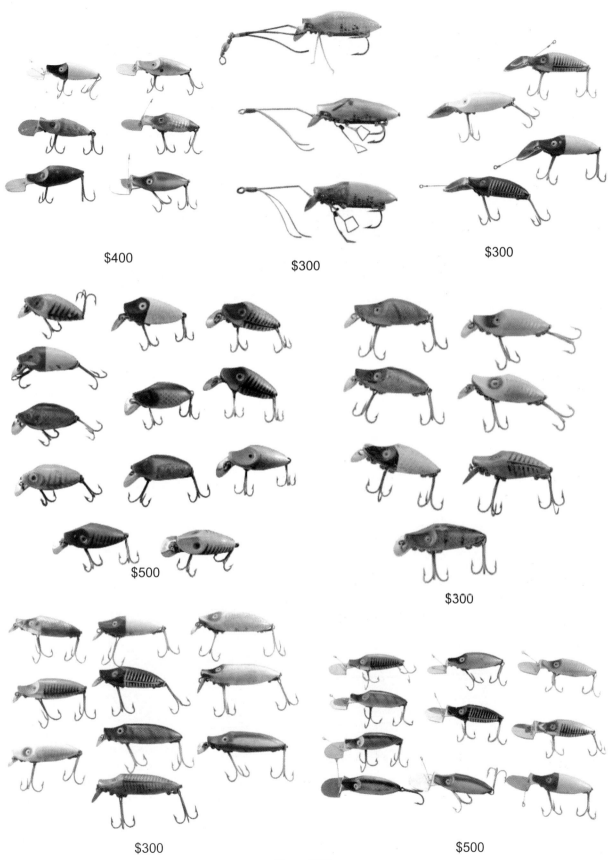

$400

$300

$300

$500

$300

$300

$500

CREEK CHUB BAITS SALESMAN'S SAMPLE
CREEK CHUB BAIT CO.,   IN   1928 VINTAGE
$20,000.00

CREEK CHUB BAITS SALESMAN'S SAMPLE
CREEK CHUB BAIT CO.,   IN   1928 VINTAGE
$10,000.00

FISHING PLUG BOXES

287-6748   4 BROTHERS
4 BROTHER NEVERFAIL MINNOW
OH $2000

287-6336   A.D. MFG. CO.
BAYOU BOOGIE
LA $20

287-6292   ABBEY & IMBRIE
ABBEY & IMBRIE LURE
NY 1920's $10

287-6307   ABBEY & IMBRIE
GO-GETTER
NY 1925 $40

287-6302   ABBEY & IMBRIE
THE GREEN SPOON
NY 1925 $30

287-6299   ABERCROMBIE & FITCH CO.
ABERCROMBIE & FITCH LURE
NY $50

287-6900   ABU GARCIA
ABU BAIT (SWEDEN)
SWE $10

287-6902   ABU GARCIA
ABU BAIT (SWEDEN)
SWE $10

287-6320   ACCETTA, TONY
ACCETTA BAIT
OH 1930's $10

287-6323   ACCETTA, TONY
ACCETTA BAIT
OH 1930's $10

287-6328   ACCETTA, TONY
RIVER DEVIL
OH 1940 $20

287-6322   ACCETTA, TONY
WEED DODGER
OH 1040 $20

FISHING PLUG BOXES

288-6308   ACTIVATED LURE CO.
HI-YO
OH 1947 $20

288-6673   ADAMS, L.D. "POP"
POP'S BASS GETTER
OK 1960 $10

288-6329   AITKEN WARNER CORP
KRAZY MINNOW
OH 1955 $10

288-6334   ALCOE LURE CO.
ALCOA LURE
FL 1958 $20

288-6350   ALLCOCK-LAIGHT & WEST-
WOOD
A.L. & W. LURE
CAN 1930's $30

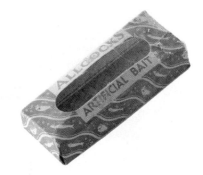

288-6303   ALLCOCKS
ALLCOCKS ARTIFICAL BAIT
UK $20

288-6324   AL'S GOLDFISH LURE CO.
AL STUART'S GOLDFISH
MA 1940'S $30

288-6312   AL'S GOLDFISH LURE CO.
DIAMOND JIM
MA 1960 $10

288-6311   AMERICAN SPORTSMAN LURES
PRO SPOON
MI $20

288-6316   ANDERSON & SON
WEEDLESS WONDER
RI 1969 $200

288-6340   AQUASPORT INC.
DOODLE BUG
OK 1965 $10

288-6290   ARBOGAST, FRED
HAWAIIAN WIGGLER
OH 1930's $60

FISHING PLUG BOXES

289-6295   ARBOGAST, FRED
HAWAIIAN WIGGLER
OH 1930's $20

289-6283   ARBOGAST, FRED
HULA DANCER
OH 1947 $20

289-6306   ARBOGAST, FRED
HULA DANCER
OH 1930's $20

289-6282   ARBOGAST, FRED
HULA PIKE
OH 1930's $10

289-6296   ARBOGAST, FRED
HULA POPPER
OH 1940's $10

289-6289   ARBOGAST, FRED
JITTERBUG
OH 1950 $20

289-6300   ARBOGAST, FRED
JITTERBUG
OH $40

289-6305   ARBOGAST, FRED
JITTERBUG
OH 1940's $20

289-6298   ARBOGAST, FRED
LIL' BASS
OH 1959 $10

289-6285   ARBOGAST, FRED
SKINNY MINNY
OH 1959 $10

289-6288   ARBOGAST, FRED
TIN LIZ
OH 1927 $100

289-6284   ARBOGAST, FRED
TWIN LIZ
OH 1947 $10

FISHING PLUG BOXES

290-6877   ATOM MFG CO
ATOM BAIT
MA 1947 $20

290-6465   ATOM MFG CO
STRIPER ATOM
MA 1947 $20

290-6310   ATOMIC MFG. CO.
STRIPER ATOM
MA 1947 $20

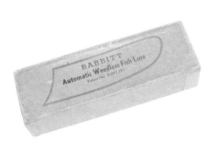

290-6363   BABBITT, E. S.
BABBITT AUTOMATIC FISH LURE
OH 1926 $100

290-6260   BAILEY & ELLIOTT
THE MANITOU MINNOW
IN 1905 $500

290-6347   BAILEY WEEDLESS BAIT CO.
WEED HOG
OH 1948 $30

290-6278   BARBER, E.E.
REEL SHAD
KY 1960 $40

290-6941   BASS-BUSTER LURES
BASS-BUSTER LURE
MO 1952 $60

290-6953   BASS-BUSTER LURES
BASS-BUSTER LURE
MO 1952 $40

290-6352   BEAN, L.L.
L.L. BEAN BAIT
ME 1948 $10

290-6938   BEAR CREEK BAIT CO
TWEEDLER
MI 1952 $40

290-6313   BEAR CREEK BAIT CO.
COHO-KING
MI 1940's $10

FISHING PLUG BOXES

291-6254   BEAR CREEK BAIT CO.
TWEEDLER
MI 1940's $40

291-6963   BEAVER BETTER BAITS TACKLE
INC
BEAVER BETTER BAIT
OH $20

291-6342   BENDER FISHING TACKLE CO.
DILLIE
FL 1955 $20

291-6688   BERRY-LEBECK MFG. CO.
OZARKA LURE
MO 1947 $30

291-6365   BIFF BAIT CO.
WHOOPEE BIFF PLUG
WI 1926 $300

291-6351   BITE-EM-BATE SALES CO.
BITE-EM-BATE
IN 1920's $400

291-6961   BLAZ-O-LURE SALES
BLAZ-O-LURE
CA $20

291-6343   BLEEDING BAIT MFG. CO.
THE BLEEDER
TX 1940's $100

291-6354   BOMBER BAIT CO.
BOMBER LURE
TX 1940's $40

291-6355   BOMBER BAIT CO.
BOMBER LURE
TX 1940's $20

291-6356   BOMBER BAIT CO.
BOMBER LURE
TX 1940's $10

291-6359   BOMBER BAIT CO.
GIMMICK
TX 1955 $10

FISHING PLUG BOXES

292-6360   BOMBER BAIT CO.
SLAB SPOON
TX 1952 $10

292-6357   BOMBER BAIT CO.
SPEED SHAD
TX 1963 $10

292-6345   BOMBER BAIT CO.
WATER DOG
TX $10

292-6362   BOSHEAR TACKLE CO.
RAZZLE DAZZLE
AR 1951 $20

292-6262   BRAIDWOOD STAMP CO.
GAYLURE
NJ 1934 $40

292-6253   BRAINERD BAIT CO.
DOCTOR SPOON
MN 1932 $20

292-6251   BRIGHTE-EYE-LURE PRODUCTS
BRIGHTE-EYE-LURE
MI 1933 $50

292-6337   BROOK'S BAITS (R-JAY INDUST.
INC.)
BROOK'S BAIT
OH 1940's $10

292-6878   BUCK'S BAITS
SPOON PLUG
NC $10

292-6939   BURMEK, TONY J.
BURMEK'S SECRET BAIT
WI 1960 $40

292-6772   BURRELLURE BAIT CO.
BURRELLURE BAIT
NJ $10

292-6383   BURTIS
THE IRRESISTABLE
           $10

FISHING PLUG BOXES

293-6382   CAPE COD LURES INC.
JIG
MA $10

293-6318   CARNES, JACK
FANCY-DANCER
AK 1953 $20

293-6276   CARPENTER'S
CARPENTER'S LURE
        $10

293-6375   CARTER BAIT CO.
CARTER'S BESTEVER WIGGLER
IN 1920'S $200

293-6944   CHALLENGE TACKLE CO
ADJUSTABLE WING LURE
PA $10

293-6280   CHALLENGE TACKLE CO
OFF SIDE VANE LURE
PA 1952 $20

293-6376   CHARMER MINNOW CO.
THE CHARMER
MO 1912 $1000

293-6348   CHASE ROD & TACKLE CO.
FISH-GETTERS
FL 1952 $10

293-6964   CHESTER, F.E.
THE DAZZLER JR.
RI 1938 $40

293-6952   CHESTER, F.E. LURES
DAZZLUM
RI 1938 $40

293-6529   CHICAGO TACKLE CO.
KING CHUB
IL 1952 $10

293-6618   CHIX FISH LURE CO.
CHIX FISH LURE
WA 1930's $30

Page 293

FISHING PLUG BOXES

294-6875   CHUM LURES
CHUM CHUM THE WONDER LURE
FL $10

294-6266   CIRCLE H. LURES
CIRCLE H LURE
OH 1949 $10

294-6372   CLARK, C.A.
POPPER SCOUT
MO 1936 $20

294-6381   CLARK, C.A.
POPPER SCOUT
MO 1936 $20

294-6380   CLARK, C.A.
WATER SCOUT
MO 1936 $20

294-6367   CLEWELL, R.L.
SNAKERBAIT
OH 1926 $200

294-6677   CLIIPPER LURES
CLIPPER LURE
          $30

294-6261   COOK, F.W.
COOK'S BEER "500"
IN $20

294-6246   COOK, F.W.
COOK'S BEER LURE
IN $20

294-6269   CORDELL
CORDELL BAIT
AR 1970's $10

294-6338   COURTNEY SPECIALTY CO.
DEEP DIVER
MO $10

294-6881   CRAZY LEGS LURES
CRAZY LEGS TOP WATER LURE
MO $20

295-6419   CREEK CHUB BAIT CO.
C.C.B. CO. LURE
IN $20

295-6421   CREEK CHUB BAIT CO.
C.C.B. CO. LURE
IN $40

295-6422   CREEK CHUB BAIT CO.
C.C.B. CO. LURE
IN $40

295-6423   CREEK CHUB BAIT CO.
C.C.B. CO. LURE
IN $100

295-6433   CREEK CHUB BAIT CO.
C.C.B. CO. LURE
IN $40

295-6434   CREEK CHUB BAIT CO.
C.C.B. CO. LURE
IN $40

295-6425   CREEK CHUB BAIT CO.
CREEK CHUB LURE
IN $20

295-6427   CREEK CHUB BAIT CO.
CREEK CHUB LURE
IN $20

295-6429   CREEK CHUB BAIT CO.
CREEK CHUB LURE
IN $10

295-6432   CREEK CHUB BAIT CO.
CREEK CHUB WIGGLER
IN 1924 $1000

295-6428   CREEK CHUB BAIT CO.
FLY ROD CREEK CHUB LURE
IN 1920's $100

295-6430   CREEK CHUB BAIT CO.
FLY ROD CREEK CHUB LURE
IN 1920's $100

FISHING PLUG BOXES

296-6418   CREEK CHUB BAIT CO.
GIANT PIKIE
IN 1957 $20

296-6424   CREEK CHUB BAIT CO.
SHUR-STRIKE MINNOW
IN 1920's $100

296-6426   CREEK CHUB BAIT CO.
SHUR-STRIKE MINNOW
IN 1920's $100

296-6431   CREEK CHUB BAIT CO.
SHUR-STRIKE MINNOW
IN 1920's $100

296-6384   D.A.M.
BOMBER SPINNER   (GERMANY)
$10

296-6387   D.A.M.
D.A.M. LURE   (GERMANy)
GER $10

296-6369   D.A.M.
D.A.M. BAIT   (GERMAN)
GER $10

296-6373   DAMYL
DAMYL LURE   (GERMAN)
GER $20

296-6277   D'ANNA'S LURE SHOP
BAYOU BOOGIE
LA 1952 $40

296-6393   DECKER ANS. B.
DECKER BASS BAIT
NJ 1910 $1000

296-6749   DECKER, ANS B.
PLUG BAIT
NJ $1000

296-6390   DEWITT, BILL
BILL DEWITT BAIT
NY 1930's $40

297-6386   DILLON-BECK MFG. CO.
DILLONBECK LURE
NJ 1960's $20

297-6957   DON J. FUELSCH & ASSOC.
SHORE PATROL #1
AR $10

297-6391   DONALY, JAMES L.
REDFIN FLOATING BAIT
NJ 1925 $1500

297-6405   DRULEY'S RESEARCH PROD-
UCTS
MINNIE THE SWIMMER
WI 1936 $40

297-6371   DUNK-CARTER
DUNK-CARTER LURE
OH 1930's $200

297-6378   DUNK'S (AMERICAN DISPLAY)
DUNK'S LURE
OH 1930's $100

297-6379   DUNK'S (AMERICAN DISPLAY)
DUNK'S SPOONFISH
OH 1930's $50

297-6395   DYNA TACKLE CO.
DYNA-MITE
TX 1952 $20

297-6888   EDSON & BOYNTON
EDSON & BOYNTON LURE
ME $20

297-6385   EGER BAIT MFG. CO.
EGER BAIT
FL 1940's $20

297-6413   EGER BAIT MFG. CO.
EGER BAIT
FL 1940's $20

297-6400   ELECTROLURE CO.
ELECTROLURE
IL $40

FISHING PLUG BOXES

298-6408   ELECTRONIC UNITS INC.
JUMPING JO
OH $20

298-6397   EPPINGER, LOU J.
DARDEVLE
MI 1920's $10

298-6374   EPPINGER, LOU J.
DARDEVLE'S IMP
MI 1921 $20

298-6394   EPPINGER, LOU J.
DARDEVLET
MI 1940's $20

298-6410   EPPINGER, LOU J.
WINGED DARDEVLE
MI 1930's $10

298-6399   ETCHEN TACKLE CO.
HELGA-DEVIL
MI $20

298-6527   EVAN'S CASE CO.
JIFFY PLUG
MA $30

298-6403   EVANS, GLEN L.
ATOMIC BASS-BUSTER
ID 1946 $20

298-6402   EVANS, GLEN L.
B-29 BASS BOMBER
ID 1946 $20

298-6388   EVER READY BAIT CO.
THE EVER READY
              $20

298-6409   EXCEL LURE CO.
THE EXCEL RUBBER LURE
IL $40

298-6471   FENNER WEEDLESS BAIT CO.
FENNER'S W.A.B. BAIT
WI $60

299-6468   FETCH-IT CO.
FETCH-IT LURE
ID $20

299-6415   FINLEY BAIT & TACKLE SHOP
FINLEY SPECIAL
IN $10

299-6462   FISHATHON BAIT CO.
DIZZY DIVER
OK 1947 $20

299-6472   FISHATHON BAIT CO.
DIZZY DIVER
OK 1947 $30

299-6463   FISHATHON BAIT CO.
DIZZY FLOATER
OK 1947 $40

299-6442   FISHMASTER SPORTING
GOODS
FISHMASTER LURE
MA $20

299-6443   FISHMASTER SPORTNG GOODS
FISHMASTER LURE
MA $20

299-6466   FLORIDA ARTIFICAL BAIT CO
SUPERSTRIKE
FL 1929 $300

299-6416   FLORIDA FISHING TACKLE CO
BARRACUDA DALTON
FL 1950's $10

299-6398   FLORIDA FISHING TACKLE CO
BARRACUDA LURE
FL 1950's $20

299-6404   FLORIDA FISHING TACKLE CO
BARRACUDA LURE
FL 1950's $20

299-6396   FLORIDA FISHING TACKLE CO
BARRACUDA REFLECTO SPOON
FL 1950's $20

FISHING PLUG BOXES

300-6406   FLORIDA FISHING TACKLE CO
PEE WEE LURE
FL 1950's $10

300-6445   FOSS, AL
PORK RIND MINNOW
OH 1930's $30

300-6448   FOSS, AL
SHIMMYETTE FLY ROD WIGGLER
OH 1930's $100

300-6474   FOSS, AL.
DRY STRIP PORK RIND
OH 1940's $200

300-6475   FOSS, AL.
POCKET KIT
OH 1940's $200

300-6476   FOSS, AL.
PORK RIND MINNOW
OH 1940's $1000

300-6484   FOSS, AL.
PORK RIND MINNOW
OH 1940's $30

300-6485   FOSS, AL.
PORK RIND MINNOW
OH 1940's $40

300-6486   FOSS, AL.
PORK RIND MINNOW
OH 1940's $30

300-6479   FOSS, AL.
PORK RIND STRIP
OH 1940's $30

300-6478   FOSS, AL.
TRUE TEMPER BAIT
OH 1940's $20

300-6435   FREEPORT HOOK
THE FREEPORT HOOK
IL 1908 $200

FISHING PLUG BOXES

301-6948   FREER, ARTHUR T.
G.M. SKINNER TROLLING SPOONS
NY $10

301-6453   FROST, C.F.
CHIPPEWA BAIT
WI 1915 $1000

301-6942   FROST, H.J.
SENATE WOODEN MINNOW
NY 1914 $1000

301-6275   FURY MFG. CO.
CHAMP
MI $20

301-6467   G.G. BAIT CO
GENE'S GEM
MN 1949 $20

301-6950   GABBARD TACKLE CO.
GAB-LUR
MI $20

301-6895   GARCIA, CHARLES
MEE-MEE   (SWEDEN)
SWE $10

301-6439   GARCIA, CHARLES (ABU)
ABU HI-LO   (SWEDEN)
SWE 1950 $10

301-6454   GARDNER SPORTS MFG. CO.
TWIN DANCER
MA 1948 $20

301-6469   GEN-SHAW BAIT CO.
GEN-SHAW BAIT
IL 1953 $20

301-6949   GETZUM TACKLE CO.
GURGLE-GITER
MN $20

301-6459   GILL, J.J. & ASSOC.
BASS BIRD
CA $30

302-6945   GILMORE TACKLE CO.
THE HOODLER
AR 1958 $10

302-6458   GLO BOY BAIT CO
GLO BOY BAIT
1941 $30

302-6361   GLO-LURE CO.
BLINKIN' BEAUTY
IL 1946 $10

302-6370   GO TOOL & STAMP CO.
MARVELURE
IL 1946 $10

302-6440   GOBLE, B.G.
GOBLE BAIT
OK 1920's $500

302-6450   GO-ITE MFG. CO.
WATER-PLANE BAIT
MI 1927 $50

302-6436   GOOD LUCK MFG. CO.
LITTLE IMP
OK 1949 $10

302-6271   GOODERHAM & WORTS
G & W SPECIAL (CANADA)
CA $20

302-6446   GREENE, F.B.
GREENE'S SPOON
CT 1917 $50

302-6943   GRUBE, W. J.
BILL'S LUCKY-STRIKE MINNOW
OH 1910's $60

302-6438   GRUBE, W. J.
FLUTTERWING CASTING FLY
OH 1910 $100

302-6444   GUDWER, HANS
COPPER WIGGLER
          $20

303-6464   GUSICK, HENRY
BONANZA LURE
WI 1959 $30

303-6567   H&H PLUG CO.
STRIP-TEASER
IA $40

303-6437   HAGEN TACKLE CO.
HAGEN SPINNER
IL 1946 $20

303-6658   HAMILTON, F.B.
MEDLEY'S WIGGLEY CRAWFISH
CA 1920 $300

303-6608   HANSON FISH LURE CO
HANSON FISH LURE
WN $30

303-6890   HARDY BROS. LTD.
FLY BOX, ENGLISH
UK $100

303-6891   HARDY BROS. LTD.
FLY BOX, ENGLISH
UK $100

303-6892   HARDY BROS. LTD.
FLY BOX, ENGLISH
UK $100

303 6893   HARDY BROS. LTD.
FLY BOX, ENGLISH
UK $100

303-6894   HARDY BROS. LTD.
FLY BOX, ENGLISH
UK $100

303-6593   HARDY, J.A.
KROU MINNOW
IN 1917 $2000

303-6592   HARDY, W.A.
HARDY INTERCHANGEABLE MINNOW
IN 1907 $3000

FISHING PLUG BOXES

304-6565   HARMON, JACK
VIBRATOR 3-IN-1 BAIT
OK 1940's $20

304-6828   HASTINGS SPORTING GOODS
WORKS
GOOD LUCK WOBBLER
MI $400

304-OX06581   HAWK, DAVE LURE CO.
LUCKYBUG
AR 1952 $20

304-6523   HAWTHORNE LURES
MONTGOMERY WARDS
          $20

304-6574   HAYDEN, BOYD & CO.
MULTI-WAG
MA 1946 $20

304-6591   HAYDEN, BOYD & CO
MULTILURES
MA $20

304-6507   HEDDON, JAMES & SONS
DOWAGIAC ARTISTIC MINNOW
MI $2500

304-6508   HEDDON, JAMES & SONS
DOWAGIAC KILLER
MI $3500

304-6487   HEDDON, JAMES & SONS
DOWAGIAC LURE
MI $40

304-6488   HEDDON, JAMES & SONS
DOWAGIAC LURE
MI $20

304-6489   HEDDON, JAMES & SONS
DOWAGIAC LURE
MI $60

304-6490   HEDDON, JAMES & SONS
DOWAGIAC LURE
MI $40

305-6505   HEDDON, JAMES & SONS
DOWAGIAC LURE
MI $40

305-6506   HEDDON, JAMES & SONS
DOWAGIAC LURE
MI $40

305-6509   HEDDON, JAMES & SONS
DOWAGIAC LURE
MI $10

305-6491   HEDDON, JAMES & SONS
DOWAGIAC MINNOW
MI $300

305-6495   HEDDON, JAMES & SONS
DOWAGIAC MINNOW
MI $300

305-6499   HEDDON, JAMES & SONS
DOWAGIAC MINNOW
MI $300

305-6501   HEDDON, JAMES & SONS
DOWAGIAC MINNOW
MI $1500

305-6512   HEDDON, JAMES & SONS
DOWAGIAC WOODEN MINNOW
MI $2500

305-6502   HEDDON, JAMES & SONS
HEDDON LURE
MI $10

305-6504   HEDDON, JAMES & SONS
HEDDON LURE
MI $10

305-6511   HEDDON, JAMES & SONS
HEDDON LURE
MI $10

305-6492   HEDDON, JAMES & SONS
HEDDON SPOOK BAIT
MI $100

FISHING PLUG BOXES

306-6494   HEDDON, JAMES & SONS
HEDDON SPOOK BAIT
MI $100

306-6497   HEDDON, JAMES & SONS
HEDDON SPOOK BAIT
MI $100

306-6498   HEDDON, JAMES & SONS
HEDDON SPOOK BAIT
MI $100

306-6496   HEDDON, JAMES & SONS
NEW CRAB WIGGLER BAIT
MI $100

306-6513   HEDDON, JAMES & SONS
RIVER RUNT SPOOK
MI $40

306-6500   HEDDON, JAMES & SONS
TAD-POLLY
MI 1923 $700

306-6514   HEDDON, JAMES & SONS
WEEDLESS PORK RIND MINNOW
MI $300

306-6493   HEDDON, JAMES & SONS
WILDER-DILG LURE
MI $100

306-6515   HEDDON, JAMES & SONS
WILDER-DILG LURE
MI $300

306-6510   HEDDON, JAMES & SONS
WILDER-DILG-SPOOK
MI $40

306-6576   HELIN TACKLE CO.
FLY ROD FLATFISH
MI $10

306-6557   HELIN TACKLE CO.
HELIN FLATFISH
MI 1933 $20

307-6579   HENZEL, J.G.
BOOSTER (EDIBLE) BAIT
IL 1907 $10

307-6532   HENZEL, J.G.
HENZEL WEEDLESS HOOK
IL 1900's $100

307-6456   HEP BAIT CO.
BLOOY LOOY
MN 1958 $20

307-6586   HERTERS INC.
HERTER'S HOOK HARNESS
MN 1950's $10

307-6525   HIGGINS, J.C.
J.C. HIGGINS LURE   (SEARS)
MI $20

307-6364   HOBBS, W.H. SUPPLY CO.
BON-NET LURE
WI 1952 $60

307-6883   HOEFER LURES
HOEFER LURE
MN $60

307-6884   HOEFER LURES
HOEFER LURE
MN $60

307-6452   HOFSCHNEIDER CORP.
RED EYE WIGGLER
NY 1949 $20

307-6559   HOFSCHNEIDER CORP.
WIGGLE PLUG
NY 1940's $20

307-6281   HORROCKS-IBBOTSON CO.
BIG BROTHER
NY 1940's $40

307-6291   HORROCKS-IBBOTSON CO.
McGINTY SHURLUCK SPINNER
NY 1947 $10

FISHING PLUG BOXES

308-6582   HORROCKS-IBBOTSON CO.
OLD HI'S FINBACK
NY $10

308-6766   HORROCKS-IBBOTSON CO.
SHMOO
NY 1947 $30

308-6286   HORROCKS-IBBOTSON CO.
SW MINNOW
NY 1940'S $40

308-6568   HOUSER FLY CO.
HOUSER HELL DIVER
MO 1949 $10

308-6584   HUMDINGER LURE MFG. CO.
HUMDINGER LURE
FL $20

308-6561   HUMPY BAIT CO.
HUMPY PLUG
IA 1950 $40

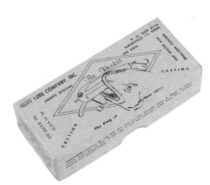

308-6566   HUNT LURE CO.
THE HOOKER
TN 1957 $20

308-6571   HUNT LURE CO.
THE HOOKER
TN 1957 $40

308-6259   INTERCHANGABLE BAIT CO.
THE QUICKIE
MI $20

308-6570   ISLE ROYALE CO.
ISLE ROYALE BAIT
MI $30

308-6578   JACK'S TACKLE MFG. CO.
LUCK-E-LURE
OK 1955 $10

308-6967   JACK'S TACKLE MFG. CO.
WIG-A-LURE
OK 1950's $20

309-6560   JAMISON, W. J.
COAXER, #3
IL $200

309-6563   JAMISON, W.J.
SHANNON TWIN SPINNER
IL $30

309-6267   JAMISON, WM J.
SHANNON SPINNING LURE
IL 1920's $10

309-6555   JAMISON, W.J.
SHANNON LURE
IL $20

309-6556   JAMISON, W.J.
SHANNON PERSUADER
IL $40

309-6546   JENSON DISTRIBUTING CO.
FROGLEGS
TX 1950 $30

309-6547   JENSON DISTRIBUTING CO.
FROGLEGS
TX 1950 $30

309-6564   JENSON FISHING TACKLE CO.
OZARK LIZARD
TX $10

309-6548   JENSON SPORTING GOODS
JENSON LURE
TX $20

309-6554   JENSON SPORTING GOODS
THE Z-I-P-P-E-R
TX $10

309-6265   JOHNSON, LOUIS CO.
JOHNSON LURE
IL 1940's $10

309-6550   JOHNSON, LOUIS CO.
JOHNSON SILVER MINNOW
IL 1928 $10

310-6551 JOHNSON, LOUIS CO.
JOHNSON SILVER MINNOW
IL 1928 $10

310-6549 JOHNSON, LOUIS CO.
JOHNSON SILVER SPOON
IL $10

310-6575 JOHNSON, LOUIS CO.
JOHNSON'S SILVER MINNOW
IL 1928 $10

310-6552 JOHNSON, LOUIS CO.
JOHNSON'S SPOON
IL $10

310-6572 JOHNSON, LOUIS CO.
JOHNSON'S SPRITE
IL 1950 $20

310-6553 JOHNSON, LOUIS CO.
LUJON
IL 1947 $10

310-6590 K&M TACKLE CO.
K & M BAIT
NH $40

310-6540 K.B. BAIT CO.
K-B SPOON
WI $20

310-6536 KAUFMAN, A.H.
NAPPANEE "YPSI" BAIT
IN 1936 $200

310-6537 KAUTZKY LAZY IKE CORP.
LAZY IKE
IA $40

310-6542 KAUTZKY LAZY IKE CORP.
LAZY IKE
IA $10

310-6544 KAUTZKY LAZY IKE CORP.
LAZY IKE
IA $10

FISHING PLUG BOXES

311-6545   KAUTZKY LAZY IKE CORP.
LAZY IKE
IA $10

311-6530   KAUTZKY LAZY IKE CORP.
LAZY IKE BAIT
IA $10

311-6543   KAUTZKY LAZY IKE CORP.
SAIL SHARK
IA $10

311-7149   KEELING, FRED C.
BABY TOM
IL 1920's $400

311-7150   KEELING, FRED C.
BASS KEE-WIG
IL 1920's $400

311-6962   KEEN BAIT MFG. CO.
KEEN KNIGHT
MI 1946 $200

311-6585   KIMMICH BAIT CO.
KIMMICH SPECIAL MOUSE
PA 1929 $200

311-6534   KINGFISHER
DIAMOND BACK LURE
            $50

311-6538   KINGFISHER
KINGFISHER WOOD MINNOW
            $200

311-6587   KNOWLES, S.F.
KNOWLE'S AUTOMATIC STRIKER
CA 1906 $20

311-6528   KRIEGER-RIGGS TACKLE CO.
THE DRAGNETTER
OK 1948 $20

311-6252   KUSH, MORRIS
KUSH SPOON
MI 1956 $10

FISHING PLUG BOXES

312-6541   KVALITETSDRAGET
DET SVENSKA (SWEDEN)
$10

312-6535   L & S BAIT CO.
JUMBO SHINER MINNOW
IL $100

312-6531   L & S BAIT CO.
MIRA-LURE
FL $20

312-6526   L & S BAIT CO.
SHINER MINNOW
IL $100

312-6272   LEON TACKLE CO.
CHASE-A-BUG
MI $10

312-6346   LINDQUIST BROS. BAIT CO.
CANADIAN WIGGLER
CAN 1940's $10

312-6349   LINDQUIST BROS. BAIT CO.
CANADIAN WIGGLER #CW-2
CAN 1940's $10

312-6518   LLOYD & CO.
LIGHTED PIRATE
FL 1940 $100

312-6517   LOBB, FLOY FERRIS
OLD LOBB
NY $100

312-6516   LONG ISLAND MFG. CO.
FLASHER LURE
NY 1934 $60

312-6653   LONGFELLOW PRODUCTS INC.
MERCURY MINNOW
MI 1947 $10

312-6407   LONN'S SALES ORG.
DANDY LURE
FL $10

313-6414   LONN'S SALES ORG.
DANDY LURES
FL $20

313-6339   LUCKY BUNNY BAIT CO.
LUCKY BUNNY
          $10

313-6613   LUCKY DAY BAIT CO.
DUBL-POP
MN 1948 $20

313-6539   LULU LURES
LULU LURE
OH $40

313-6666   LULU LURES
LULU LURE
OH $10

313-6344   MACATAWA BAIT CO.
MACATAWA BAIT
MI $50

313-6642   MACK, ARTIE
BIG SILVER SHINER
RI $50

313-6612   MAGIC MINNOW BAIT CO.
MAGIC MINNOW
MA 1939 $20

313-6617   MAKINEN TACKLE CO.
MAKINEN BAIT
MI 1940's $40

313-6595   MANN, J.H.
MANN'S PIKE SPOON
NY 1880's $30

313-6594   MARATHON BAIT CO.
FROG AND MINNOW HOOK
WI $30

313-6656   MARATHON BAIT CO.
KITTYCLAW
WI 1940's $10

FISHING PLUG BOXES

314-6610   MARTIN FISH LURE CO.
HOTTER 'N' HELL
WA $40

314-6607   MARTIN FISH LURE CO.
MARTIN FISH LURE
WA 1930's $30

314-6619   MARTIN FISH LURE CO.
MARTIN FISH LURE
WA 1930's $30

314-6605   MARTIN FISH LURE CO.
MARTIN PLUG
WA 1930's $30

314-6606   MARTIN FISH LURE CO.
MARTIN SPOON
WA 1930's $30

314-6603   MARTIN, JACK
LIZZARD
OK $40

314-6645   MARVELUS LURES
MARVELUS WOODEN MINNOW
          $500

314-6599   MAYGARD TACKLE CO.
SPARX-PLUG
WA 1946 $30

314-6601   McCAGG, BARNEY
TOPWATER LURE
NY 1947 $40

314-6903   METEOR BAIT CO.
METEOR BAIT
          $10

314-6596   MILLER LURES
TOP KICK
MO 1958 $10

314-6616   MILLS PRODUCTS INC.
DEEPSTER
FL $20

315-6885   MILLS, WM AND SONS
ENGLISH DRY FLIES
NY $40

315-6598   MILLS, WM. & SONS
MILLS BAIT
NY $30

315-6597   MILLSITE TACKLE CO.
MILLSITE BAIT
MI 1940's $20

315-6880   MILWARDS
SPINMASTER REVERSIBLE SPIN DEVON
          $30

315-6609   MINSER TACKLE CO.
LUCKY LOUIE
WA 1935 $30

315-6392   MITTIG MFG. CO.
TRIGGER-FISH
MI $60

315-6686   MOBY DICK MFG. CO.
MOBY DICK LURE
NE $10

315-6659   MONTPELIER BAIT CO.
HOOTENANNA
OH 1939 $100

315-6648   MOONLIGHT BAIT CO.
DREADNOUGHT
MI 1918 $1000

315-6647   MOONLIGHT BAIT CO.
MOONLIGHT BAIT
MI $400

315-6651   MOONLIGHT BAIT CO.
MOONLIGHT FLOATING BAIT
MI $1000

315-6650   MOONLIGHT BAIT CO.
THE TROUT BOB
MI $1000

316-6652   MOORE, JOE BAITS, INC.
SILVER DRAGON
TX $100

316-6319   MUSKEGON BAIT CO.,
MUSKEGON SPOON JACK MINNOW
MI $300

316-6250   NATIONAL DYNAMICS
COLORAMA FISH LURES
          $10

316-6638   NATIONAL EXPERT BAIT CO.
FLASH
MN 1932 $30

316-6633   NATIONAL EXPERT BAIT CO.
MUSK-E-FLASH
MN 1932 $20

316-6622   NATURALURE BAIT CO.
NATURALURE BAIT
CA 1950 $10

316-6621   NEAL BAIT MFG. CO.
NEAL ARTIFICIAL LURE
IN $50

316-6636   NEON MICKEY BAIT CO.
NEON MICKEY
OR 1955 $20

316-6635   NESS, JOS. M. CO.
NIFTY MINNIE
MN 1913 $2500

316-6646   NEWTON MFG. & SALES CO.
NEWTON'S COMET SPOON
OK $20

316-6640   NICHOLS LURE CO.
NICHOLS SHRIMP
TX 1937 $50

316-6687   OLIVER & GRUBER
GLOWURM
WA 1920 $1000

FISHING PLUG BOXES

317-6965   ORCHARD INDUSTRIES
KICK-N-KACKLE
MI 1946 $20

317-6889   OSBORNE, ASA C.
FLY BOX, ENGLISH
MA $60

317-6966   OUACHITA TRAVELER BAIT CO.
OUACHITA TRAVELER BAIT
AR $20

317-6694   OUTING MFG. CO.
OUTINGS' GETUM LURE
IN 1920's $500

317-6696   OZARK LURE CO.
LITL-LIZ
OK 1950's $50

317-6655   OZARK LURE CO.
OZARK LIZARD
OK 1948 $20

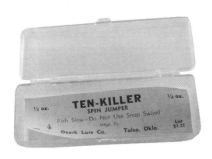

317-6685   OZARK LURE CO.
TEN-KILLER SPIN JUMPER
OK 1950's $10

317-6699   PACHNER & KOLLER INC.
DR. DEERING'S SOFTY THE WONDER CRAB
IL 1940's $20

317-6679   PACHNER & KOLLER INC.
P & K WHIRL-A-WAY
IL 1946 $20

317-6674   PACHNER & KOLLER INC.
P & K BAIT
IL 1946 $20

317-6698   PACHNER & KOLLER INC.
P & K LURE
IL 1940's $20

317-6700   PADRE ISLAND CO.
PICO PERCH
TX 1940's $10

318-6683   PARK MFG. CO.
JAKE'S FLY BAIT
OH 1959 $20

318-6680   PAUL BUNYAN BAIT CO.
"66" TROLLER
MN 1940's $20

318-6676   PAUL BUNYAN BAIT CO.
"66" LURE
MN 1946 $20

318-6681   PAUL BUNYAN BAIT CO.
"66" LURE
MN 1940's $10

318-6675   PAUL BUNYAN BAIT CO.
PAUL BUNYAN BAIT
MN 1940's $30

318-6625   PAW PAW BAIT CO.
LUCKY LURE
MI $200

318-6639   PAW PAW BAIT CO.
LUCKY LURES
MI $50

318-6624   PAW PAW BAIT CO.
PAW PAW BAIT
MI $40

318-6632   PAW PAW BAIT CO.
PAW PAW BAIT
MI $200

318-6641   PAW PAW BAIT CO.
PAW PAW BAIT
MI $200

318-6630   PAW PAW BAIT CO.
PAW PAW BAIT DISPLAY
MI $200

318-6643   PAW PAW BAIT CO.
TROUT FLIES
MI $200

FISHING PLUG BOXES

319-6693   PEPPER, JOE E. BAIT CO.
COPPER CITY MINNOW
NY 1920's $20

319-6691   PEPPER, JOE E. BAIT CO.
DELTA BUG SPINNER
NY 1920's $20

319-6672   PEPPER, JOE E. BAIT CO.
NATIONAL MINNOW
NY 1905 $800

319-6690   PEPPER, JOE E. BAIT CO.
PEARL ROMAN SPINNER
NY 1920's $20

319-6692   PEPPER, JOE E. BAIT CO.
PEARL ROMAN SPINNER
NY 1920's $20

319-6669   PEPPER, JOE E. BAIT CO.
REVOLVING MINNOW
NY 1900's $1500

319-6670   PEPPER, JOE E. BAIT CO.
ROMAN REDTAIL MINNOW
NY 1910 $1500

319-6689   PEPPER, JOE E. BAIT CO.
THE NEW CENTURY BALL SPINNER
NY 1910 $20

319-6660   PFEFFER, JIM
BANANA LURE, PLASTIC
FL 1952 $50

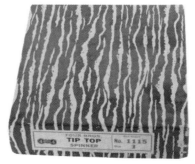

319-6671   PFEFFER, JIM
PFEFFER TOP LURE
FL 1952 $50

319-6725   PFLUEGER
4-BROTHERS TIP TOP SPINNER
OH $20

319-6730   PFLUEGER
GOLD SEAL WOODEN MINNOW
OH $1500

FISHING PLUG BOXES

320-6745   PFLUEGER
INDIANA SPINNER
OH $50

320-6723   PFLUEGER
JUNE BUG SPINNER
OH $20

320-6750   PFLUEGER
LIVEWIRE MINNOW
OH $20

320-6726   PFLUEGER
MARION SPINNERS
OH $100

320-6742   PFLUEGER
MUSKILL BAIT
OH $10

320-6743   PFLUEGER
NEVERFAIL MINNOW
OH $20

320-6722   PFLUEGER
PFLUEGER BAIT
OH $20

320-6733   PFLUEGER
PFLUEGER BAIT
OH $50

320-6736   PFLUEGER
PFLUEGER BAIT
OH $50

320-6737   PFLUEGER
PFLUEGER BAIT
OH $200

320-6738   PFLUEGER
PFLUEGER BAIT
OH $200

320-6739   PFLUEGER
PFLUEGER BAIT
OH $50

FISHING PLUG BOXES

321-6740   PFLUEGER
PFLUEGER BAIT
OH $50

321-6744   PFLUEGER
PFLUEGER BAIT
OH $50

321-6751   PFLUEGER
PFLUEGER BAIT
OH $20

321-6731   PFLUEGER
PFLUEGER'S SIMPLEX MINNOW
OH   1905 $1500

321-6724   PFLUEGER
PILOT FLY SPINNER
OH $20

321-6727   PFLUEGER
SILVER KING
OH $10

321-6752   PFLUEGER
WIZARD
OH $10

321-6747   PFLUEGER
WIZARD WIGGLER
OH $500

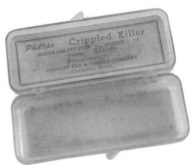

321-6664   PHILLIPS FLY & TACKLE CO.
CRIPPLE KILLER
PA   1948 $10

321-6662   PHILLIPS FLY & TACKLE CO.
FLASH-O-MINO
PA $10

321-6678   PIERSON BAIT CO.
CHE'-GEGON WOBBLER
MI $20

321-6473   PLUCKY LURE CO
PLUCKY LURE   (FRANCE)
FRA $20

322-6668   PORTER BAIT CO.
SCOOTER POOPER
FL 1955 $10

322-6580   PROGRESSIVE TOOL & MFG.
PYRALIN SPOON BALL BAIT
IL 1927 $20

322-6667   PROVEN BAIT CO.
WIGGLEFISH
OH 1946 $50

322-6779   R.K. TACKLE CO
HOLLOWHEAD
MI $20

322-6786   RAILEY MFG CO
KNOCKOUT
              $20

322-6785   RAPALA, LOURI
RAPALA LURE   (FINLAND)
FIN 1960 $20

322-6767   REEAL LURES INC
FLOYD ROMAN POPPER
MA $30

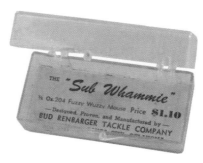

322-6960   RENBURGER, BUD TACKLE
CO.L
SUB WHAMMIE
OK $20

322-6710   RHODES, FRED D.
RHODES PERFECT CASTING MINNOW
MI $1500

322-6863   RINEHART TACKLE CO
JINX
OH 1947 $20

322-6867   RINEHART TACKLE CO
JINX
OH 1947 $10

322-6850   RINEHART TACKLE CO.
JINX
OH 1947 $20

323-6946   ROCHESTER BAIT MFG. CO.
ROCHESTER SPOON BAIT
NY $400

323-6959   ROGERS
CRAW-PAP
            $20

323-6951   ROSS MFG. CO.
BASSNIK
TN 1952 $20

323-6777   RUSSELURE MFG CO
RUSSELURE BAIT
CA 1940's $10

323-6627   SAM-BO LURE CO.
SAM-BO LURE
            $30

323-6770   SAN LUCO INC
SAN LUCO LURE
CA 1952 $30

323-6756   SCHALLER BAIT CO
THREE-BAGGER
IL 1938 $100

323-6886   SCHLITZ
SCHLITZ SPOON LURE
            $10

323-6936   SCHMELZER ARMS CO.
SCHMELZER'S BASS BAIT
MO $600

323-6947   SCOOTERPOOPER SALES INC.
SCOOTERPOOPER LURE
SC 1945 $100

323-6757   SENECA TACKLE
WOB-L-RITE
NY 1946 $50

323-6754   SEVDY ENTERPRISES
WEED KING
MN 1952 $300

324-6602   SHAD-O-LURE CO.
SHAD-O-LURE
          $50

324-6720   SHAKESPEARE, WILLIAM CO.
REVOLUTION MINNOW
MI 1910 $2000

324-6706   SHAKESPEARE, WILLIAM CO.
SHAKESPEARE BAIT
MI $50

324-6707   SHAKESPEARE, WILLIAM CO.
SHAKESPEARE BAIT
MI $50

324-6709   SHAKESPEARE, WILLIAM CO.
SHAKESPEARE BAIT
MI $50

324-6713   SHAKESPEARE, WILLIAM CO.
SHAKESPEARE BAIT
MI $300

324-6714   SHAKESPEARE, WILLIAM CO.
SHAKESPEARE BAIT
MI $20

324-6716   SHAKESPEARE, WILLIAM CO.
SHAKESPEARE BAIT
MI $20

324-6717   SHAKESPEARE, WILLIAM CO.
SHAKESPEARE BAIT
MI $1000

324-6718   SHAKESPEARE, WILLIAM CO.
SHAKESPEARE BUCKTAIL BAIT
MI $1000

324-6711   SHAKESPEARE, WILLIAM CO.
SHAKESPEARE WOODEN MINNOW
MI $1500

324-6703   SHAKESPEARE, WILLIAM CO.
T. ROBB CASTING FLY
MI $300

325-6705   SHAKESPEARE, WILLIAM CO.
TRICKY BUCKIE
MI 1935 $150

325-6558   SHANNON, J.P. & CO.
SHANNON TWIN SPINNERS
IL $20

325-6562   SHANNON, J.P. & CO.
WEED MASTER
IL $30

325-6782   SHUREBITE
SHUREBITE BAIT
MI $60

325-6761   SILVER CREEK NOVELTY
WORKS
SILVER CREEK MINNOW
MI 1920's $500

325-6784   SILVER-TIP TACKLE CO
SILVER-TIP HELLDIVER
OK 1945 $50

325-6765   SIREN LURE CO.
SIREN
CA 1947 $10

325-6755   SMITHWICK, JACK K. AND SON
DEVIL'S HORSE LURE
LA 1959 $20

325-6802   SOUTH BEND BAIT CO.
BABE-ORENO
IN 1930'S $200

325-6808   SOUTH BEND BAIT CO.
BASS-ORENO
IN $200

325-6792   SOUTH BEND BAIT CO.
BEST-O-LUCK LURE
IN $100

325-6800   SOUTH BEND BAIT CO.
BEST-O-LUCK LURE
IN $100

FISHING PLUG BOXES

326-6801   SOUTH BEND BAIT CO.
BEST-O-LUCK LURE
IN $100

326-6791   SOUTH BEND BAIT CO.
CALLMAC BUG
IN $100

326-6818   SOUTH BEND BAIT CO.
DIVE-ORENO
IN 1938 $50

326-6803   SOUTH BEND BAIT CO.
DUAL-ACTION LURE
IN $50

326-6814   SOUTH BEND BAIT CO.
FINN-ORENO
IN $200

326-6821   SOUTH BEND BAIT CO.
FISH-OBITE
IN $20

326-6793   SOUTH BEND BAIT CO.
FISH-ORENO
IN 1926 $200

326-6820   SOUTH BEND BAIT CO.
FLIPIT
IN 1953 $20

326-6822   SOUTH BEND BAIT CO.
FLIPIT
N 1953 $20

326-6815   SOUTH BEND BAIT CO.
KETCH-EM WOODEN MINNOW
IN $1500

326-6804   SOUTH BEND BAIT CO.
ORENO-TEASER
IN $200

326-6805   SOUTH BEND BAIT CO.
SOUTH BEND BAIT
IN $200

327-6816   SOUTH BEND BAIT CO.
SOUTH BEND BAIT
IN $50

327-6817   SOUTH BEND BAIT CO.
SOUTH BEND BAIT
IN $200

327-6809   SOUTH BEND BAIT CO.
SOUTH BEND CASTING SPOON
IN $50

327-6789   SOUTH BEND BAIT CO.
SOUTH BEND LURE
IN $10

327-6819   SOUTH BEND BAIT CO.
SPIN-I-DUZY
IN 1953 $20

327-6788   SOUTH BEND BAIT CO.
SUPER-DUPER
IN 1953 $20

327-6811   SOUTH BEND BAIT CO.
SURF-ORENO NITE-LUMING
IN $200

327-6797   SOUTH BEND BAIT CO.
TARPON SPECIAL
IN $200

327-6796   SOUTH BEND BAIT CO.
TEASER
IN 1925 $200

327-6813   SOUTH BEND BAIT CO.
THE KETCH-EM WOODEN MINNOW
IN $1500

327-6799   SOUTH BEND BAIT CO.
TROLL-ORENO
IN 1919 $200

327-6807   SOUTH BEND BAIT CO.
WIZ-ORENO
IN $200

FISHING PLUG BOXES

328-6806   SOUTH BEND BAIT CO.
ZANE GRAY TEASER
IN 1950 $200

328-6781   SOUTHERN BAIT CO
SOUTHERN BAIT
FL $40

328-6940   SPARK-DART CO.
SPARK-DART BAIT
OK 1948 $60

328-6778   SPLIT FISH LURE CO
SPLIT FISH LURE
OH 1951 $10

328-6520   SPORT KING LURES
MONTGOMERY WARDS
              $20

328-6522   SPORT KING LURES
MONTGOMERY WARDS
              $20

328-6773   SPORTSLAND MFG INC
SHIMMY SHINER
OK 1944 $10

328-6377   SPRINGFIELD NOVELTY MFG.
THE REEL LURE
MO 1930's $60

328-6760   STANLEY & CHAPMAN
THE STANLEY SMELT
NY 1895 $500

328-6783   STEEL FISH LURE CO
STEEL FISH BAIT
OH 1953 $20

328-6769   STREICH MFG. CO.
ACRO-BAIT
IL 1924 $300

328-6256   STRIP TEASER BAIT CO
STRIP TEASER
              $50

FISHING PLUG BOXES

329-6879   SUICK LURE CO
SUICK MUSKIE THRILLER
WI $20

329-6882   SUICK LURE CO
SUICK MUSKIE THRILLER
WI $10

329-6533   SUNNYBROOK LURE CO
LAYFIELD LURE
TX $30

329-6661   SUN-RAY BAIT CO.
SUN-RAY FLOATING BAIT
           $100

329-6577   SUPERIOR DOOR CATCH CO.
K&B FISHING SPOON (B. GALLINGER)
WI $10

329-6314   SUPPLEE-BIDDLE HARDWARE
CO.
CONGRESS MINNOW
PA $300

329-6758   SURE-CATCH BAIT INC.
STRIKE-MASTER LURE
OH 1920's $150

329-6855   T.C. BAIT CO
DOODLE BUG
WI 1948 $10

329-6870   TACKLE INDUSTRIES
SWIMMING MINNOW
LA 1958 $10

329-6873   TAR HEEL BAIT CO
TAR HEEL FLAPPER
NC 1954 $40

329-6335   THE ACTUAL LURE CO.
ACTUAL LURE
NY 1950 $10

329-6333   THE ACTUAL LURE CO.
TINY TROUTER
NY 1950 $10

330-6417   THE COLT DISTRIBUTING CO.
SERV-A-LURE "PONY LURE"
FL $10

330-6746   THE ENTERPRISE MFG CO
PFLUEGER KENT-KENT FLOATER
OH $500

330-6589   THE HALIK CO.
HALIK FROG JUNIOR
MN 1947 $40

330-6583   THE HOUSE OF HOUSER
HOUSER'S HELL DIVER
MO $20

330-6719   THE KALAMAZOO FISHING
TACKLE CO.
RHODES WOODEN MINNOW
MI 1904 $1500

330-6771   THE PRESCOTT SPINNER CO
PRESCOTT PIKE HOOK
WI $10

330-6294   THE REB MFG. CO.
BAYOU SPECIAL
            $20

330-6776   THE ROBINSON BAIT CO
ROBINSON BAIT
FL 1940's $30

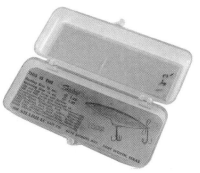

330-6774   THE SHADRAC BAIT CO
SHADRAC BAIT
TX $10

330-6763   THE SPORTMAN'S LURE CO
FLASH MINNOW
TX 1940's $30

330-6775   THE SWIMMY BAIT CO
SWIMMY BAIT
IA $10

330-6569   TRANS-LURE BAIT CO. (JOHN
INGALLS)
THE TRANSPARENT LURE
IL 1946 $40

331-6274   TRANSPARENT FISHING TACKLE
CO.
LURETTE   (CANADA)
1920'S $500

331-6864   TRENTON MFG CO
SURFACE DOODLER
KY 1940's $40

331-6852   TRENTON MFG CO
TRENTON BAIT
KY 1940's $20

331-6871   TRENTON MFG CO
WHAM DOODLER
KY 1940's $40

331-6869   TRIUMPH MFG CO
TRIUMPH WOOD MINNOW
MO $1000

331-6604   TROLLER TACKLE
PIRATE
OR $30

331-6874   TROPICAL BAIT CO
FUZZY DUCK
IN 1952 $20

331-6483   TRUE TEMPER
HELL CAT
OH 1940's $30

331-6482   TRUE TEMPER
SPEED SHAD
OH 1940's $20

331-6455   TRUE TEMPER
TRUE TEMPER CRIPPLED SHAD
OH 1940's $20

331-6461   TRUE TEMPER
TRUE TEMPER CRIPPLED SHAD
OH $20

331-6477   TRUE TEMPER
TRUE TEMPER CRIPPLED SHAD
OH 1940's $20

332-6860   TULSA FISH TACKLE
BEE-POPPER
OK 1940's $10

332-6854   TULSA FISH TACKLE
DI-DIPPER LURE
OK 1940's $10

332-6866   TYNE-LYNE BAIT CO
TYNE-MYTE BAIT
OK 1952 $10

332-6780   U.S. SPECIALTY CO
RUSH TANGO SWIMMING MINNOW
NY $100

332-6787   U.S. SPECIALTY CO
RUSH TANGO SWIMMING MINNOW
NY $100

332-6588   UNCA HUBS ENTERPRISES
DOOFER
FL 1946 $10

332-6954   UNCLE ASHER'S BAIT & TACKLE
UNCLE ASHER BAIT
AR $10

332-6270   UNCLE ASHER'S BAIT & TACKLE
UNCLE ASHER'S LURE
AR $10

332-6862   UNILINE MFG
SPINNO MINNOW
TX 1947 $30

332-6823   UNION SPRINGS SPECIALTY CO
MILLER'S REVERSIBLE SPINNER
NY 1916 $800

332-6865   UNION SPRINGS SPECIALTY CO
MILLER'S REVERSIBLE SPINNER
NY 1916 $500

332-6753   UNKNOWN MAKER
PHANTOM MINNOW
              $500

FISHING PLUG BOXES

333-6759   UNKNOWN MAKER
SURE THING WOOD MINNOW
$1500

333-6876   UNKNOWN MAKER
THE PREZ
$10

333-6768   UNKNOWN MAKER
UNKNOWN WOOD BOX
$1000

333-6573   VACUUM BAIT CO.
HOWE'S VACUUM BAIT
IN 1909 $400

333-6837   VAL PRODUCTS CO
VAL-LURE
IL 1930's $50

333-6845   VAL PRODUCTS CO.
PIKY-LUR
IL 1930's $40

333-6868   VAUGHN TACKLE CO
VAUGHN'S LURE
MI 1932 $300

333-6872   VERMILION BAIT CO.
VERMILION MEADOW MOUSE
OH 1922 $200

333-6851   WADHAM, PERCY
PERCY WADHAM BAIT   (ENGLAND)
UK 1920's $40

333-6853   WADHAM, PERCY
PERCY WADHAM BAIT (ENGLAND)
UK 1920's $40

333-6263   WASWYLER, C.S. DR.
MARVELOUS ELECTRIC GLOW MINNOW
WI 1915 $1000

333-6368   WATER SCOUTS BAIT CO.
WATER SCOUT BAIT
MO $20

FISHING PLUG BOXES

334-6836   WATT TACKLE CO
TWIRLING TWIRP
MI 1950's $20

334-6887   WEBER TACKLE CO,
DRY FLY BOX
WI $40

334-6857   WEBER TACKLE CO.
MUSKY-DUCK
WI 1960 $10

334-6833   WEEZEL BAIT CO
WEEZEL BOPPER
OH 1946 $40

334-6856   WEEZEL BAIT CO.
WEESNER'S BABY WEEZEL BAIT
OH $10

334-6844   WELLER, ERWIN
WELLER MOUSE
IA 1925 $40

334-6366   WESTERN AUTO STORES
WESTERN FISHING LURE
          $20

334-6838   WHIRLING DERVISH BAIT CO
WHIRLING DERVISH
OK $30

334-6835   WHOPPER-STOPPER BAIT CO
SHIMMY
TX 1940's $10

334-6834   WHOPPER-STOPPER BAIT CO
WHOPPER-STOPPER BAIT
TX 1958 $20

334-6858   WINCHESTER REPEATING
ARMS
WINCHESTER BAIT
CT 1920's $1500

334-6273   WINCHESTER REPEATING
ARMS CO.
WINCHESTER FISHING TACKLE
CT 1910's $20

335-6827   WONDER STATE PRODUCTS
BUG-R-BIRD BAIT
AK 1946 $50

335-6847   WOOD MANUFACTURING CO
DEEP-R-DOODLE
AR 1950 $20

335-6839   WOOD MANUFACTURING CO
DIPSY DOODLE
AK 1947 $20

335-6848   WOOD MANUFACTURING CO
SPOT TAIL MINNOW
AR 1950 $20

335-6840   WOODS, F.C.
EXPERT WOODEN MINNOW
OH 1903 $1000

335-6264   WORTH BAIT CO.
MUSKY MAULER
MI 1940 $10

335-6843   WRIGHT & McGILL CO
EAGLE CLAW LURE
CO $20

335-6829   WRIGHT & McGILL CO
MIRACLE MINNOW
CO $20

335-6846   WRIGHT & McGILL CO
WIGGLING MINNOW
CO $40

335-6825   WRIGHT & McGILL CO.
SWIMMING MOUSE
CO 1929 $600

335-6826   WRIGHT & McGILL CO.
WRIGHT & McGILL BAIT
CO $600

335-6861   YAKIMA BAIT CO
WORDEN'S WIZARD
WA $10

FISHING PLUG BOXES

336-6859   YORK BAITS
KER-PLUNK
PA 1960 $10

336-6849   ZOL I INC.
ZOLI DETACH-O-LURE
NJ $20

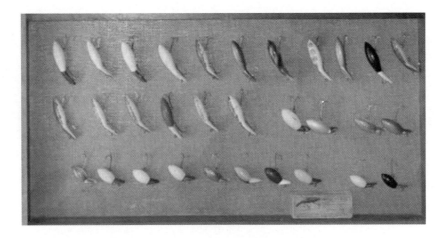

RUSH TANGO JR., S.O.S, & MIDGET TANGO
COLOR SET
RUSH, J.K. (RUSH TANGO LURES) NY
$5,000.00

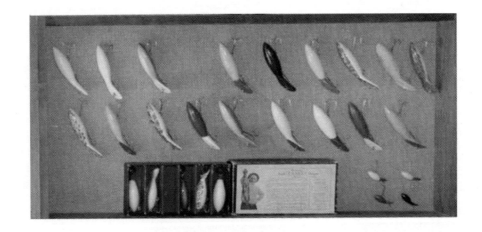

DELUXE TANGO AND TROUT TANGO
COLOR SET
RUSH, J.K. (RUSH TANGO LURES) NY
$10,000.00

INDEX BY MANUFACTURER

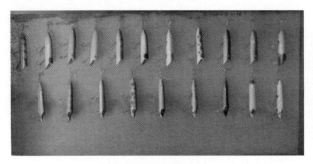

VAMPS AND BASSERS
COLOR SET
JAMES HEDDON & SONS, MI

$3,000.00

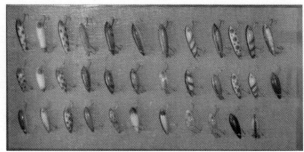

CRAB WIGGLERS &
BABY CRAB WIGGLERS COLOR SET
JAMES HEDDON & SONS, MI

$3,000.00

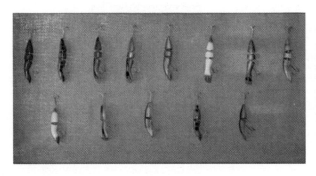

GAMEFISHERS & BABY GAMEFISHERS
COLOR SET
JAMES HEDDON & SONS, MI

$3,000.00

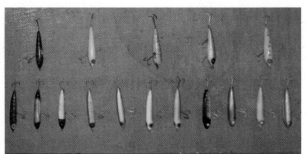

ZARA-SPOOKS & ZARAGOSSAS
COLOR SET
JAMES HEDDON & SONS, MI

$3,000.00

INDEX BY NAME

INDEX BY NAME

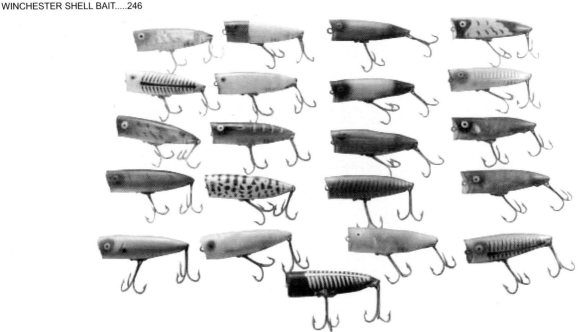

CHUGGER COLOR SET, - JAMES HEDDON & SONS, MI $2000.00

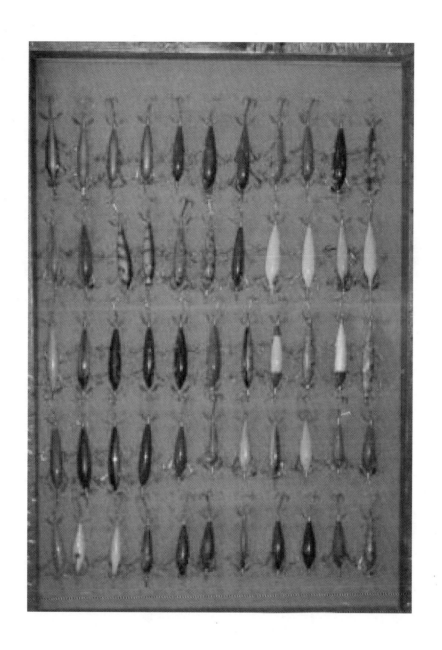

#100 AND #150 DOWAGIAC MINNOW
COLOR SET
JAMES HEDDON & SONS, MI

$50,000.00

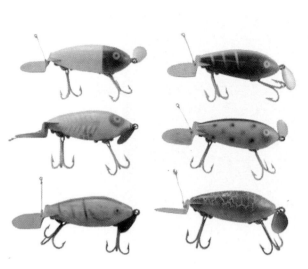

CRAB WIGGLER COLOR SET
JAMES HEDDON & SONS, MI
$200.00

PUNKINSEED COLOR SET
JAMES HEDDON & SONS, MI
$500.00

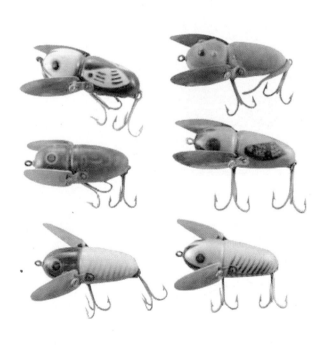

CRAZY CRAWLER COLOR SET
JAMES HEDDON & SONS, MI
$500.00

HI-TAIL COLOR SET
JAMES HEDDON & SONS, MI
$300.00